CITROEN RELAY
PEUGEOT BOXER
1.9 AND 2.5 LITRE DIESEL
WORKSHOP MANUAL
1994 - 2001

OWNERS EDITION

BROOKLANDS BOOKS LTD.
P.O. BOX 146, COBHAM,
SURREY, KT11 1LG. UK
sales@brooklands-books.com

ABOUT THIS MANUAL

This 'Owners Edition' workshop manual covers the Citroen Relay and the Peugeot Boxer diesel powered with two 1.9 litre engines, a naturally aspirating diesel engine and a turbodiesel engine, known as the XUD engines. Two 2.5 Litre engines were also fitted to both makes, without or with turbocharger, known as DJ5 engines. Details of these models can be found on the following pages.

This manual has been compiled for the practical owner who wants to maintain their vehicle in first-class condition and contains comprehensive step-by-step instructions to enable them to carry out the bulk of their own servicing and repairs. With easy-to-follow instructions and hundreds of illustrations to amplify the text, many aspects of service, overhaul and repair are within the scope of an owner with a reasonable degree of mechanical aptitude.

Some operations, however, demand more skill whilst other jobs require the use of special tools and, in some cases, testing facilities and techniques that are not generally available. Only you can judge whether a job is within your capabilities. Whilst we do try to assist the reader to ensure that the information is correct it is obviously not possible to guarantee complete freedom from errors or omissions.

Information found in the driver's handbook is not necessarily duplicated here. It is not possible within this volume to cover every aspect to be found in the manufacturer's own workshop manual which is of greater size and complexity. However, it should be consulted if more detailed information is needed.

Always remember that you are responsible for your own safety, and that of others, when working on a vehicle. Particular care should be taken with safety related systems like the brakes and steering. If in any doubt professional advice should be sought. Never work under a vehicle unless it is properly supported (a single jack is not enough). Care should be taken with power tools and potentially harmful fuel, lubricants, solvents and sealers. These should always be stored in labelled, sealed containers. Always obtain your spare parts from an officially appointed dealer.

With care and common sense the practical owner can make an excellent job of maintenance and overhaul. You will be adding to your knowledge too, knowing more about what needs to be done even if it does, in some instances, have to go to a professional repair shop.

Given regular servicing and maintenance they will provide long and reliable service.

ISBN 9781783180561   CRPBWH

Brooklands Books Ltd. PO Box 146, Cobham, Surrey, KT11 1LG, England
Tel. 01932 865051   email: sales@brooklands-books.com

www.brooklandsbooks.com

CONTENTS

0.	**INTRODUCTION**

Our 'Owners Manuals' are based on easy-to-follow step-by-step instructions and advice enabling you to carry out many jobs yourself. This manual will give you the means to avoid delays and inconveniences which may result from not knowing the correct procedures for carrying out repairs, which are often of a comparatively simple nature.

Whilst special tools are required to carry out certain operations, this manual shows you – whenever possible – how to improvise or use alternative tools. Experience shows that it is preferable to use only genuine parts since these give the assurance of a first class job. You will find that many parts are identical in the various makes covered, so our advice is to find out before purchasing new parts and suggests that you always buy your replacement parts from an authorised dealer.

0.0.   General Information

After 13 successful years, the two Vans Citroen C25 and Peugeot J5 were replaced during February 1994 by two new models, i.e. the Citroen Relay and the Peugeot Boxer. The Fiat Ducato, up to then nearly identical in design and available engines, is now fitted with different diesel and turbodiesel engines. The version with 1.9 litre engine has its own Fiat engine, the larger 2.5 litre engine is supplied by Sofim. The new models are manufactured in the way of a partnership between Citroen, Peugeot and Fiat and are built in Italy.

Many different body versions, marketed under the name of "steel" van, Combi "Club", Combi "Comfort" and "Minibus" in the van range and the special versions chassis cab, double chassis cab, cab and platform, platform and double cab are available. Also available are vehicles with a load carrying capacity between 2.7 and 3.5 tons and three different wheelbases between 2.85 m (short wheelbase), 3.20 m (medium wheelbase) or 3.70 m (long wheelbase). Boxer 1000, 1400 or 1800 are used in the Peugeot range.

The engine range within the various models is also extensive. Originally two 1.9 litre engines were fitted, a naturally aspirating diesel engine of 1905 c.c. with a performance of 51 kW (70 B.H.P.) at 4600 rpm and a turbodiesel engine with a performance of 67.5 kW (92 B.H.P.) at 4000 rpm. These engines belong to the well known family of "XUD" engines, with two valves per cylinder.

Two 2.5 Litre engines were also fitted to both makes, without or with turbocharger. These engines are also produced by Citroen and have the designation "DJ5". New on these engine is the fitting of three valves per cylinder, two inlet valve and one exhaust valves. Both engines have a capacity of 2446 c.c. and a performance of 63 kW (86 B.H.P.) at 4350 rpm without turbocharger or 75 kW (104 B.H.P.) at 4200 rpm with turbocharger.

Other engines have been added to the range within the model years covered in this manual, which will be mentioned in the technical data or whenever necessary.

The fuel injection system is, however, not identical for the given engines. A Bosch system is fitted to the two 1.9 litre engines and the 2.5 litre engine without turbocharger. The 2.5 litre engine with turbocharger is fitted with a Lucas fuel injection system.

All models use a five-speed transmission with cable gearchange, but different transmission types are used, depending on the engine. The transmission drives the front wheels in standard version. Later a 4 x 4 vehicle was added to the range.

Various modifications were introduced since the introduction of the new models, which will be mentioned whenever necessary.

0.1. Identification

The type identification plate is riveted to the centre of the upper crossmember, near the bonnet lock at the position shown in Fig. 01 and contains the following information:

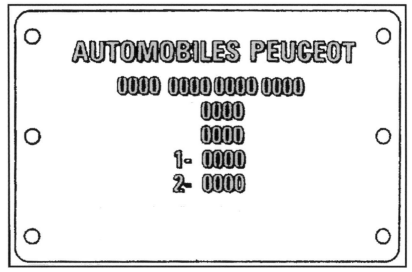

Fig. 0.1 – The type identification plate.

The name of the manufacturer, the chassis number, the max. permissible all-up weight and the max. weight on the front and rear axles. The chassis number can also be found in the inside of the R.H. wheel arch, immediately before the passenger seat and can be seen with the door open.

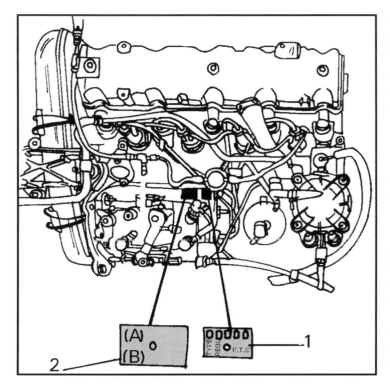

Fig. 0.2a. The location of the engine number of a XUD 1.9 litre engine.

Another important identification is the engine number. The number always commences with the engine type code. Without referring to every single engine, you will find the engine number always on a plate on the upper part of the cylinder block, before the injection pump support bracket. Figs. 0.2a to 0.2c show the various engines with the location of the type identification plate. The list below will enable you to identify which engine is fitted to your particular vehicle, but it should be

General Information

noted that some have had the engine code changed within the model years covered. The following information is based on the engines fitted during the initial production.

Important is the model year of the vehicle. This should always be quoted when parts are required. The type identification of the vehicle commences with the numbers "231", "232" or "233".

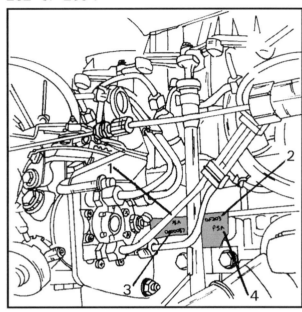

Fig. 0.2b – The location of the engine number of a 2.5 litre engine (except without direction injection).
1   Code (i.e. T9B)
2   Engine type
3   Engine serial number
4   Manufacturer (PSA)

Important is the model year of the vehicle. This should always be quoted when parts are required. The type identification of the vehicle commences with the numbers "231", "232" or "233".

1.9 litre engine:
- Without turbocharger   XUD9AU (D9B) or XUD9AU/W2 (D9B)
- With turbocharger   XUD9TFU (D8C), XUD9UTF (D8C) or
                                XUD9UTF/X3 (DHX)

2.5 litre engine:
- Without turbocharger   DJ5 (T9A)
- With turbocharger   DJ5T (T8A or THZ)
- With direct injection   DJ5TED (THX)

0.2   Dimensions

Wheelbase
- Short wheelbase . . . . 2850 mm (113.3 in.)
- Intermediate wheelbase. . . . . 3200 mm (127.14 in.)
- Long wheelbase . . . . .3700 mm (147.0 in.)

Front track . . . . .1720 mm (68.34 in.)
Rear track . . . . 1710 mm (67.54 in.)
Overall length (typical van) . . . . 5005 mm (198.5 in.)
Overall height . . . . 2145 mm (85.22 in.)
Overall width . . . . 1998 mm (79.4 in.)
Ground clearance (depending on tyres) . . . . 170 to 210 mm (6.76 – 8.3 in.)

0.3   Filling Capacities

Fuel tank . . . . 80 litres
Engine:
-      Without oil filter – 1.9 litre engine . . . . 6.3 litres
-      Without oil filter – 2.5 litre engine . . . . 9.0 litres

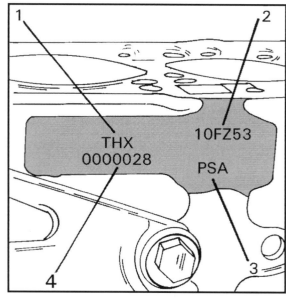

Fig. 0.2b – The location of the engine number of a 2.5 litre engine with direct injection.
1   Code letters (THX)
2   Component number
3   Manufacturer
4   Engine serial number

- With oil filter – 1.9 litre engine . . . . 6.6 litres
- With oil filter – 2.5 litre engine . . . . 9.5 litres

Between "Max." and "Min." marks on oil dipstick:
-    1.9 litre engine . . . . .3.3 litres
-    2.5 litre engine, without turbo charger . . . . .3.5 litres
-    2.5 litre engine, with turbo charger . . . . 4.0 litres

Cooling System:
-    1.9 litre engine . . . . 10.2 litres
-    2.5 litre engine without A/C system . . . . 13.0 litres
-    2.5 litre engine with A/C system . . . . 13.5 litres

Transmission:
-    ME5TU gearbox . . . . 1.85 litres
-    ME5GU gearbox . . . . 2.75 litres

Power assisted steering . . . . .1.3 litres

0.4.   General Servicing Notes

The servicing and overhaul instructions in this Workshop Manual are laid out in an easy-to-follow step-by-step fashion and no difficulty should be encountered, if the text and diagrams are followed carefully and methodically. The "Technical Data" sections form an important part of the repair procedures and should always be referred to during work on the vehicle.

In order that we can include as much data as possible, you will find that we do not generally repeat in the text the values already given under the technical data headings. Again, to make the best use of the space available, we do not repeat at each operation the more obvious steps necessary - we feel it to be far more helpful to concentrate on the difficult or awkward procedures in greater detail. However, we summarise below a few of the more important procedures and draw your attention to various points of general interest that apply to all operations.

Always use the torque settings given in the various main sections of the manual. These are grouped together in separate sub-sections for convenient reference.

General Information

Bolts and nuts should be assembled in a clean and very lightly oiled condition and faces and threads should always be inspected to make sure that they are free from damage burrs or scoring. DO NOT degrease bolts or nuts.

All joint washers, gaskets, tabs and lock washers, split pins and "O" rings must be replaced on assembly. Seals will, in the majority of cases, also need to be replaced, if the shaft and seal have been separated. Always lubricate the lip of the seal before assembly and take care that the seal lip is facing the correct direction.

References to the left-hand and right-hand sides are always to be taken as if the observer is at the rear of the vehicle, facing forwards, unless otherwise stated.

Always make sure that the vehicle is adequately supported, and on firm ground, before commencing any work on the underside of the car. A small jack or a make shift prop can be highly dangerous and proper axle stands are an essential requirement for your own safety.

Dirt, grease and mineral oil will rapidly destroy the seals of the hydraulic system and even the smallest amounts must be prevented from entering the system or coming into contact with the components. Use clean brake fluid or one of the proprietary cleaners to wash the hydraulic system parts. An acceptable alternative cleaner is methylated spirit, but if this is used, it should not be allowed to remain in contact with the rubber parts for longer than necessary. It is also important that all traces of the fluid should be removed from the system before final assembly.

Always use genuine manufacturer's spares and replacements for the best results.

Since the manufacturer uses metric units when building the cars it is recommended that, these are used for all precise units. Inch conversions are given in most cases but these are not necessarily precise conversions, being rounded off for the unimportant values.

Removal and installation instructions, in this Workshop Manual, cover the steps to take away or put back the unit or part in question. Other instructions, usually headed "Servicing", will cover the dismantling and repair of the unit once it has been stripped from the vehicle. It is pointed out that the major instructions cover a complete overhaul of all parts but, obviously, this will not always be necessary and should not be carried out needlessly.

There are a number of variations in unit parts on the range of vehicles covered in this Workshop Manual. We strongly recommend that you take care to identify the precise model, and the year of manufacture, before obtaining any spares or replacement parts.

Std.: To indicate sizes and limits of components as supplied by the manufacturer. Also to indicate the production tolerances of new unused parts.

O/S: Parts supplied as Oversize or Undersize or recommended limits for such parts, to enable them to be used with worn or re-machined mating parts.

U/S: O/S indicates a part that is larger than Std. size U/S may indicate a bore of a bushing or female part that is smaller than Std.

Max.: Where given against a clearance or dimension indicates the maximum allowable If in excess of the value given it is recommended that the appropriate part is fitted.

TIR: Indicates the Total Indicator Reading as shown by a dial indicator (dial gauge).

TDC: Top Dead Centre (No. 1 piston on firing stroke).

MP: Multi-Purpose grease.

0.5.   Jacking up of the Vehicle

For small jobs, jack up the vehicle as described in the Owner's Manual, with the jack supplied in the vehicle. If a mobile jack is used, make sure it can be inserted between the lowest point of the vehicle and the ground. If necessary, use the vehicle jack to lift the vehicle slightly, until the mobile jack can be inserted. Due to the construction of the vehicle, a mobile jack and/or chassis stands should only be placed under the vehicle as follows, noting that a piece of rubber or wood should always be inserted between the jack head and the jacking point to protect the part in question.

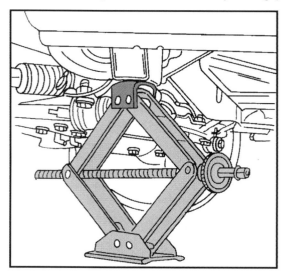

Fig. 0.3 – Lifting the front end of the vehicle with a scissor-type jack.

Never apply a mobile jack or a hydraulic jack underneath the engine oil sump, the transmission, the rear axle (except with 4DW), the front axle or underneath the front crossmember, as these parts or surrounding parts can either be damaged or distorted.

The recommendation is to first jack up one side of the vehicle, placing a chassis stand underneath the body and then jacking up the other side. The following instructions should be followed at all times:

Fig. 0.4 – Lifting the front end of the vehicle with a mobile jack, as used in a workshop.

- To lift the front wheel with a scissor jack, refer to Fig. 0.3.
- To lift a front wheel with a mobile jack, use the jacking point shown in Fig. 0.3, but insert a wooden plank between jack head and jacking point. Fig. 0.4 shows this arrangement.

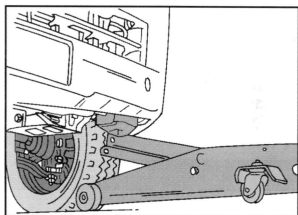

Fig. 0.5 – Chassis stands are placed in the position shown when supporting the front of the vehicle.

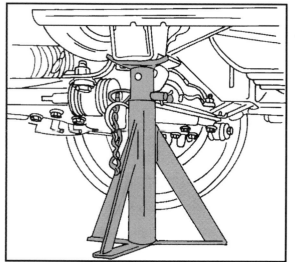

- Chassis stands are placed underneath the front end of the vehicle at the same positions as the jack. In this case the lifting jack must be placed underneath the inner crossmember. This will enable you to insert the chassis stands. A properly placed stand is shown in Fig. 0.5. Note that chassis stands with flat head are used. If you only have stands with "V" shaped head, fill the "V" in suitable manner. Make sure the vehicle cannot slip off the stands.

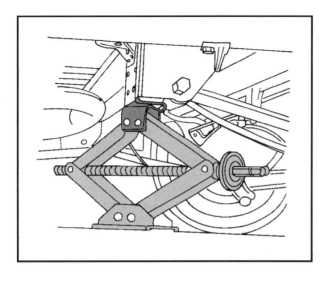

Fig. 0.6 – Jacking up the rear end of the vehicle with a scissor jack.

- The rear end of the vehicle is jacked up and supported in the following manner:
- A scissor jack is used as shown in Fig. 0.6. The jacking point is located before the rear spring.
- A mobile jack is arranged as shown in Fig. 0.7. The jacking point is the same as shown in Fig. 0.6, but a wooden plank should be placed between jack head and jacking point.

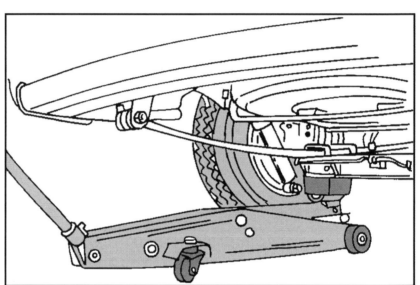

Fig. 0.7 – Jacking up the rear end of the vehicle with a mobile jack as used in the workshop.

Chassis stands are placed under the jacking points. To insert the chassis stands, lift the vehicle at the connection between the rear spring and the crossmember, to place the jack underneath the position shown in Fig. 0.8. As already explained, use only chassis stands with flat heads.

Fig. 0.8 – Chassis stands placed underneath the rear end of the vehicle.

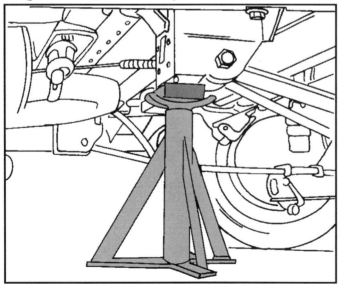

Make sure that the chassis stands and the jack are strong enough to carry the vehicle. Always chock the front and rear wheels on the other side of the vehicle with a brick, to prevent the vehicle from rolling off the jack. Also apply the handbrake.

Note: *It is always difficult to raise a vehicle first on one side and then on the other. Take care that the vehicle cannot tip-over when the first side is lifted. Ask a helper to support the vehicle from the other side.*

1. ENGINES

1.0 Main Features

Model Identification:
- Model 10Q   1.9 litre engine
- Model 14Q   1.9 or 2.5 litre engine
- Model 18Q   2.5 litre engine

Type – 1.9 litre Engine:

Four-cylinder diesel engine with indirect injection, transversely mounted, tilted 7° towards the front, overhead valves (2 per cylinder) and camshaft in cylinder head, driven by toothed belt. Cylinder head made of aluminium alloy. With or without turbo charger.

Type – 2.5 litre Engine:

Four-cylinder diesel engine with indirect injection (DJ5 TED engine with direct injection), transversely mounting at an angle of 17.5° towards the front. Cylinder head and cylinder block made of aluminium alloy. Overhead valves (3 per cylinder) with hydraulic tappets. Camshaft mounted in separate housing on top of cylinder head with toothed belt drive. Crankshaft mounting in separate housing below cylinder block. DJ5 engine without turbo charger, DJ5T engine with turbo charger.

Number of cylinders: 4

Engine capacity
- 1.9 litre engine   1905 cc
- 2.5 litre engine   2446 cc

Cylinder bore:
- 1.9 litre engine   83.00 mm (3.2976 in.)
- 2.5 litre engine   92.00 mm (3.6552 in.)

Piston stroke:
- 1.9 litre engine   88.00 mm (3.4962 in.)
- 2.5 litre engine   92.00 mm (3.6552 in.)

Compression ratio
- 1.9 litre engine   21.8 : 1
- 2.5 litre engine without turbo charger   24.0 : 1
- 2.5 litre engine with turbo charger   21.0 : 1
- With direct injection   20.0 : 1

Max. Power:
- 1.9 litre engine:
- XUD9AU (D9B), without turbo charger   51 kW (70 BHP) at 6000 rpm
- XUD9AU (DJY), without turbo charger   50 kW (68 BHP) at 6000 rpm
- XUD9TFU (D6C), with turbo charger   67.5 kW (92 BHP) at 4000 rpm

Engines

- XUD9UTF (DHX), with turbo charger — 67.5 kW or 66 kW (90 BHP) at 4000 rpm

- DJ5 (T9A) without turbo charger — 63 kW (86 BHP) at 4350 rpm
- DJ5T (T8A) with turbo charger — 76 kW (103 BHP) at 4200 rpm
- DJ5T (THY) with turbo charger — 76 kW (103 BHP) at 4200 rpm
- DJ5T TED (THX) with turbo charger — 79 kW (107 BHP) at 4000 rpm

Max. Torque:
- D9B engine — 12.0 kgm (86.5 ft.lb.) at 2000 rpm
- DJY engine — 12.0 kgm (86.5 ft.lb.) at 2000 rpm
- D8C engine — 19.6 kgm (141 ft.lb.) at 2250 rpm
- DHX engine — 19.6 kgm (141 ft.lb.) at 2250 rpm
- DJ5 T9A engine — 15.3 kgm (110 ft.lb.) at 2250 rpm
- DJ5T T8A engine — 23.0 kgm (165.5 ft.lb.) at 2200 rpm
- DJ5T THY engine — 23.0 kgm (165.5 ft.lb.) at 2200 rpm
- DJ5 TED THX engine — 25.0 kgm (180 ft.lb.) at 2250 rpm

Oil pressure — See Section "Lubrication"
Fuel injection type — See relevant section

Valve Timing

	1.9 litres (all)	*2.5 litres*
Inlet valve opens	- 4° ATDC	13° ATDC
Inlet valve closes	35° ABDC	38° ABDC
With turbo charger		32° ABDC
Exhaust valve opens	43° BBDC	56° BBDC
Exhaust valve closes	0° (TDC)	12° BTDC

Valve Timing – DJ5 TED Engine (direct injection)

Inlet valve opens	5.5 ° ATDC
Inlet valve closes	12.7° ATDC
Exhaust valve opens	37.5° BBDC
Exhaust valve closes	4° BTDC

BTDC = Before dead centre
ATDC = After top dead centre
BBDC = Before bottom dead centre
ATDC = After top dead centre

Valve Clearances – 1.9 litre only:
- Engine cold – Inlet valves — 0.15 +/- 0.008 mm
- Engine cold – Exhaust valves — 0.30 +/- 0.08 mm
- Engine hot — Not permissible

Some changes within the model years

Model Year 1995
New 1.9 litre engine "DHX" (XUD9UTF/X3) and new 2.5 litre engine "THZ" (DJ5T/X3). Increased performance (see above). Both engines have an exhaust gas return system (EGR) and an oxidation catalyser.

Model Year 1996
New glow plugs and new glow plug relay. Post-glow system fitted to extend the operation of the glow plugs after the engine has started. 4DW models introduced.

Model Year 1997
Main change can be found in the exhaust system (all engines). The vacuum pump is fitted with quick-connectors.

Model Year 1998
Engines with Bosch injection system have a new injection pump with electronically operating anti-theft system. Modifications on the 1.9 litre engine include crankshaft, cylinder block, cylinder head and the crankshaft timing belt sprocket.

Model Year 1999
The 1.9 litre engine without turbo charger has been re-named and is now known as XUD9AU (DJZ) engine. The power of all engines has changed slightly.

Model Year 2000
The 2.5 litre engine with turbo charger has a new, direct injection system with charge air cooler. The vacuum pump drive on this engine is from the end of the camshaft.

1.1   Engine – Removal and Installation

The removal and installation of the engine is not the same for all models. Follow the instructions for the engine in question.

2.1.1   1.9 LITRE – REMOVAL OF POWER UNIT

The engine and transmission are removed from the vehicle as a complete unit. The following description tries to cover engines with and without turbo charger. In the workshop a special lifting table is used to take out the unit, which will not be described in the following text. The power unit is removed towards the front, i.e. the front end of the vehicle must be removed as necessary to lift out the assembly. You will need a hoist or small crane, which must have the necessary carrying capacity. The same applies to the lifting brackets. Fig. 1.1 shows a suitable appliance to lift out the unit.

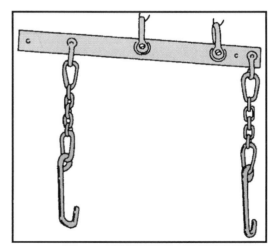

Fig. 1.1 – A lifting bracket and suitable chains can be used to lift the engine and transmission out of the engine compartment.

The bonnet should be removed or placed in vertical position and tied up.

Hose clamps are require a special pair of pliers to open and tighten them. Otherwise cut them and use screw-type clamps during installation.

Removal can now be attempted as follows:

- Disconnect the battery cables. If a radio with anti-theft code is fitted, make sure you have the code handy for later. Also remember that pre-programmed stations will be lost. The battery can be removed if preferred.

- Drain the cooling system (engine cold). A drain plug is inserted into the bottom of the radiator. Open the expansion tank cap to speed-up the draining. The anti-freeze can be collected if it appears to be in good condition. A plug can be fitted into the cylinder block. In this case remove it.

Engines

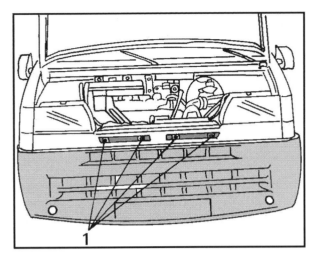

Fig. 1.3 – Remove the protective panels in the inside of each wheel arch. The support strut for the front bumper, shown in Fig. 1.11 can also be removed.

- The next operations are carried out by referring to Fig. 1.5. Remove the air cleaner (1), the air intake hoses (2), the bonnet lock (3) and the bracket for the power steering fluid container (if fitted).

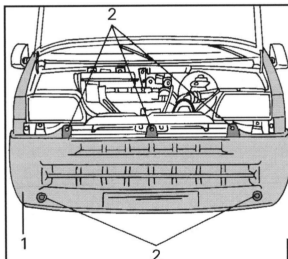

Fig. 1.5 – Removal of the 1.9 litre engine.
1   Air cleaner
2   Air intake hoses
3   Bonnet lock
4   Heat exchanger

- Disconnect the coolant hoses from the radiator and, if fitted the hoses from the heat exchanger (4) in Fig. 1.5.
- Disconnect all electrical connections from the radiator.

Fig. 1.2 – Remove the screws (1) and take off the front panel.

- Drain the transmission oil.
- Unscrew the four bolts shown by the arrows in Fig. 1.2 and remove the complete front of the vehicle.
- In the inside of the wheel arches remove the protective panel shown in Fig. 1.3. You will see a stay between the body and the front bumper, which must be, unscrewed at the top and the bottom (see also Fig. 1.11). The bumper is now removed by referring to Fig. 1.4.

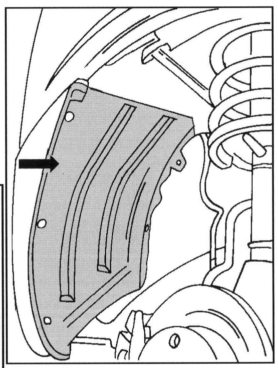

Fig. 1.4 – The front bumper (1) is secured with screws (2) at the positions shown.

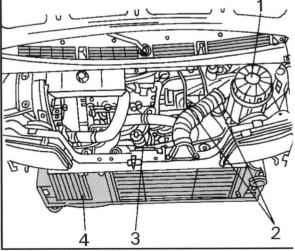

14

- Withdraw the cable plugs from the headlamps, remove the flasher lamps and dismount the front panel. Remove the radiator together with the cooling fan assembly. Remove the bolts (3) in Fig. 1.6 and take out the lower crossmember.

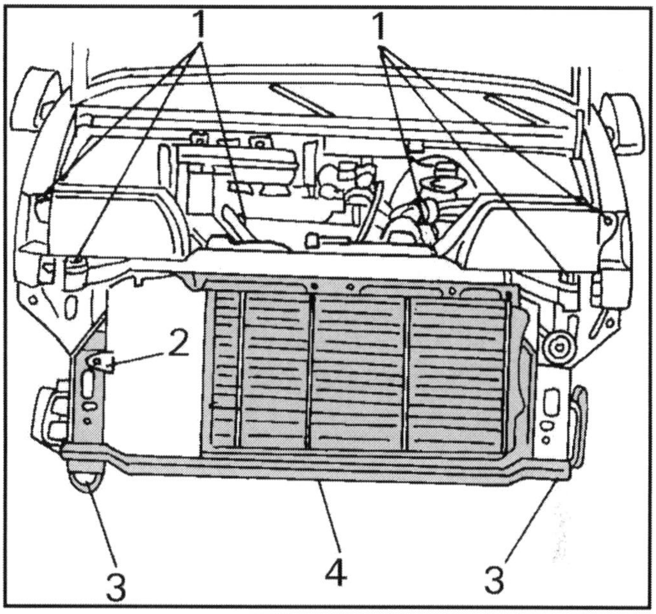

Fig. 1.6 – Removal of the 1.9 litre engine.

1	Bolts
2	Bolt
3	Bolts of lower crossmember
4	Lower crossmember

- Remove the connecting tube between the turbo charger and the heat exchanger.

- Disconnect the following electrical leads or pull off the cable connector plugs: from the alternator, from the starter motor, from all sensors, from the injection pump, unscrew the earth cable and disconnect the reversing light switch cable.

- The following items are disconnected: The fuel feed and return pipes, the clutch cable, the throttle operating cable, the vacuum hose from the brake servo unit, the heater hoses, the hoses from the cooling system expansion tank. Completely remove the expansion tank as it may be in the way.

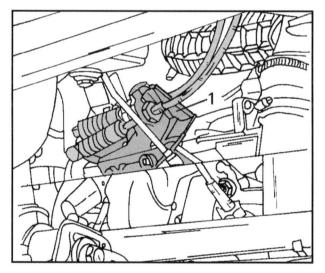

Fig. 1.7 – The gear change cable support bracket.

- Remove the drive shafts as described in the relevant section.

- Push the ball joints off the gearchange levers (screwdriver) and unscrew the gearchange control at the position shown in Fig. 1.7 and remove. Also the speedo-meter cable and withdraw it from the transmission.

- If power steering is fitted, locate the various pipes/hoses and disconnect them, and a union nut and the clamp from the return hose. Unscrew the pipe clamps where attached.

- Remove the cover underneath the flywheel housing.

- Unscrew the torque strut at the rear of the engine.

In the workshop the power unit is now lifted with the lifting table referred to above and removed towards the front. Under DIY conditions, you will need ropes or chains to lift up the assembly until it is no longer under tension. Make sure that the power unit is well supported and remove the L.H. engine mounting (Fig. 1.8) and the R.H. mounting (shown in Fig. 1.9). Nuts and bolts must be removed. The third mounting is the torque strut, which has already been removed.

Engines

Fig. 1.8 – The LH engine mounting.
1   Bolts, 5.0 kgm
2   Nuts, 8.0 kgm

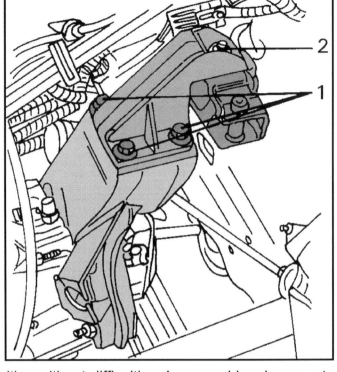

• Slowly lift the assembly towards the front out of the engine compartment. Check once more that all connections, hoses, etc. have been freed before lifting out the unit.

The installation of the engine and transmission is a reversal of the removal procedure. The following points should be noted in particular:

• Always replace self-locking nuts, lock plates, lock washers and other parts.

• Prepare the engine compartment to lift the engine and transmission in position without difficulties. Loose cables, hoses, etc. should be pushed well aside and fastened with sticky tape or tank tape.

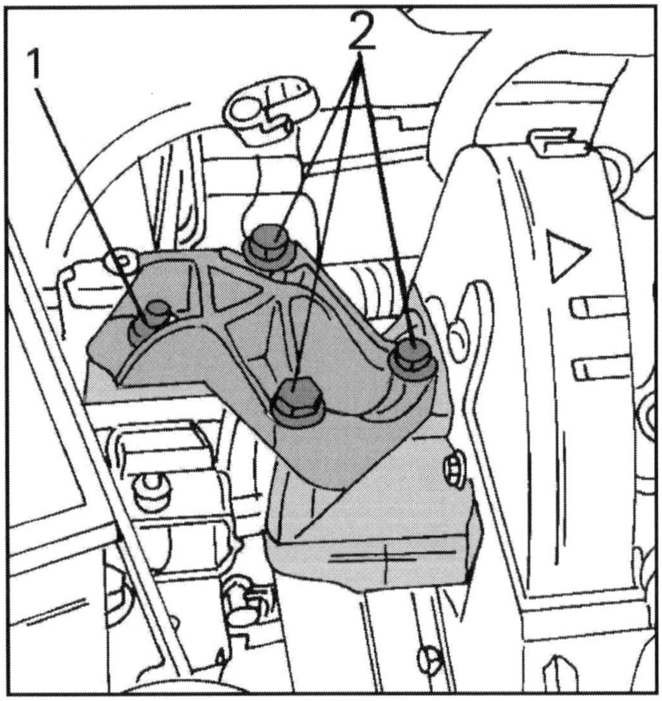

Fig. 1.9 – The RH engine mounting.
1   Nut, 8.0 kgm
2   Bolts, 5.0 kgm

• These are shown in Fig. 1.10. The following instructions refer, however to Figs. 1.8 and 1.9. Tighten the bolts and nuts with the torque values given in the illustrations. The torque strut (2) in Fig. 1.10 is tightened to 9.0 kgm (65 ft.lb.) after it is in the correct position.

• Refit the drive shafts as described in Chapter 4.

• Lift the engine and transmission in position and tighten the engine mountings.

• Refit the transmission, the steering fluid container and the cooling system as described in the relevant section. The cooling system must be bled of air.

• After fitting the power unit, start the engine and move the steering wheel from one lock into the other, to bleed the system. Check the fluid level in the container and correct if necessary. Lower the vehicle onto its wheels after the steering is free of air.

• Tighten the wheel bolts.

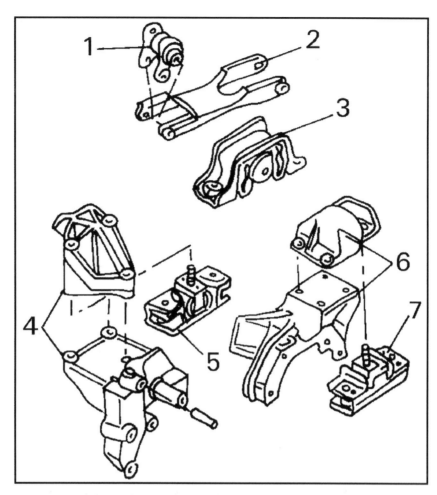

Fig. 1.10 – The engine and transmission mountings.

1	Rubber mounting, torque strut
2	Torque strut
3	Rubber mounting, torque strut
4	Mounting bracket, RH side
5	Rubber mount, RH mounting
6	Mounting bracket, LH side
7	Rubber mount, LH mounting

1.1.2   2.5 LITRE ENGINE

The instructions given for the 1.9 litre engines also apply to this engine. Proceed as follows:

- Disconnect the battery cables. If a radio with anti-theft code is fitted, make sure you have the code handy for later. Also remember that pre-programmed stations will be lost. The battery can be removed if preferred.
- Empty the container for the steering fluid.
- Place the front end of the vehicle on chassis stands, take off the front wheels and remove the protective cover underneath the vehicle.
- Drain the cooling system (engine cold). A drain plug is inserted into the bottom of the radiator. Open the expansion tank cap to speed-up the draining. The anti-freeze can be collected if it appears to be in good condition. A plug can be fitted into the cylinder block. In this case remove it.
- Drain the transmission oil.
- Unscrew the four bolts shown by the arrows in Fig. 1.2 and remove the complete front panel of the vehicle.

Engines

- In the inside of the wheel arches remove the protective panel shown in Fig. 1.3. You will see a stay between the body and the front bumper, which must be, unscrewed at the top and the bottom (see Fig. 1.11). The bumper is now removed by referring to Fig. 1.4.

Fig. 1.11 – In each wheel arch you will find a stay for the front bumper, which must be removed after taking off the protective panels.

- The next operations are carried out by referring to Fig. 1.12. Remove the air cleaner (1), the bonnet lock (2) and the bracket for the cooling system expansion tank.
- Disconnect the coolant hoses from the radiator and remove them.
- Disconnect all electrical connections from the radiator.

Withdraw the cable plugs from the headlamps, remove the flasher lamps and dismount the front panel. Remove the radiator together with the cooling fan assembly. Remove the bolts (3) in Fig. 1.6 and take out the lower crossmember.

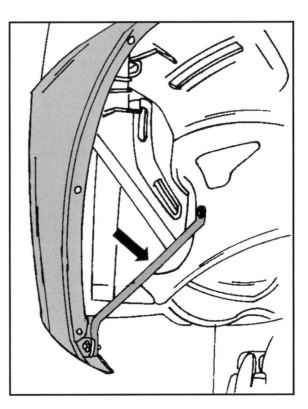

Fig, 1.12 – Parts to be removed in the engine compartment – 2.5 litre.

1	Air cleaner with intake hose
2	Bonnet lock
3	Mounting bracket
4	Expansion tank

- Remove the connecting tube between the turbo charger and the heat exchanger.
- Disconnect the following electrical leads or pull off the cable connector plugs from the alternator, from the starter motor, from all sensors, from the injection pump, unscrew the earth cable and disconnect the reversing light switch cable.
- The following items are disconnected: The fuel feed and return pipes, the clutch cable, the throttle operating cable, the vacuum hose from the brake servo unit and the heater hoses.
- Remove the drive shafts as described in the relevant section.
- Push the ball joints off the gearchange levers (screwdriver) and unscrew the gearchange control, similar as shown in Fig. 1.7 and remove. Also and the speedometer cable and withdraw it from the transmission.

- **On the power assisted steering:** Locate the various pipes/hoses and disconnect them, and a union nut and the clamp from the return hose. Unscrew the pipe clamps where attached.
- Remove the cover underneath the flywheel housing.
- Unscrew the torque strut at the rear of the engine. Fig. 1.10 shows where the strut is attached. The mounting is similar, if not the same, on the 2.5 litre engine.
- In the workshop the power unit is now lifted with the lifting table referred to above and removed towards the front. Under D.I.Y. conditions, you will need ropes or chains to lift up the assembly until it is no longer under tension. Make sure that the power unit is well supported and remove the engine mounting in Fig. 1.13 and the mounting in Fig. 1.14. Nuts and bolts are used, but only the bolts are removed. The third mounting is the torque strut, which has already been removed.

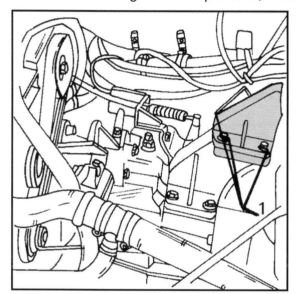 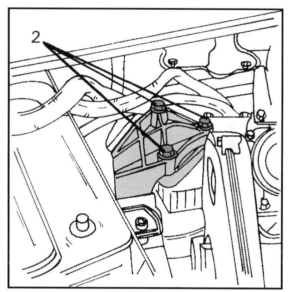

Fig. 1.13 (left) and 1.14 (right). Tighten the bolts (1) to 5.0 kgm and the bolt (2) to 6.0 kgm.

- Slowly lift the assembly towards the front out of the engine compartment. Check once more that all connections, hoses, etc. have been freed before lifting out the unit.

The installation is a reversal of the removal procedure. The instructions already given for the 1.9 litre engine will also apply to this engine. Note the different oil capacity when filling the engine. The same applies when the transmission has been drained.

After installation start the engine and check for leaks from the cooling system.

1.2   Engine - Dismantling

Before commencing dismantling of the engine, all exterior surfaces should be cleaned, as far as possible, to remove dirt or grease. Plug the engine openings with clean cloths to prevent any foreign matter entering the cavities and openings. Detailed information on engine dismantling and assembly is given in the sections dealing with servicing and overhaul (sections commencing at 1.4.) and these should be followed for each of the sub-assemblies or units to be dealt with.

Follow the general dismantling instructions given below. The two engine types are described under different headings:

Dismantling must be carried out in an orderly fashion to ensure that parts, such as valves, pistons, bearing caps, shells, tappets and so on, are replaced in the same positions as they occupied originally. Mark them clearly, but take care not to scratch or stamp on any rotating or bearing surfaces. A good way to keep the valves in order is by piercing them through an upside-down cardboard box, as shown in Fig. 1.15 and writing the number against each valve (refer to previous page). Segregate together the tappets, the springs and retainers with collets for each valve, if possible in small plastic bags for each individual valve.

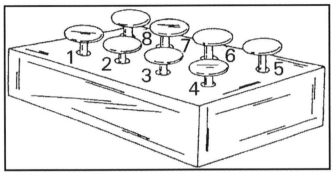

Fig. 1.15 – Valves can be pushed through the bottom of an upside down cardboard box.

- If a proper engine dismantling stand is not available, it will be useful to make up wooden support blocks to allow access to both the top and bottom faces of the engine. The cylinder head, once removed from the block, should be supported by a metal strap, screwed to the manifold face and secured by two nuts onto the manifold studs.

- The normal order of removal of parts for a complete engine strip-down is given below but this may, of course, be modified if only partial dismantling is required.

1.2.0   XUD ENGINE (1.9 LITRE)

- Drain the engine oil, remove the bolts between engine and transmission and remove the transmission from the engine without resting the weight of the transmission on the clutch shaft.

- Remove the oil filter. A suitable oil filter wrench should be used for this operation. Accessory shops have these as a stock item and it is a good investment to purchase one, as it is needed more than once in the lifetime of an engine. The filter is located at the top of the engine.

- Unscrew the support bearing for the drive shaft from one side of the cylinder block (4 bolts). Remove the oil return pipe when a turbo-charged engine is dismantled.

- Withdraw the oil dipstick.

Fig. 1.16 – Locking a flywheel.

- Mark the position of the clutch plate in relation to the flywheel by punching two marks in the clutch and the flywheel on opposite points. Unscrew the clutch and remove the driven plate. The flywheel should be held against rotation by inserting a screwdriver into the flywheel teeth or by means of a toothed sector as shown in Fig. 1.16. If the driven plate looks in good condition, take care not to contaminate it with oily fingers.

The next operations are carried out on the side of the injection pump by referring to Fig. 1.18 on the next page. If fitted, remove the heat exchanger (1), the fuel filter (2) with the filter bracket, the oil separator (4) with the connected hoses, unscrew the cover (5), lift out the thermostat and unscrew the coolant outlet housing (3). Remove the union nuts for the injector pipes (6) and pull the pipes out of their connectors. Protect the ends of the pipes against entry of dirt. Also on the same side of the engine remove the alternator, the steering pump (if fitted) and the accessory plate. Also disconnect the fast idle operating cable. Not all items mentioned are shown in the illustration.

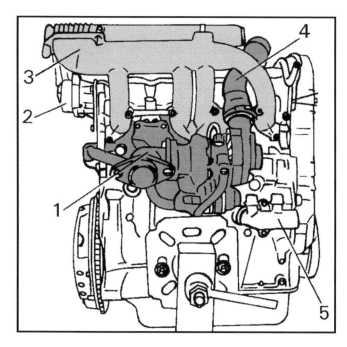

Fig. 1.17 – View of the engine from the exhaust manifold side.

1	Exhaust manifold
2	Vacuum pump
3	Inlet manifold
4	Air duct
5	Coolant inlet elbow

- On the side of the exhaust manifold, remove the items shown in Fig. 1.17.
- Remove the oil sump. To do this, place the engine on its side and remove 23 securing bolts. Lift off the oil sump (Fig. 1.19).

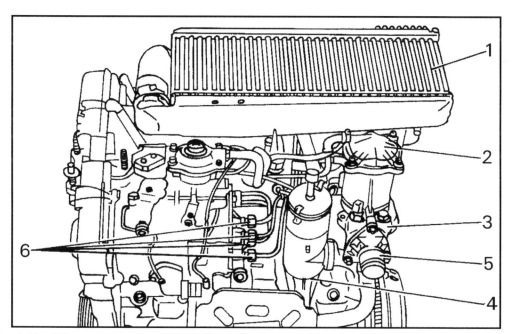

Fig. 1.18 – View of the engine from the injection pump side. Remove the parts shown.

1	Heat exchanger (if fitted)	4	Oil separator
2	Fuel filter	5	Closing cover
3	Coolant outlet elbow	6	Union nuts, injection pipes

Note: The above instructions are valid for a sheet metal sump. Vehicles with A/C system have an aluminium sump and the attachment is slightly different. There are also 23 screws, but 20 have the same length, two other screws have a different length and a further screw has a different length. Fig. 1.20 shows this sump. During installation insert the screws accordingly.

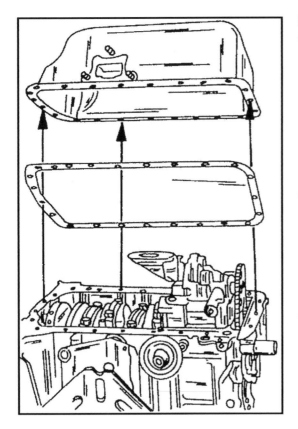

Fig. 1.20 – Attachment of the aluminium oil sump (with A/C system).

1	Bolts (20), 22 mm long
2	Oil sump
3	Bolts (2), 40 mm long
4	Bolt (1), 20 mm long

Fig. 1.19 – Removal of the oil sump.

- Lock the flywheel as shown in Fig. 1.16 and remove the crankshaft pulley bolt. Also unscrew the bolts securing the flywheel to the crankshaft and with a mallet tap off the flywheel. There is no need to mark the flywheel, as it can only be fitted in one position. Counterhold the flywheel as shown in Fig. 1.16 once more.

- Remove the crankshaft pulley from the other end of the engine. Two tyre levers can be placed under the pulley on opposite sides to pry it off. Otherwise use a puller with two extractor bolts which can be screwed into the holes of the pulley.

- Remove the two toothed belt covers from the front of the engine, removing the spring clip in the centre of the covers with a strong screwdriver (push it out). Also remove the covering panel at the bottom of the timing belt. Fig. 1.21 shows a view of the engine thus dismantled (Page 23).

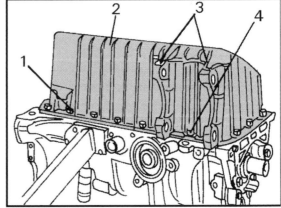

- Obtain three 8 mm x 40 mm bolts, insert one of the bolts into position (1) in Fig. 1.22 into the camshaft timing wheel and the two others into positions (2) and (3) of the injection pump drive gear. This will lock the timing mechanism. If the engine is to be dismantled completely, ignore this instruction. Only if it is to be prevented to re-adjust the timing setting, lock the mechanism as described.

- Remove the nut (4) and the bolt (5) securing the timing belt tensioner pulley. Insert the square of a 3/8 in. socket set into the square hole (6) in Fig. 1.22 (next page) of the pulley bracket and push the assembly to the outside until the belt is slack. Then re-tighten the bolt (5) in Fig. 1.22 to retain the pulley in its new position.

- Carefully remove the timing belt from the timing gearwheels.

- Remove the cylinder head as described in Section 1.4.0.1.

- Remove the five screws securing the water pump and remove the pump. Take off the gasket.

- Remove the two screws securing the thermostat housing and take off the housing. Remove the gasket.

- Remove the parts from the exterior of the engine. These include the oil cooler, the pulley for the vacuum pump, the engine breather assembly, etc.

• Remove the cover in front of the oil pump (6 screws, see Fig. 1.24). The cover is located on two dowel pins and must be carefully levered off.

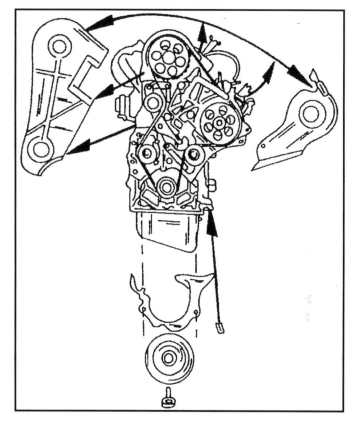

Fig. 1.21 – Parts removed from the front of the engine.

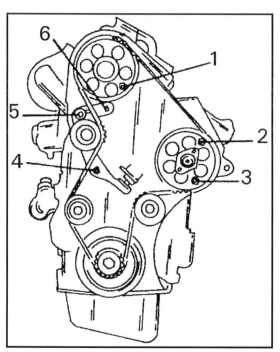

Fig. 1.22 – Removal of the timing mechanisms.

1	Inserted bolt	4	Securing screw
2	Inserted bolt	5	Securing screw
3	Inserted bolt	6	Square hole

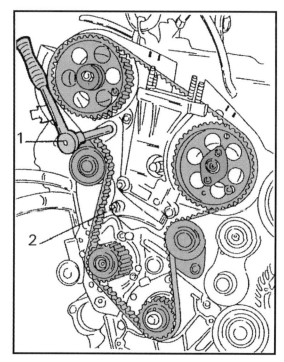

Fig. 1.23 – Removal of the timing belt. Slacken the nut (2) and a nut hidden by the ratchet and rotate the belt tensioner with a socket (1), to compress the spring.

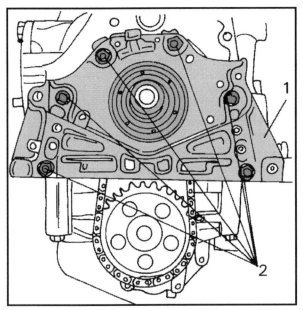

Fig. 1.24 – Removal of the front cover (1). Six screws (2) hold the cover in position.

- Remove the three screws securing the oil pump to the bottom face of the crankcase. Remove the spacer plate in the direction as shown in Fig. 1.25 (not on all engines); disengage the drive chain from the sprocket and lift out the oil pump. Fig. 1.26 shows the removal.

- Remove the chain sprocket and the key from the end of the crankshaft and take off the chain.

- Refer to Fig. 1.27 and remove the camshaft timing gearwheel and the injection pump drive wheel. Remove the injection pipes and the injection pump. Use a flat spanner to hold the hexagon when slackening the pipe union nuts.

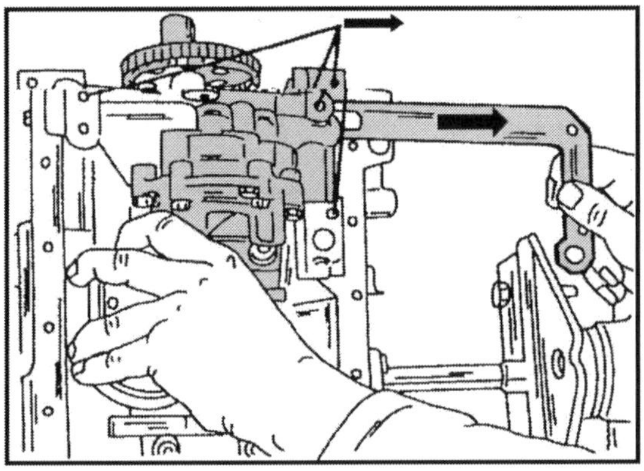

Fig. 1.25 – Remove the spacer plate before taking off the oil pump.

- Turn the cylinder block upside down, with the open crankcase uppermost and rotate the crankshaft until two of the crankpins are in the bottom dead centre position.

- Mark the two accessible bearing caps and the connecting rods with a centre punch and remove the connecting rod bearing cap nuts (Fig. 1.28). Remove the bearing caps and bearing shells and put the parts aside. Using a hammer handle now push the pistons out of the cylinder bores. The upper bearing shell will be stuck either to the connecting rod or to the crankpin. Retrieve the shell and immediately fit the other shell and the bearing cap to the removed connecting rod/piston assembly.

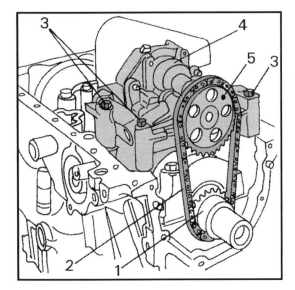

Fig. 1.26 – The fitted oil pump.

1	Sprocket on crankshaft
2	Drive chain
3	Pump bolts
4	Oil pump
5	Oil pump sprocket

- Rotate the crankshaft until the remaining crankpins are at bottom dead centre and remove the pistons and connecting rods in the same manner.

- Mark the main bearing caps and their bearing locations on one side of the engine and remove the caps one after the other. Remove the bearing shells out of the caps, thoroughly clean them and mark the back of each cap with the bearing number.

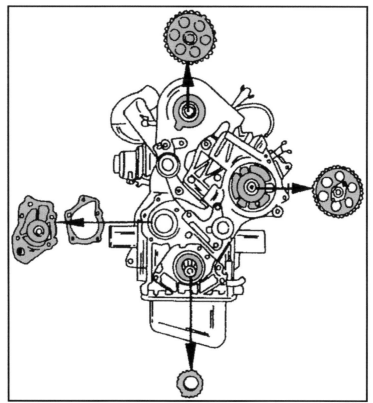

Fig. 1.27 – Dismantling of the engine.

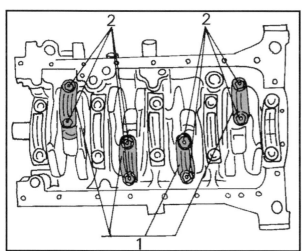

Fig. 1.28 – Big end bearing caps (1) are secured with two nuts each.

- Remove the oil seal from the flywheel end of the crankshaft. The seal must be replaced, once removed.
- Carefully lift the crankshaft out of the bearing bores and remove the five bearing shells from the crankcase. Also remove the two half thrust washers from the second crankshaft main bearing journal. Attach the bearing shells of each bearing to the respective main bearing cap, if the same shells are to be fitted. Also mark where each half of the thrust washer has been removed from.
- Dismantle the pistons as described in Section 1.4.1.1 and the cylinder head as described in Section 1.4.0.2.

1.2.1   DISMANTLING THE 2.5 LITRE ENGINE

The dismantling of the 2.5 litre engine follows in general as described for the 1.9 litre engine. Special instructions for specific operations, for example on the cylinder head or the timing mechanisms are given under the relevant headings.

1.3   Engine - Assembly

The following general instructions are applicable to all engines. When assembling the engine, follow the general proceedings outlined in this section and refer to the later sections, commencing at 1.4 for any detailed information that is necessary. In the following description, it is assumed that all sub-assemblies have been overhauled or replaced, if necessary.

Carefully clean the cylinder block, paying particular attention to the crevices, which are easily overlooked. Note that the cylinder block is made of aluminium-alloy and should therefore not be scraped in order to clean the gasket faces.

Lubricate each rotating or moving part with engine oil BEFORE it is assembled. Lubricating it after the assembly has little purpose, as the oil cannot reach the gliding surfaces at all times. Oil seals should be replaced as a matter of course. The same goes for the lock washers or lock plates. Check that all oilways are thoroughly clean.

Assemble the engine in the following general order. The assembly is based on the 1.9 litre engine. Any differences, which apply to the other engine, can be found in the specific sections later on in the manual.

Fig. 1.29 – Fit the connecting rod and the bearing cap with the marks (1) on the same side. Oil the bearing shells (2) before installation into the connecting rod and bearing cap.

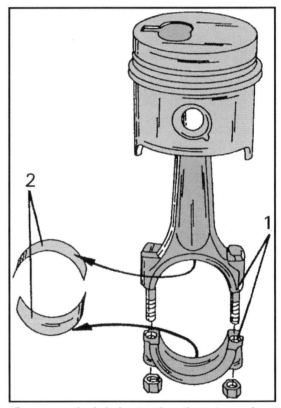

- Assemble the pistons and connecting rods as described in Section 1.4.1.1.

- Fit the bearing shells into the connecting rods and the big end bearing caps in accordance with Fig. 1.29, if the original parts are re-used. Make sure the lugs on the shells engage into the holes in the bearing bore.

- Generously lubricate the main bearing shells with oil and place them into the crankcase bores. These are the shells with the oil grooves.

- If fitted, fit the oil splash jets to the bottom of the cylinder block.

- Fit the half thrust washers to the No. 2 main bearing (No. 1 is next to the flywheel) so that the washer friction faces are against the crankshaft flange. Generously lubricate the thrust washers with oil.

- Once more, check that the bearing shells are well lubricated and slowly lift the crankshaft into the crankcase. Rotate the crankshaft a few times to settle the bearing shells. Fit the lower bearing shells into the bearing caps (half thrust washers to No. 2 bearing cap) and fit the bearing caps in accordance with the marks made on dismantling. The numbering must be on the side of the oil filter. The rear cap is not fitted at this stage.

The crankshaft end float is now checked, and if necessary corrected, as described below:

Fit a dial gauge with a suitable bracket to the front end of the cylinder block and set the stylus and place the stylus onto the end of the crankshaft, as shown in Fig. 1.30. If a dial gauge with a magnetic case is used, place the base against the crankshaft end face, with the stylus resting against the cylinder block face.

Fig. 1.30 – Checking the crankshaft end float.

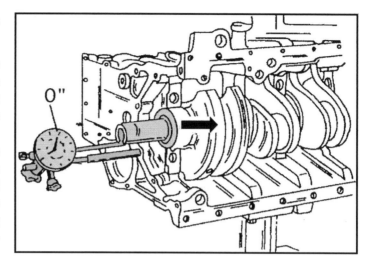

- Move the crankshaft to one side as shown by the arrow in the illustration and set the dial gauge to "Zero".
- Move the crankshaft to the other side in the same manner and read the dial gauge indication. The value should be between 0.07 – 0.32 mm (0.0003 – 0.013 in.).
- If the end float exceeds the upper value, replace the half thrust washers. The crankshaft must be partially removed to take out the washers. Washers are available in thicknesses of 2.35, 2.40, 2.45 and 2.50 mm, apart from the standard thickness. Two washers of the same thickness must always be fitted to one side of the crankshaft.

A special tool is required to fit the rear main bearing cap to prevent damage to the cap side seals. First coat the mounting faces for the bearing cap (on the crankcase face) with sealing compound. Then proceed as follows:

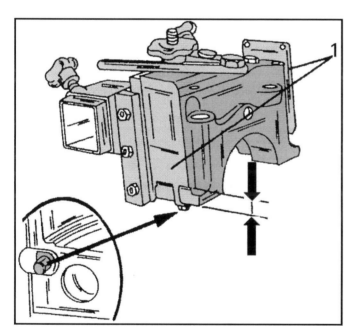

Fig. 1.31 – Fitting the side seals of the rear bearing cap. The guide plates (1) push the seals into the grooves. The seals must protrude at the bottom as shown in the inset.

- Fit the two guide plates to the special tool, as shown in Fig. 1.31. The screws are only tightened finger-tight.
- Fit two new side seals to the sides of the rear bearing cap with the holder. Fit the holder to the main bearing cap, using the clamp screw. Lubricate the guide plates with engine oil.
- Push the guide plates together with one hand and insert the whole assembly at an angle into the cylinder block opening, until the cap is in the correct position. Push the tool downwards until this is the case.
- Fit the two main bearing cap bolts and tighten them finger-tight.
- Unscrew the tool body from the cap and remove the tool together with the guide plates from the cylinder block.
- Commencing at the centre and working towards the outside, evenly tighten all main bearing cap bolts to 7.0 kgm (50.5 ft.lb.).
- Fit two of the flywheel bolts into the crankshaft flange and insert a screwdriver between the bolts to rotate the crankshaft, check the crankshaft for binding before proceeding with the assembly.

Engines

- Coat the outside of a new rear oil seal with oil and drive it in position into the crankcase and the rear bearing cap. Take care not to damage the oil seal. Use a mandrel that will cover the complete outer face of the seal.

Fig. 1.32 – Fitting a piston.

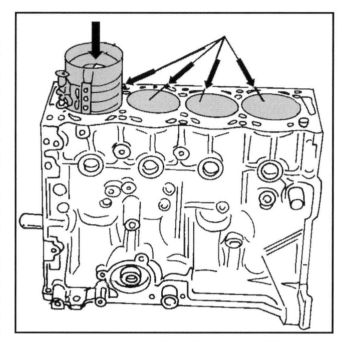

- Arrange the assembled piston and connecting rods in their cylinder order. Fit a piston ring clamp band around the piston rings, as shown in Fig. 1.32, and guide the connecting rod into the cylinder bore and over the crankpin (bearing shell must be in connecting rod).

- Check that the piston bowl is in the correct position and use a hammer handle to push the piston into the bore. The clamp band will slide off the piston as soon as all piston rings have entered the bore. Make sure that the connecting rod is guided over the crankpin at the same time. The cylinder block can be placed onto its side to facilitate the installation. Two of the crankshaft pins should be at the bottom dead centre position and connecting rod/piston assemblies of these two should be fitted.

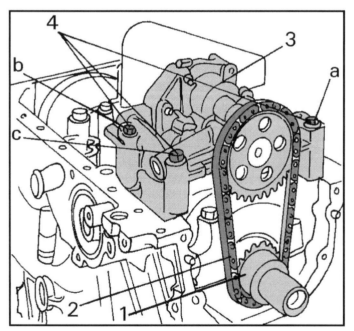

Fig. 1.33 – The location of the various securing screws for the oil pump.

1	Crankshaft sprocket
2	Drive chain
3	Oil pump
4	Securing screws
a	Bolt, 80 mm long
b	Bolt, 70 mm long
c	Bolt, 65 mm long

- Fit the pistons of the other cylinders in the same manner.

- Fit the bearing shells in accordance with the marks made during dismantling into the bearing caps of the two fitted connecting rods and lubricate the shell faces with oil. Fit the bearing caps over the connecting rod bolts and check that both cylinder marks on rod and cap are on the same side of the cylinder block.

- Fit new nuts and evenly tighten the two nuts to 2.0 kgm (14.5 ft.lb.). From the final position each nut must then be tightened by a further 70°. Either estimate the angle (1/4 of a turn is 90°) or use a graduated disc.

- Rotate the crankshaft a few times to check for binding and then rotate the shaft until the two remaining crankpins are at bottom dead centre.

- Fit the other two pistons and connecting rod assemblies in the manner described, always checking that the marking is strictly adhered to.

- Fit the oil pump drive sprocket with the key and the drive chain to the end of the crankshaft. The cylinder block should be with the cylinder head gasket face uppermost, with the chain hanging down, engaged with the sprocket.

- Fit the front oil seal cover with a new gasket. The six screws must be inserted in accordance with their length. The screws at the top on the L.H. side in Fig. 1.24 are 35 mm long, the others 10 mm. Tighten all screws to 1.2 kgm (9.5 ft.lb.).

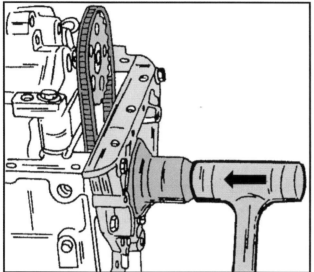

Fig. 1.34 – Fitting the front crankshaft oil seal after installation of the oil pump.

- When fitting the oil pump, engage the chain over the oil pump sprocket, place the oil pump in position and slide the spacer, if fitted, between the pump and the cylinder block, in reverse to the arrow shown in Fig. 1.25.

- Insert the screws, shown in Fig. 1.33. The screws are of different length (see illustration, a to c), but all screws are tightened to 1.8 kgm (13 ft.lb.).

- Coat the outside and the sealing lip of the front crankshaft oil seal with engine oil and fit the seal over the end of the crankshaft and into the oil seal cover. Use a suitable mandrel, which covers the outside face of the seal, as shown in Fig. 1.34 on the next page. Take care not to damage the seal.

Fig. 1.35 – Measuring the protrusion of the piston above the cylinder block face. The stylus is placed onto the block face and set to "Zero".

- Fit the oil sump with a new gasket and tighten the 23 screws evenly to a torque setting of 1.6 kgm (11.5 ft.lb.). Insert the screws in accordance with the markings during removal. An aluminium oil sump is guided on the crankcase by means of a dowel pin. No gasket is used, but the block face must be coated with sealing compound. Again insert the screws as marked during removal. The same torque setting applies.

- Fit the flywheel. Always use new bolts. Rotate the flywheel until all bolt holes are aligned. Coat the threads with "Loctite" before installation. Tighten the bolts evenly to 5.0 kgm (36 ft.lb.). The flywheel must be held against rotation. Either insert a screwdriver into the teeth of the flywheel ring gear or use a locking sector as shown in Fig. 1.16.

- Fit the clutch driven plate and the clutch pressure plate. Align the clutch driven plate with a centring mandrel (mandrel sets are available from tool hire companies

Engines

and one will fit the driven plate). Tighten the clutch plate securing screws to 2.0 kgm (14.5 ft.lb.).

Cylinder head gaskets are available in different thicknesses and the gasket to be used depends on the protrusion of the piston above the cylinder block face. To check the protrusion, rotate the crankshaft until each piston in turn is at top dead centre position. Measure the amount the piston end is above the cylinder block face (protrusion) as follows:

*   Place a dial gauge with a suitable holder onto the well cleaned cylinder block face and place the dial gauge stylus next to the piston to be measured onto the cylinder block face. Set the dial gauge to "Zero" in this position, as shown in Fig. 1.35 (previous page).

Fig. 1.36 – Measuring the protrusion of the pistons above the cylinder block face. The stylus is placed onto the piston crown, as far as possible near the centre of the piston.

*   Leave the dial gauge holder in position on the block face and swing the stylus over the piston, as far as possible to the centre, as shown in Fig. 1.36. Read the indicated value on the dial gauge and make a note to which pistons it applies.
*   Measure the remaining pistons in the same manner, always rotating the crankshaft until each piston is at top dead centre position. Write down each value.
*   The greatest dimension determines the thickness of the cylinder head gasket, but the difference between two of the pistons must not exceed 0.12 mm (0.0047 in.).

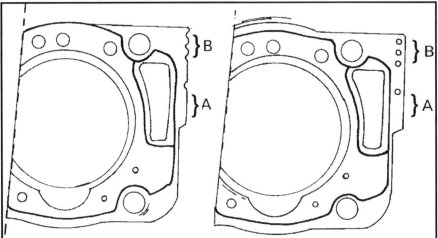

Fig. 1.37 – View of the cylinder head gasket for earlier engines. At "A" the engine type can be recognised, "B" indicates the thickness. Gaskets can have holes (left) or notches (right).

The protrusion must now be evaluated with the help of Figs. 1.37 and 1.38:

Referring to Fig. 1.37:

*   If the greatest dimension is between 0.54 and 0.65 mm, fit a gasket which has no notch at position "A" and one notch at position "B", if a naturally aspirating engine

is assembled. The gasket for a turbo diesel engine must have 3 notches at "A" and 1 notch at "B".

- If the greatest dimension is between 0.65 and 0.77 mm, use a gasket without notch or hole at position "A" and 2 notches or holes at position "B", if a normal diesel engine is being dealt with. A gasket for a turbo diesel engine must have 3 notches or holes at position "A" and 2 notches or holes at position "B".

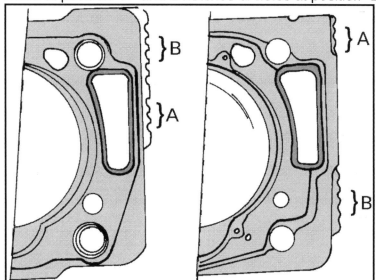

Fig. 1.38 – View of the cylinder head gasket on later engines. The engine type can be recognised at "A", the thickness at "B". The notches are either close together or apart (right),

- If the greatest dimension is between 0.78 and 0.82 mm, use a gasket without notch or hole at position "A" and 3 notches or holes at position "B".
- A gasket for a turbo diesel engine must have 3 notches or holes at position "A" and 3 notches or holes at position "B".

Referring to Fig. 1.38:

- If the greatest dimension is between 0.56 and 0.67 mm use a gasket without notch or hole at position "A" and 1 notch or hole at position "B". A gasket for a turbo diesel engine must have 3 notches or holes at position "A" and 1 notch or hole at position "B".
- If the greatest dimension is between 0.68 and 0.71 mm use a gasket without notch or hole at position "A" and 2 notches or holes at position "B" (standard engine). A gasket for a turbo diesel engine must have 3 notches or holes at position "A" and 2 notches or holes at position "B".
- If the greatest dimension is between 0.72 and 0.75 mm use a gasket without notch or hole at position "A" and 3 notches or holes at position "B" (standard engine). A gasket for a turbo diesel engine must have 3 notches or holes at position "A" and 3 notches or holes at position "B",
- If the greatest dimension is between 0.76 and 0.79 mm use a gasket without notch or hole at position "A" and 4 notches or holes at position "B" (standard engine). A gasket for a turbo diesel engine must have 4 notches or holes at position "A" and 4 notches or holes at position "B".
- If the greatest dimension is between 0.80 and 0.83 mm use a gasket without notch or hole at position "A" and 5 notches or holes at position "B" (standard engine). A gasket for a turbo diesel engine must have 3 notches or holes at position "A" and 5 notches or holes at position "B".

Engines

Note: As can be seen from the above instructions, you will have to follow it to the letter in order to select the correct gasket. We recommend therefore, to measure the protrusion as described and go to the parts department to have the correct gasket selected – remember standard diesel or turbo-charged diesel are different.

After the protrusion has been measured, turn the crankshaft until all four pistons are approx. In the centres of their bores, before continuing with the assembly.

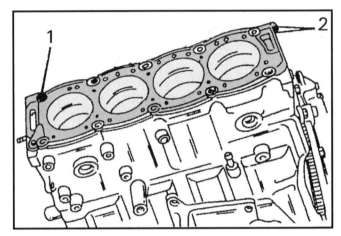

Fig. 1.39 – View of the fitted cylinder head gasket, with the position of the dowel sleeve (1) and the identification notches (2).

- Check that the dowel pin (1) in Fig. 1.39 is in position in the cylinder block face and place the cylinder head gasket in position. The notches on the outer edge of the cylinder head gasket must be located on the flywheel side of the engine. No sealing compound must be used for the gasket. Fit it dry.
- Fit the cylinder head in accordance with the instructions in Section 1.4.0.4 and check and if necessary adjust the valve clearances as described in Section 1.4.0.5.
- Fit the water pump with a new gasket and tighten the screws to 1.5 kgm (11.5 ft.lb.).
- Fit the thermo switches into the adapter housing for the thermostat and tighten them to 1.5 kgm (11.5 ft.lb.).
- Fit the thermostat with two new gaskets and attach the adapter housing to the thermostat housing. Fit the complete thermostat housing with a new gasket to the cylinder head.
- Remove the camshaft timing gear (which should be still in position, as it is required for the adjustment of the valve clearance) and fit the camshaft oil seals with a suitable mandrel, without damaging the seal lips. Coat the seal lips with a little grease.
- Fit the camshaft timing gearwheel. Tighten the centre bolt to 4.3 kgm (31 ft.lb.). The gearwheel must be held against rotation. To do this, insert a metal rod into one of the timing gear holes and rest the rod against the head.
- Refit the injection pump in accordance with the instructions in the relevant section.
- Rotate the crankshaft, the camshaft and the injection pump shaft into the timing position. To do this, refer to Fig. 1.40. The arrows point to the position of the Woodruff keys.
- Fit the injection pump drive gear and tighten the bolt in the centre. The gear must be counterheld against rotation. Insert a metal rod into one of the openings. Tighten the bolt to 5.0 kgm (36 ft.lb.).
- Fit the crankshaft timing gear over the end of the crankshaft, using a piece of tube. Make sure that the Woodruff key is fitted.
- Fit the timing belt. First place the belt over the crankshaft timing gearwheel, then over the fixed pulley in the centre, the injection pump drive gear and finally over the camshaft timing gearwheel. Hold the driving side of the belt tight and then

place it over the tensioning roller and the water pump wheel. Check that the timing belt has engaged correctly with all gearwheels and tension the belt as described in the relevant section.

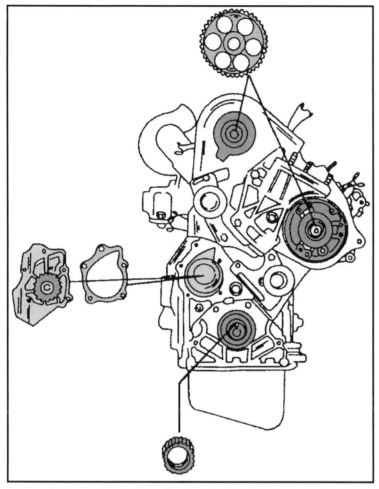

Fig. 1.40 – The arrows point to the position of the Woodruff keys in the shafts for the adjustment of the timing and fitting of the timing belt.

- Lock the injection pump drive gear by inserting two M8 x 40 mm bolts into the bores (2) and (3) in Fig. 1.22. The drive gear is now in position for the injection timing for the 1st cylinder.

- Lock the crankshaft by inserting an 8 mm metal rod from the rear into the cylinder block and guide into the hole of the flywheel, as shown in Fig. 1.41.

- Adjust the injection pump timing as described in the relevant section.

- Fit the crankshaft pulley. Coat the bolt thread with "Loctite". The bolt is tightened to 4.0 kgm (30 ft.lb.). From this position tighten the bolt a further 60°. The crankshaft must be prevented from rotation, as shown earlier on.

Fig. 1.41 – Locating the crankshaft in the timing position.

- Fit the injectors and tighten to 9 kgm (65 ft.lb.). Fit the injection pipes. Tighten the union nuts to 2.0 kgm (14.5 ft.lb.).

- Fit the glow plugs and tighten to 2.2 kgm (15 ft.lb.). Connect the glow plug bus bar to the plugs and tighten the nuts 0.4 kgm (3 ft.lb.).

- Fit the two timing belt covers with the spring clips. The clip in the centre is pushed in position with a large screwdriver.

- Refit the remaining parts to the engine. Tighten the exhaust manifold nuts to 2.0 kgm (14.5 ft.lb.) and the inlet manifold nuts to 2.3 kgm (17 ft.lb.). Fit the oil filter with a new sealing ring and tighten to 1.4 kgm (10 ft.lb.).

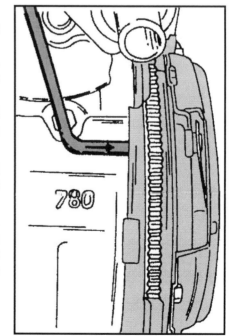

Engines

1.4. Engine – Servicing and Overhaul

1.4.0   CYLINDER HEAD AND VALVES

1.4.4.0   Technical Data

1.9 Litre Engines

Cylinder Head:

- Cylinder head height, face to face	140 mm +/- 0.05 mm
- Min. permissible height	139.56 mm
- Max. distortion of head surface	0.07 mm
- Grinding of head surface	Not permissible
- Valve faces below cylinder head face	See under "Valves"

Cylinder Head Bolt Length

Bolts without guide spigots:

- Without turbo charger – New/wear limit	129 mm/121.50 mm
- With turbo charger	145 mm/146.50 mm

Bolts with guide spigots:

- Without turbo charger – New/wear limit	123.0 mm/125.5 mm
- With turbo charger	150.0 mm/150.5 mm

Camshaft Bearing Bores in Cylinder Head:

- No. 1, flywheel end	27.500 – 27.533 mm
- No. 2	28.000 – 28.033 mm
- No. 3	28.500 – 28.533 mm

Cylinder Head Gasket

See description during installation of cylinder head. Different gaskets are used for non-turbo and turbo diesel engines.

Valve Guides

Nominal outside diameter	13.981 – 14.013 mm
Repair size 1 – 1 groove	14.211 – 14.083 mm
Repair size 2 – 2 grooves	14.511 – 14.543 mm

Locating Bore in Cylinder Head:

- With nominal outside diameter	14.009 – 14.020 mm
- Repair size 1 14.279 – 14.290 mm	
- Repair size 2 14.579 – 14.590 mm	

Inside diameter of guides	8.020 mm
Installation height, guide to head face	36.5 +/- 0.5 mm

Valve Shaft Clearance in Guides:

- Inlet valves	0.015 – 0.230 mm
- Exhaust valves	0.035 – 0.250 mm

Valve Seats

Seat angle, inlet and exhaust valves	90°
Width of valve seat faces – Inlet/Exhaust	2.45/3.00 mm

Valve Seat Outer Diameters – Inlet Valves:

- Nominal diameter	40.136 – 40.161 mm
- Repair size 1	40.336 – 40.461 mm
- Repair size 2	40.636 – 40.661 mm

Valve Seat Outer Diameters – Exhaust Valves:
- Nominal diameter   34.112 – 34.137 mm
- Repair size 1   34.412 – 34.437 mm
- Repair size 2   34.612 – 34.737 mm

Locating Bore in Cylinder Head – Inlet valves:
- Nominal diameter   40.000 mm
- Repair size 1   40.300 mm
- Repair size 2   40.500 mm

Locating Bore in Cylinder Head – Exhaust Valves:
- Nominal diameter   34.000 mm
- Repair size 1   34.300 mm
- Repair size 2   34.500 mm

Valves
Valve Shaft Diameters:
- Inlet valves   7.790 – 8.005 mm
- Exhaust valves   7.970 – 7.985 mm
Valve seat angle   90°
Valve Head Diameters:
- Inlet valves   38.50 +/- 0.10 mm
- Exhaust valves   33.50 +/- 0.20 mm
Min. Valve Length:
- Inlet valves   112.4 mm
- Exhaust valves   111.85 mm
Valve Stem Diameter:
- Inlet valves   7.996 mm +/- 0.03 mm
- Exhaust valves   7.970 mm +/- 0.01 mm
Stem end, max. grinding allowance   0.20 mm
Stem to guide clearance, max.   0.10 mm
Valve Shaft Clearance in Guides:
- Inlet valves   0.015 – 0.230 mm
- Exhaust valves   0.035 – 0.250 mm

Valve Springs
Wire diameter   3.80 mm
Coil diameter   29.60 mm
Length under load of 32 kg   42.80 mm
Length under load of 55 kg   33.30 mm

Valve Clearances
Engine cold – Inlet valves   0.15 mm +/- 0.08 mm
Engine cold – Exhaust valves   0.30 mm +/- 0.08 mm)
Engine warm   Not permissible

Valve Timing, all engines
Inlet valve opens   -4° BTDC
Inlet valve closes   35° ABDC
Exhaust valve opens   43° BBDC
Exhaust valve closes   0° (TDC)

Camshaft
Camshaft end float   0.025 – 0.114 mm

Engines

Camshaft bearing running clearance	0.04 – 0.082 mm
Camshaft Journal Diameter (standard):	
- No. 1	27.50 mm
- No. 2	28.00 mm
- No. 3	28.50 mm
Camshaft Journal Diameter (Repair Diameters):	
- No. 1	28.00 mm
- No. 2	28.50 mm
- No. 3	29.00 mm
Camshaft identification	Colour ring on No. 1 cam

2.5 Litre Engine

Cylinder head	Aluminium alloy
Cylinder head height, face to face	117.0 mm +/- 0.05 mm
Max. distortion of cylinder head face	0.03 mm
Length of cylinder head bolts:	
- M12 diameter	152.50 mm
- M10 diameter	162.50 mm

Cylinder Head Gasket

Protrusion of Pistons above Block Face:	
- Except with direct injection	0.5 mm +/- 0.05 mm
- With direct injection	0.63 mm +/- 0.05 mm
Thickness of gasket:	
- Except with direct injection	1.6 mm (one thickness)
- With direct injection	1.4 mm (one thickness)
Fitting direction	Identification tag on side of injection pump
Piston protrusion	By selection of pistons with different height, only applicable when pistons are replaced. Cylinder head is fitted without measuring protrusion.

Valve Guides

Outer diameter – Nominal	13.026 mm
Repair size	13.579 – 13.590 mm
Inner diameter	7.020 – 7.042 mm
Installation height, guide to cyl. head face	93.17 mm +/- 0.20 mm
Valve shaft clearance in guides:	
- Inlet valves	0.015 – 0.230 mm
- Exhaust valves	0.035 – 0.250 mm

Valve Seats

Valve seat angle	90°, all valves
Valve seat width – All valves	2.25 mm
Valve seat outer diameter – All valves:	
- Nominal diameter	39.112 – 39.137 mm
- Repair size 1	39.612 – 39.637 mm

Valves

Valve Shaft Diameter:	
- Inlet valves	6.790 – 7.005 mm
- Exhaust valves	6.970 – 6.985 mm

Valve seat angle	90°
Valve head diameter, all valves	36.90 mm
Min. Valve Length:	
- Inlet valves	127.91 mm
- Exhaust valves	127.51 mm
Valve Lift:	
- Inlet valves	9.40 mm (8.40 mm turbo)
- Exhaust valves	9.25 mm (all engines)

Valve Springs

Number of springs	1, same for all valves
Coil diameter	29.30 mm
Length under load of 30 kg	36.40 mm
Length under load of 53 kg	27.15 mm
Valve Clearance	Automatic by means of hydraulic compensating elements

Valve Timing	Except DJ5 TED	DJ5 TED
Inlet valve opens	13° BTDC	5.5° ATDC
Inlet valve closes	38° ABCD*	12.7° BBDC
Exhaust valve opens	56° BBDC	37.5° BBDC
Exhaust valve closes	12° ATDC	4° BTDC

* = 32° ABDC in case of turbo-charged engine

1.4.0.1. Cylinder Head – Removal

The cylinder head can be removed with the engine fitted to the vehicle, but it should be pointed out that the timing belt must be partially removed and a dial gauge with a magnetic base must be available to determine the thickness of the cylinder head gasket required, when the gasket of a 1.9 litre engine is replaced. Provided that these conditions are met, proceed as follows for the two engine capacities.

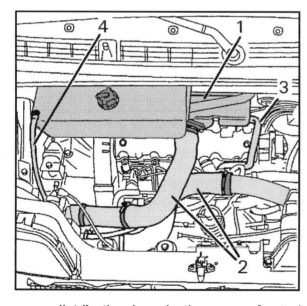

Fig. 1.42 – Removal of the cylinder head (1.9 litre).

1	Inlet manifold
2	Air intake hoses
3	Hose
4	Breather hose on head

1.9 litre engine – Cylinder Head Removal

- Disconnect the battery earth cable.
- Place the front end of the vehicle on chassis stands and remove the protective panel underneath the vehicle.
- Remove the air cleaner with its connections. In the case of a non-turbo engine, remove the air distribution box, in the case of a turbo engine, remove the heat exchanger from the top of the engine (1, Fig. 1.17).
- Drain the cooling system.
- Disconnect the front exhaust pipe from the exhaust manifold or directly from the turbo charger.

Engines

- Referring to Fig. 1.42 remove the following items: The fluid reservoir for the power steering (if fitted), the air intake hoses (2) and the inlet manifold (1), if fitted the turbo charger. Disconnect the heater hoses from the cylinder head, the hose from the vacuum pump, the hose (3), the breather hose (4) from the cylinder head and the fuel heating hoses for the fuel supply.
- **Remove:** The upper part of the fuel pre-heater, the three bolts from the water outlet housing and the injection pipes.
- **Disconnect:** The glow plug leads and the cable from the glow plug connection of No. 1 cylinder.

The cylinder head is now removed as follows:

- Remove the timing belt covers from the front of the engine. Remove the clip in the centre of the covers (screwdriver) and take off the covers. Also remove the cover at the lower end.
- Insert the locking rod at the position shown in Fig. 1.41 into the crankcase. The crankshaft must be rotated to obtain the top dead centre position.

Fig. 1.43 – View of the engine with details for the removal of the timing belt.

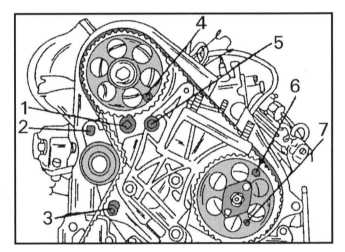

1	Square hole
2	Bolt tensioner bolt
3	Bolt tensioner bolt
4	Timing lock bolt
5	Engine mounting bolt
6	Timing lock bolt
7	Timing lock bolt

- Obtain three M8 x 1.5 bolts (40 mm long). Screw one of the bolts into hole (4) in Fig. 1.43 into the camshaft sprocket and two of the bolts into holes (6) and (7) into the injection pump gearwheel. If the crankshaft is in the correct position, there should be no problems to screw in the bolts. The timing mechanism is now locked.
- Remove the two bolts (2) and (3) securing the timing belt tensioner. Insert the square drive of a 3/8 in. Socket set into the square opening (1) and push the tensioning roller towards the outside against the tension of the spring. Re-tighten the bolt (2) to lock the tensioning roller in position.
- Carefully lift the timing belt from the gearwheels towards the front.
- Remove the camshaft timing gear from the camshaft. The shaft must be held against rotation. Either insert a metal rod into one of the holes and rest it against the cylinder head or counterhold the wheel with the help of a restraining tool. Remove the camshaft wheel and the inserted lock bolt.
- Remove the cylinder head cover.
- Slacken the cylinder head bolts in the reverse order of Fig. 1.44 in several stages and remove the bolts. ***Note that the length of each bolt must be measured before re-use.*** As the cylinder head is located by means of a dowel pin, it may be difficult to remove the head. Workshops use two angled levers, as shown in Fig. 1.45, which are inserted into the side of the head. Lift the two levers together until the head is free of the cylinder head gasket. Lift off the head completely and remove the cylinder head gasket. Also remove the dowel pin if it is attached to the cylinder head. It must be tapped into the cylinder block before the head is refitted.

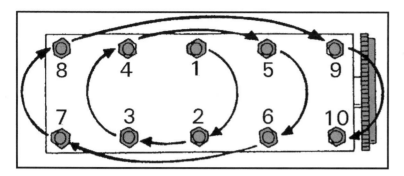

Fig. 1.44 – The cylinder head bolts of 1.9 litre engines are tightened in the order shown. Reverse the order when the bolts are slackened.

- Clean the cylinder block and cylinder head surfaces with a suitable solvent. Never use a scraper or emery cloth to clean the gasket faces. Re-grinding the cylinder head face is not permitted. If the cylinder head must be dismantled, refer to the next section.

Fig. 1.45 – Removal of the cylinder head with the two special levers.

2.5 litre Engine – Head Removal

- Disconnect both battery leads and remove the battery.

- Place the front of the vehicle on chassis stands and remove the protective panel underneath the engine. Immediately drain the cooling system.

- Remove the parts already shown in Fig. 1.12, i.e. the coolant expansion tank, the air cleaner with the connected hoses and the bracket for the steering system fluid reservoir.

- **Disconnect:** The parts shown in Fig. 1.46. Also disconnect the vacuum hose for the brake servo unit, the breather hose from the cylinder head.

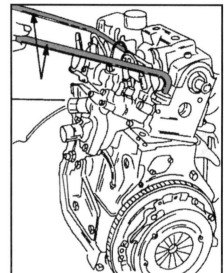

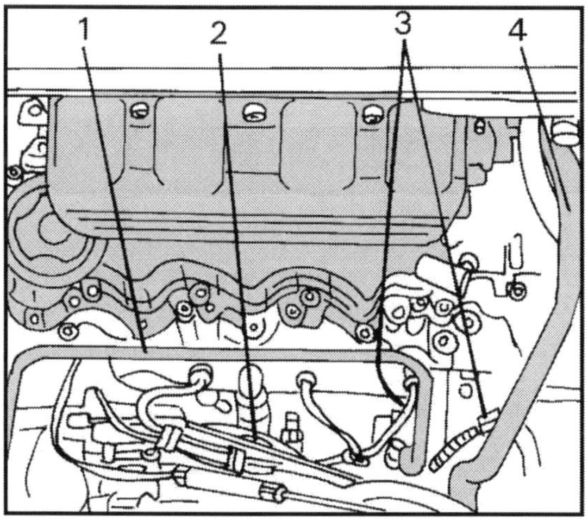

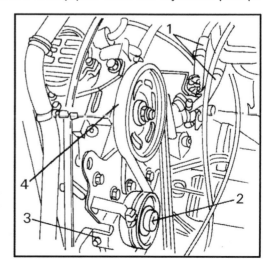

Fig. 1.46 – Removal of the cylinder head (2.5 litre).

1	Connecting hose
2	Fast idle speed cable
3	Coolant temperature sensor
4	Heater hose

- The fuel return pipe, the glow plug feed cable and pipes from the injection pump.

Fig. 1.47 – Removal of the cylinder head (2.5 litre).

1	Fuel pipes
2	Belt tensioner bolt
3	Belt tension adjusting bolt
4	Water pump drive belt

- Free the fuel feed and return pipes from the clips on the injection pump and disconnect the pipes from the fuel pre-heater (refer to Fig. 1.47).

Engines

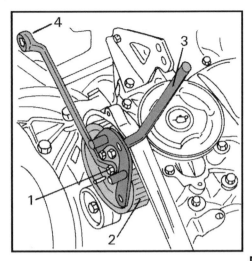

Fig. 1.49 – Remove the cylinder head cover (1) and the vacuum pump (2).

- Lock the camshaft gearwheel to prevent it from rotating and slacken and remove the bolt in the centre. A suitable holder is shown in Fig. 1.48. Remove the gearwheel and remove the cover panel behind it.

- Remove the front exhaust pipe from the exhaust manifold or directly from the turbo charger and push it to one side.

- Remove the exhaust manifold and the inlet manifold.

Fig. 1.48 – The camshaft timing gearwheel can be held with a holder as shown.
1　　　Timing gearwheel bolt
2　　　Camshaft timing gearwheel
3　　　Holding lever
4　　　Ring spanner

- Remove the bolt (2) in Fig. 1.47 and turn the bolt (3) in clockwise direction, to free the water pump drive belt. Remove the belt. Remove any other belts from the front of the engine.

- Remove the toothed timing belt, as described for this engine under separate heading.

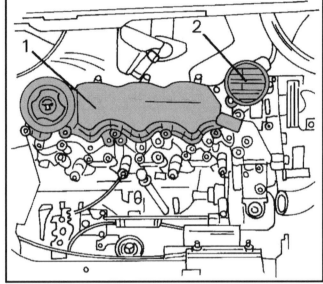

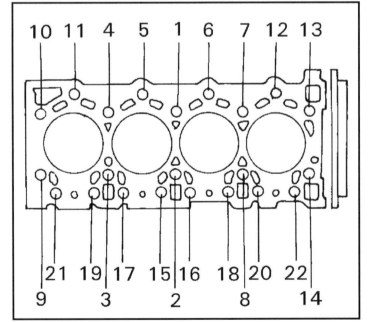

Fig. 1.50 – Tightening sequence for the cylinder head bolts. Slacken the bolts in reverse order.

- Hold the steering pump pulley to prevent it from rotating, remove the three pulley screws and take off the pulley. Remove the three bolts situated behind the pulley.

- Remove the cylinder head cover (1) in Fig. 1.49 and the vacuum pump (2). This is the original arrangement. Note that some engines have a camshaft driven vacuum pump, which will be referred to later on.

- Slacken the cylinder head bolts in the reverse order of Fig. 1.50 in several stages. Leave the bolts in the head at this stage.

- Place a jack underneath the engine (wooden plank between jack head and engine) and lift the engine until the engine mounting is under slight tension. Remove the R.H. engine mounting, already shown in Fig. 1.14. Remove the nut (1) and the three bolts (2). After removal of the mounting bracket, unscrew the mounting carrier from the cylinder head (2 bolts, fitted from above).
- Fully remove the cylinder head bolts and lift off the cylinder head, if necessary using a small hand crane. Remove the cylinder head gasket.
- Clean the sealing faces as described for the other engines.

1.4.0.2   Cylinder Head – Dismantling

Figs. 1.51 and 1.55 show exploded views of the cylinder heads in question. If the head is replaced, remove the parts shown in the illustrations. The component parts of the valves together with the camshaft and the timing mechanism parts are shown in later illustrations during the description of operations on the timing gear.

Fig. 1.51 – Dismantled cylinder head (1.9 litre). Note that the cylinder head bolts are different for non-turbo and turbo engines.

1	Cylinder head cover
2	Cover gasket
3	Camshaft bearing cap
4	Cylinder head bolt (turbo)
5	Cylinder head bolt (non turbo)
6	Cover nut
7	Cylinder head
8	Cylinder head gasket
9	Centring ball
10	Pre-combustion chamber
11	Closing cover
12	Screw plug
13	Closing cover

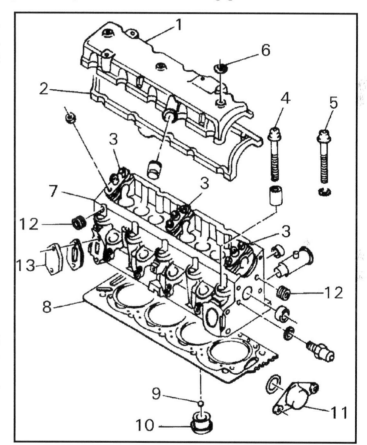

1.9 litre Engine

- Mark the camshaft bearing caps and the cylinder head with a centre punch. Unscrew the camshaft bearing cap nuts and lift out the camshaft. Remove the oil seals from both ends of the camshaft. Always replace the seals. After dismantling you will have the parts shown in Fig. 1.53 removed from the head (refer to next page).
- Remove the valve tappets and the valve clearance adjusting shims. Keep the shims together with the tappets, if the parts are to be re-fitted.
- A valve lifter is required to remove the valves from the cylinder head. Valve lifters are available from most tool hire companies and there should be no problem obtaining one. Fig. 1.52 shows a suitable valve lifter, which can be used. It is also possible by placing a piece of wood into the combustion chamber, to support the valve head, and then to proceed as follows:
- Use a piece of tube, the same diameter as the valve spring cap, and place the tube over the valve spring. With a hammer give a short blow onto the tube. The

Engines

valve springs will be compressed and the valve cotter halves remain inside the tube. The operation may be slightly tricky, due to the inclination of the valves.

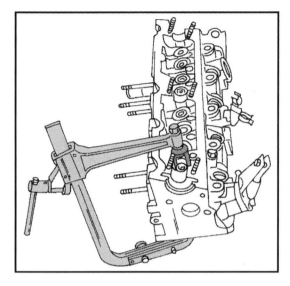

Fig. 1.52 – Using a valve lifter.

- Take the parts off the valve and withdraw the valve from the other side. If fitted, remove the valve stem seals. Mark the valves with the number. No. 1 valve is the nearest to the timing end of the engine.

2.5 litre Engine

Slacken the camshaft housing securing bolts in reverse order to Fig. 1.54 and lift the housing from the cylinder head. In a later chapter you find the removal of the camshaft for an engine with direct injection (type DJ5 TED).

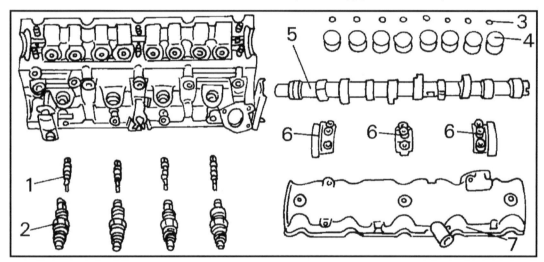

Fig. 1.53 – The cylinder head of a 1.9 litre engine after dismantling.

1	Glow plugs	5	Camshaft
2	Injectors	6	Camshaft bearing caps
3	Valve adjusting shims	7	Cylinder head cover
4	Valve tappets		

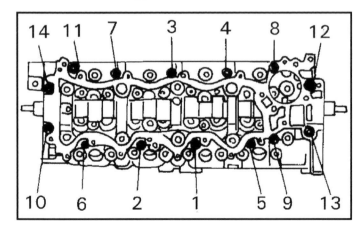

Fig. 1.54 – Tightening sequence for the cylinder head bolts of a 2.5 litre engine. Slacken the bolts in reverse order.

- Remove the two oil seals from the two ends of the camshaft housing (screwdriver).
- Remove the camshaft keeper plate from one side of the cylinder head and withdraw the camshaft to-wards the flywheel side out of the cylinder head.

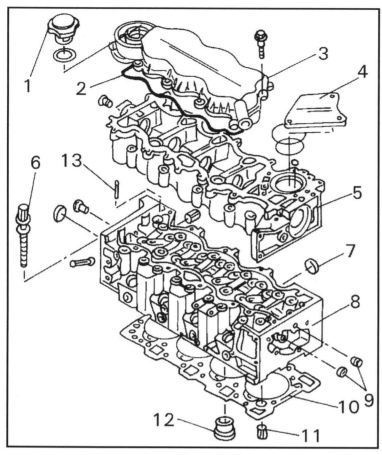

Fig. 1.55 – The dismantled cylinder head of a 2.5 litre engine.
1　Oil filler cap
2　Cylinder head cover gasket
3　Cylinder head cover
4　Closing cover
5　Camshaft housing
6　Cylinder head bolt
7　Closing plug
8　Cylinder head
9　Screw plug
10　Cylinder head gasket
11　Dowel sleeve
12　Pre-combustion chamber
13　Dowel pin, housing

- Remove the tappet operating levers and the hydraulic compensating elements from the head and keep them in their order of removal.
- Remove the valves as described above for the other engine. Take special care not to mix

up the 12 valves on this engine.

Fig. 1.56 – Observe the minimum permissible value of 0.5 mm, measured between the arrows.

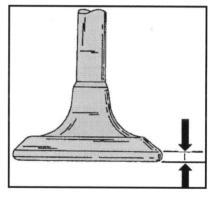

1.4.0.3.　Cylinder Head Overhaul

Refer to Section 1.4.0.0. and compare the values given for the engine in question.

Valves: Check the valve faces for wear or grooving. If the wear is only slight, re-grind the valves to their appropriate angle in a valve grinding machine. All valves have the same angle. The valve head thickness, shown in Fig. 1.56 must not be less than 0.5 mm.

Check the valve stem diameters and in this connection the inside diameters of the valve guides. If there is a deviation from the nominal values, it may be necessary to replace the valve guides (see below). Also check the ends of the valve stems. There should be no visible wear in this area. Valve ends can be re-ground to a maximum value.

Valve Seats: Valve seats can be re-machined to their original angle with the appropriate cutters. All seats have the same angle (45°). If this operation is carried out properly, there should be no need to grind-in the valves. Use correction cutters to bring the valve seating area in the centre of the valve head. Make sure that the valve seat, given in Section 1.4.0.0. is obtained (different values for 1.9 and 2.5 litre engines). We recommend, however, to have the valves re-furbished in an engine shop.

Fig. 1.57 – Diagram showing the inlet valve heads (A) and the exhaust valve heads (B) below the cylinder head face.

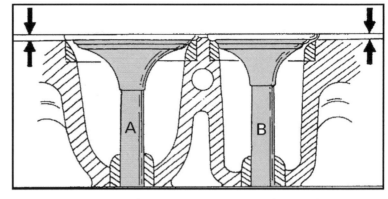

1.9 litre Engine only

After valve seats have been re-cut, measure the distance between the valve heads and the cylinder head surface. To do this, place a dial gauge with a magnetic base onto the cylinder head face, with the stylus on the surfaces of the valves shown in Fig. 1.58.

Fig. 1.58 – Measuring the height of the valve head surfaces below the cylinder head face.

The indicated value is the height from the valve head to the cylinder head face. If this is not 0.5 – 1.10 mm in the case of the inlet valves or 0.90 – 1.40 mm in the case of the exhaust valves, replace the cylinder head. The measurement is carried out as shown in Fig. 1.57.

Valves should be ground into re-cut seats. To do this, coat the valve seat with lapping compound and use a suction tool, as shown in Fig. 1.59. Move the valve backwards and forwards. Every so often lift the suction tool, move it forward by ¼ of a turn, and continue grinding. Work the seat until an uninterrupted ring is visible around the face of the valve. After grinding-in, clean the cylinder head, and even more important the inside of the valve guide bores thoroughly. Any lapping paste inside the cylinder head will accelerate the wear of the new parts.

Use a pencil and mark across the valve seat closely spaced. Drop the valve into the respective valve guide and turn the valve by 90°, using the suction tool, applying slight pressure to the tool. Remove the valve and if the pencil marks have been removed from the entire circumference. The gap created will indicate the width of the valve seat and can be measured with a ruler or caliper. Otherwise repeat the grinding until this is the case.

Fig. 1.59 – Grinding in of valves.

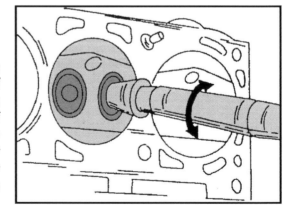

Valve Springs: Springs should be compared with new springs and rejected if weak or cracked. Lay each spring on a surface plate and check that the ends of the springs are square. Slide the originally fitted spring and a new spring together over a long bolt (with large washers under bolt head and nut) and screw a nut onto the end of the bolt. Clamp the bolt head.

Valve Guides: Valve guides and valve stems should first be inspected for visible wear. Clean the inside of the valve guides with a rag moistened in petrol, inserting the rag into the guides and move it to and fro to clean the inside of the bore. Valve stems are best cleaned by clamping them into an electric drill and using a wire brush to clean off any carbon deposits.

Measure the inside diameter of the guides. As an inside micrometer is necessary for this operation, which is not always available, you can insert the valve into its guide and withdraw it until the valve head is approx. level with the cylinder head face. Rock the valve to and fro and check the play. Although no exact values are available, it can be assumed that the play should not exceed 1.0 – 1.2 mm (0.04 – 0.047 in.)

Valve guides are available with oversize outside diameters (see Section 1.4.0.0.) and the locating bores in the cylinder head must be bored out to take the new guides. This may be a job for an engine shop. Drive out the guide with a suitable mandrel. The cylinder head can be heated in boiling water to facilitate the operation. Measure the protruding end of the guide (write it down) before driving the old guide out and drive in the new guide to obtain the same dimension.

New valve guides always require the fitting of new valves and the valve seats must be re-cut and the valves ground into the seats.

Valve guides must be reamed after installation to the diameter given in Section 1.4.0.0. Use an adjustable reamer. The correct running clearance of the valve stem is automatically obtained when the guides have the correct internal diameter.

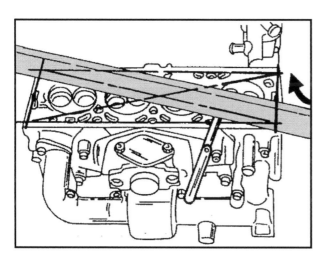

Fig. 1.60 – Checking the cylinder head gasket face for distortion. Check in the directions shown.

Cylinder Head: Thoroughly clean the cylinder head surface and measure the surface for distortion. To do this, place a fine-edge steel ruler across the cylinder head face as shown in Fig. 1.60 and measure the gap between ruler and head with feeler gauges. If a feeler gauge of more than specified in Section 1.4.0.0. can be inserted, replace the cylinder head. The head of some "XUD" engines can be re-ground. Consult your dealer before the head is replaced.

Camshaft: Camshafts are allocated to a certain engine. Check the bearing journal diameters with a micrometer. The camshaft of a 1.9 litre engine has journals with different diameters. If the measurements are outside the limits, fit a new camshaft.

Place the camshaft with the two end journals into V- blocks or clamp the shaft between the points of a lathe and apply a dial gauge to the centre journal. Slowly rotate the camshaft and read off the dial gauge. If the indication is more than 0.01 mm, replace the shaft, as it is bent.

To check the camshaft end float, place the shaft into the cylinder head without fitting the tappets in order to avoid the pressure of the valve springs onto the camshaft.

Arrange a dial gauge, with the stylus of the gauge resting against the end of the camshaft. Move the camshaft to and fro and read off the dial gauge. The dial gauge reading must not exceed the value given in Section 1.4.0.0. for the end float.

Engines

1.4.0.4. Cylinder Head – Assembly

All Engines

- If the cylinder head has been replaced, transfer all parts from the old to the new head. Thoroughly clean all parts and lubricate all moving parts with engine oil.
- Insert the valves into their guides. If valves have been replaced, fit them into the respective guides. The same applies to the originally fitted valves.

Fig. 1.61 – Fitting a valve.

1	Tube to fit valve stem seals
2	Valve stem seal
3	Valve spring cup
4	Valve spring
5	Washer

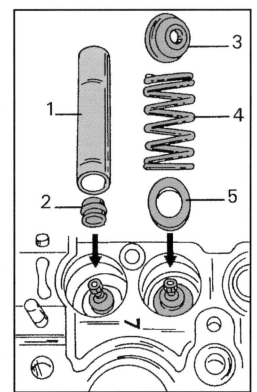

- Assemble the valves. First place the valve spring seat over the cylinder head and push the valve stem seals over the valve stems and the valve guides, as shown in Fig. 1.61. Fit the upper valve spring cup over the valve spring and compress the valve spring with a valve spring compressor. When the valve stem end protrudes from the valve spring cup, insert the two valve cotter halves with a pair of pointed pliers. Slowly release the valve spring compressor, checking continuously that the valve cotter halves are kept in position.
- With a plastic mallet tap against the end of all valve stems. If the valve cotter halves have not engaged properly, they will jump out. A piece of rag should be placed over the valve stem ends – just in case.

1.9 litre Engine

- Lubricate the valve clearance adjusting shims and the valve tappets with engine oil and insert them into the original bores (in accordance with their markings). If a tappet must be partially removed, always withdraw it completely to check the proper seating of the shim, as the shim can be dislodged, if the tappet is removed.
- Coat the bearing journals and the cams with engine oil and insert the camshaft into the bearing bores. Fit the three bearing caps. The caps are marked with numbers. Cap with No. 3 is fitted to the timing wheel side. The seating faces of caps No. 1 and No. 3 must be coated with sealing compound. Tighten the nuts evenly to a torque setting of 1.8 kgm (14 ft.lb.).
- Fit the two oil seals into the cylinder head, using a suitable mandrel. Take care not to damage the sealing lips. The oil seal on the clutch side is not fitted to all engines.
- Adjust the valve clearances as described in Section 1.4.0.6.

2.5 litre Engine

The camshaft housing is fitted with sealing compound. You will have to enquire which type is used.

- Coat the camshaft bearing bores with engine oil and insert the shaft into the housing. Attach the shaft on one side with the keeper plate. Fit new oil seals to both sides of the housing.
- Place the cylinder head on the left-hand and right-hand side on wooden blocks, to make sure that protruding valves cannot be damaged.
- Clean the upper surface of the cylinder head and the lower surface of the camshaft housing. No scraper or emery cloth must be used.
- Coat the upper face of the cylinder head with the sealing compound and place the camshaft housing over the head. Fit the bolts and tighten them in the order shown in Fig. 1.55 in several stages to a final torque setting of 2.0 kgm (14 ft.lb.).
- The cylinder head can now be refitted as described below.

1.4.0.5   Cylinder Head - Installation

Thoroughly clean the threaded bores for the cylinder head bolts. The bores must be free of grease and dry. If necessary use an M12 x 150 threaded tap to re-cut the thread (in the case of a 2.5 litre engine an M10 x 150 tap is also required). The threads must be cleaned after re-cutting them.

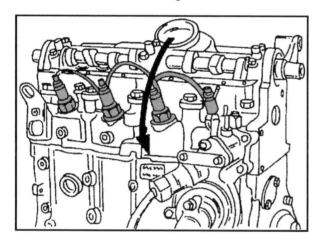

Fig. 1.62 – Fitting the cylinder head. Position the head at the rear and then lower it in the direction of the arrow until the gap at the front is closed.

1.9 litre Engine
- Rotate the camshaft until the valves of No. 1 and No. 4 cylinders are closed.
- Knock the dowel pin into the cylinder head, at the position shown in Fig. 1.39. Select the thickness of the cylinder head gasket as described during the assembly of the engine and place the gasket in dry condition over the cylinder head face, with the identification notches (2) in Fig. 1.39 on the side of the flywheel.
- Place the cylinder head over the block at an angle to observe the engagement of the locating dowel. Once engagement has taken place, lower the front of the cylinder head, as shown in Fig. 1.62.
- Check the length of the cylinder head bolts. As different bolts are used on the XUD engines, first establish which type is fitted. Bolts are either flat at their ends or have a small pilot spigot.
  - **Bolts without pilot spigot:** Measure the length between the underside of the bolt head and the end of the thread. Replace bolts if they are longer than 121.5 mm (non-turbo) or 146.5 mm (turbo), as they have stretched
  - **Bolts with pilot spigot:** Measure between the end of the thread and the underside of the bolt head. Replace the bolts if they are longer than 125.5 mm (non-turbo) or 150.5 mm (Turbo), as they have stretched.
- Lubricate the bolt heads and the washers and the threads with engine oil and insert the bolts. Tighten the bolts in the order shown in Fig. 1.44. A "Torx" head insert and possibly a graduated disc are required to tighten the bolts.
- Tighten the bolts in the order shown to 2.0 kgm (14 ft.lb.), followed by a second stage to 6.0 kgm (43 ft.lb.).

Engines

- After all bolts have been tightened, tighten each bolt in the tightening sequence to a specific angle. In the case of an engine without turbo charger, tighten the bolts by 180° (half a turn). In the case of a turbo-charged engine the angle is 220°. The graduated disc, mentioned above, is here a great help. Otherwise you will have to estimate the angle (somewhere between ½ and ¾ of a turn). There is no need to re-tighten the cylinder head bolts at a later stage.
- Fit the camshaft gearwheel. The gearwheel must be held against rotation by inserting a metal rod into one of the holes and resting it against the cylinder head. Tighten the bolt to 4.5 kgm (33 ft.lb.).
- Adjust the valve clearances as described below.
- Rotate the camshaft gearwheel until an M8 x 40 mm bolt can be inserted at position (4) in Fig. 1.43. The camshaft gearwheel is now set to the timing position to fit the timing belt.
- Fit the bolt (2) in Fig. 1.63 to 2.0 kgm (14 ft.lb.).
- Re-connect the exhaust pipe to the exhaust manifold or turbo charger. Also connect the all pipes and hoses to the cooling and fuel injection systems and all electrical cables to the cylinder head.
- Check that all parts that will be in contact with the timing belt are free from oil or grease and that the tensioning roller is fully locked in the outer position.
- Lock the injection pump drive gear by inserting the two M8 x 40 mm bolts (7) and (9) in Fig. 1.43. The drive gear is now in the injection position.
- Lock the crankshaft in the timing position by inserting the special tool shown in Fig. 1.41 or a metal rod into the crankcase and the flywheel.

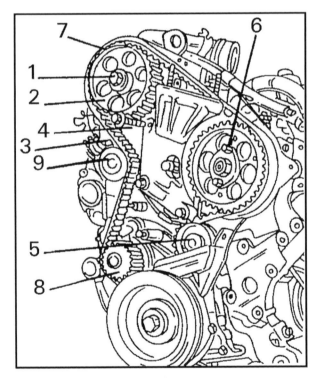

Fig. 1.63 – Fitting the timing belt.

1	Bolt, 4.5 kgm
2	Camshaft timing gear
3	Bolt, 2.0 kgm
4	Bolt, 2.0 kgm
5	Fixed roller
6	Injection pump drive gear
7	Timing belt
8	Water pump wheel
9	Belt tensioner roller

- Refer to Fig. 1.63 and fit the timing belt. First place the belt over the crankshaft timing gear, then over the fixed centre roller (5), the injection pump drive gear (6) and then over the camshaft timing gearwheel. Keep the driving side of the belt under tension and place the belt on the L.H. side over the water pump drive gear (8) and the tensioning roller (9). Check that the belt has engaged with the teeth on all gearwheels in the proper manner.
- Fit the washer and the bolt into the end of the crankshaft and temporarily tighten the bolt.
- Slacken the bolt (1) and the nut (2) in Fig. 1.64 to release the tensioning roller.
- Remove all timing bolts (camshaft gearwheel and injection pump drive gear).
- Rotate the crankshaft by at least two turns in the direction of rotation. Never *backwards*, and slacken the bolt and nut in Fig. 1.64 once more. The tensioner will

spring towards the inside and tension the timing belt. In this position, tighten the bolt (1) and the nut (2) to 1.8 kgm (14 ft.lb.).

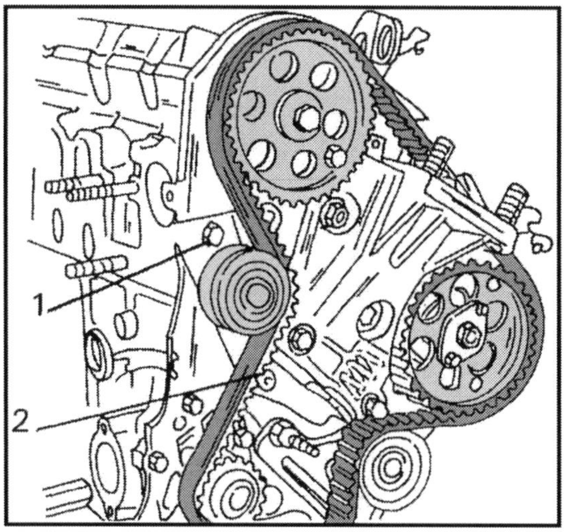

Fig. 1.64 – Slacken and tighten the bolt (1) and the nut (2) as described in the text, when tensioning the timing belt.

- Rotate the engine a few times and re-insert the three timing bolts in the positions shown in Fig. 1.43. If one of the bolts or all of the bolts cannot be inserted, re-adjust as described, as the timing is incorrectly adjusted.

- Fit the two timing belt covers with the clips and insert spring clip in the centre of the covers, using a large screwdriver.

- Remove the bolt and washer and fit the crankshaft pulley. Coat the threads of the pulley bolt with "Loctite", insert it into the crankshaft end (with washer) and tighten the bolt to 4.0 kgm (30 ft.lb.). From the end position, tighten the bolt a further 60°. The shaft must be held against rotation.

- All other operations are carried out in reverse order to the removal procedure.

2.5 litre Engine

- Clean the surfaces of cylinder head and cylinder block. Scrapers and emery cloth must not be used.

- Measure the length of each cylinder head bolt. Measure between the ends of the bolts. M10 bolts must be 162.5 mm long, M12 bolts must still have a length of 153.5 mm. These is the min. permissible length. Bolts which exceed the given values must be replaced. Coat the underside of the bolt heads and the bolt threads with a little graphited grease.

- Check that the dowel sleeves are in position in the corners of the cylinder block and place the cylinder head gasket in position (dry). Check that the gasket is fitted the correct way round.

- Check that crankshaft and camshaft are still in the correct position. Otherwise turn crankshaft and camshaft until the locking bolts can be inserted.

- Lower the cylinder head, engaging it with the dowel sleeves and tap it in position with a rubber or plastic mallet.

The cylinder head bolts are now tightened in accordance with the diagram in Fig. 1.51. If no graduated disc is available, you will have to estimate the angle given below.

- Tighten bolts (1) to (14) in several stages in the order shown to 5.0 kgm (36 ft.lb.). These are the M12 bolts.

- Tighten the bolts (15) to (22) in several stages in the order shown to 3.5 kgm (25 ft.lb.).

- Tighten all bolts (M10 and M12) in the order shown a further 120°, with a tolerance of 5° more or less. When estimating, remember that 90° is a quarter of a turn. Once tightened as explained, there is no need to re-tighten them again.

- Fit the R.H. engine mounting by referring to Fig. 1.65 (see Page 60). Tighten the bolts (3) to 5.0 kgm (36 ft.lb.), the nut (1) with 8.0 kgm (58 ft.lb.) and the bolts (2) to 5.8 kgm (42 ft.lb.). Lower the engine into its mountings after the tightening has been completed.

Engines

- Fit the vacuum pump (Fig. 1.49) with a new gasket (1.5 kgm/10 ft.lb.) and the cylinder head cover (0.8 kgm/6 ft.lb.).

Fig. 1.65 – The engine mounting of a 2.5 litre engine.

1	Nut, 8.0 kgm
2	Bolts, 5.8 kgm
3	Bolts, 5.0 kgm

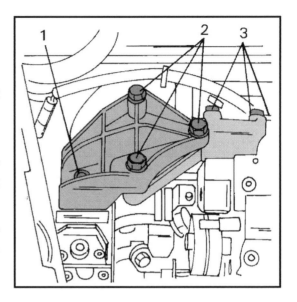

- Fit the cover below the crankshaft pulley with a new gasket (0.8 kgm). Fit the steering pump pulley and tighten the three bolts.
- Fit the following parts with new gaskets in the given order: Inlet manifold (2.2 kgm), exhaust manifold (2.0 kgm), standard diesel, (3.0 kgm) (turbo diesel), the bracket in front of the manifolds, the exhaust pipe (1.0 kgm) and the cover on the front end of the engine.

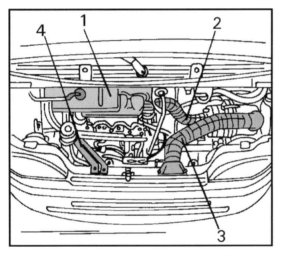

Fig. 1.66 – Parts to be removed in the engine compartment (2.5 litre).

1	Coolant expansion tank
2	Air intake hose
3	Air intake hose
4	Bracket, fluid reservoir

- Fit the camshaft gearwheel, hold the shaft against rotation and tighten the bolt to 4.3 kgm (31 ft.lb.).
- Fit the timing belt as described under separate heading.
- Fit the drive belt and also the water pump drive belt (described later on).
- Re-connect or refit the following items: Fuel pipes (1, Fig. 1.47), fast idle speed cable (2, Fig. 1.46), heater hose (4, Fig. 1.46), coolant temperature sensor (3, Fig. 1.46), the connecting hose (1, Fig. 1.46), the leak-off pipes to the injectors, the breather hose to the cylinder head cover, the vacuum hose to the brake servo unit, the feed pipe for the injection advance.
- Refit the following parts: The bracket for the steering fluid reservoir (4, Fig. 1.66), the air intake hoses (2) and (3), the coolant expansion tank (1) with the hoses.
- Refit and connect the battery and the panel underneath the vehicle. Fit the wheel and lower the vehicle to the ground.
- Finally refill the cooling system and the oil sump. Tighten the wheel bolts.

1.4.0.6. Adjusting the Valve Clearances

Adjusting the valve clearance requires the removal of the camshaft. The following description assumes that the camshaft is removed. If the valve clearances are checked with the engine fitted, carry out all preliminary operations to gain access to the valves. This involves the removal of the complete cylinder head cover.

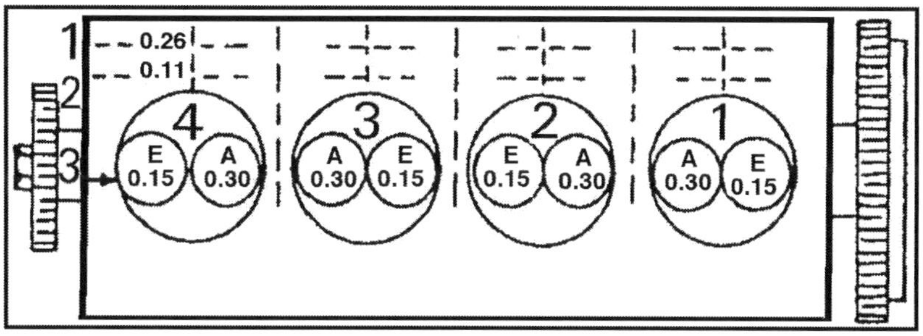

Fig. 1.67 – Diagram for the valve adjustment check.
1   Measured valve clearance
2   Difference between measured clearance
      and actual clearance
3   Required valve clearance

- Jack up the R.H. side of the vehicle front and place a chassis stand underneath the side of the body. If a gear is engaged, the wheel can be rotated to turn over the engine as necessary. The glow plugs can be removed to facilitate the rotation of the engine.
- Prepare a table as shown in Fig. 1.67, to enter the measured valve clearances.
- Turn the engine in direction of rotation by turning the fitted front wheel until the cam of the first valve is pointing straight upwards. This is the inlet valve (flywheel side). Insert a feeler gauge of the specified thickness between the back of the cam and the valve tappet (gap "S" in Fig. 1.68).

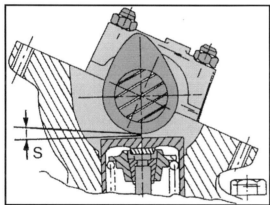

Fig. 1.68 – Measure the gap "S" at the position shown.

- Insert the measured value into the column "1" in the table in Fig. 1.67.
- Measure the exhaust valve of the 4th cylinder in the same manner, but with a feeler gauge of 0.30 mm thickness and enter the measured value into column "2" above and the exhaust valve "A".
- Turn the engine by half a turn in the direction of rotation, until the next set of valves is in the position shown in Fig. 1.68. Measure as described above and enter the values in the respective columns.
- Continue rotating the engine until all valves have been measured in the manner described. Line "1" of all cylinders must now have a value entered.

A tolerance of plus or minus 0.05 mm is permissible. If the measured value is not within the adjustment range, the shim between the bottom of the valve tappet and the end of the valve stem must be changed to correct the clearance. If the valve clearance is excessive fit a thinner shim.

Adjust the valve clearances as follows, as this may be the case when the engine is being assembled. Otherwise remove the camshaft in a similar manner as the removal of the cylinder head, until the camshaft bearing caps can be unscrewed and the shaft lifted out.

- Remove the first valve tappet and the adjusting shim underneath, as shown in Fig. 1.69. Thoroughly clean the adjusting disc and measure the thickness. The new shim thickness is established by use of the following equation:

Correction = Measured clearance less valve clearance

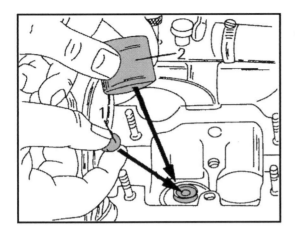

Fig. 1.69 – Removal of the valve tappet (2) and the shim (1).

Fig. 1.70 shows on the example of the inlet valve for the No. 4 cylinder how the values and calculations are entered. These must be carried out on all valves.

The correction can either be positive or negative. If the measured clearance is above the valve clearance, increase the thickness of the shim. In the example this value is 0.11 mm more than the measured shim thickness of 2.54 mm, i.e. a new shim with a thickness of 2.55 mm must be used during installation.

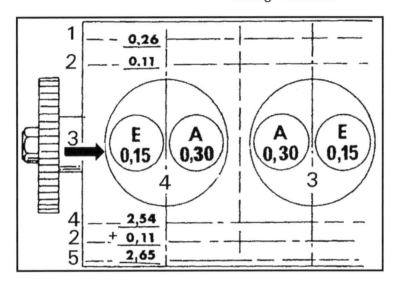

Fig. 1.70 – Example of adjusting shim calculation in the case of the inlet valve of No. 4 cylinder.

1	Measured clearance	4	Thickness of old shim
2	Difference	5	Thickness of new shim
3	Valve and clearance		

Select a shim as near as possible to the required thickness. Shims are available in thicknesses between 2.425 and 3.550 mm, in steps of 0.075 mm between sizes.

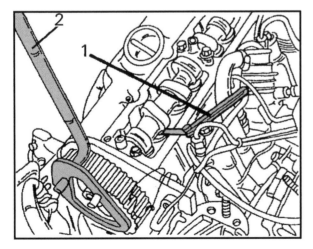

Fig. 1.71. – Checking the valve clearance with a feeler gauge (1). The camshaft can be rotated with a lever (2) as shown.

Lubricate the valve tappet with engine oil and insert it into the tappet bore. If the tappets should be lifted, even slightly, it may cause the shim to be dislodged. In this case, remove the tappet and fit the shim back into the housing bore before inserting the tappet once more.

Refit the camshaft and rotate it by two turns. Again measure the valve clearances as described. Use feeler gauges as shown in Fig. 1.71.

The remaining operations are carried out in reverse order. The installation of the timing belt has already been described during the installation of the cylinder head.

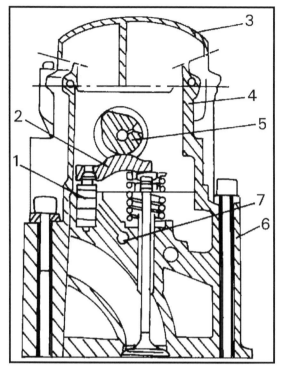

Fig. 1.72 – Sectional view of the valve mechanism of a 2.5 litre engine.
1   Hydraulic compensating element
2   Rocker lever
3   Cylinder head cover
4   Camshaft housing
5   Camshaft
6   Cylinder head
7   Oil bore to compensating element

Valve Clearances – 2.5 Litre Engines

Fig. 1.72 shows a sectional view of the valve operation with a hydraulic compensating element. The rocker levers are located at the ends of the valve shafts and the hydraulic elements. Valve adjustment is not required.

Hydraulic elements cannot be repaired and must be replaced, if faulty. Some noises after starting the engine from cold are no cause for concern. They will disappear after the elements are filled with oil.

To replace an element, remove the timing belt and the camshaft bearing housing as described during the removal of the cylinder head. After refitting the tappets allow the engine to stand at least 30 minutes, to drain the oil inside the tappets. If this is not observed, it may be possible for the valves and pistons to make contact.

1.4.1   PISTONS AND CONNECTING RODS

1.4.1.0.   Technical Data

Type:

- 1.9 litre engines | Aluminium alloy pistons with 3 piston rings. Turbo-charged engines with oil cooling jets for pistons

- 2.5 litre engines | Similar as above, all engines with cooling jets for pistons. Pistons for turbo-charged engines different

Piston pin fit | Floating fit in piston and connecting rod small ends. Circlips on both sides of the piston pins (all engines)

Piston fitting direction | Piston bowl on side of injection pump (all engines).

Piston Crown Protrusion above Cylinder Block | See under "Cylinder Head"

Piston Diameters - 1.9 litre – Marking in Piston Crown:
- Piston marking "1" | 82.921 – 82.939 mm
- Piston marking "2" | 82.951 – 82.969 mm
- Repair size 1 | 83.130 mm

Engines

- Repair size 2   83.430 mm
- Repair size 3   83.730 mm

Turbo-charged 1.9 litre Engines:
- Nominal diameter   82.920 mm
- Repair size 1   83.420 mm
- Repair size 2   82.720 mm

2.5 litre engines (marked in piston crown):
- Nominal diameter – non-turbo   91.939 mm
- Nominal diameter - Turbo   91.020 mm
- Repair size diameter – non-turbo 92.439 mm
Repair size diameter – Turbo   92.420 mm

Piston Height – Pin centre to Piston Crown – 2.5 litre:

	Without Turbo	**With Turbo**
Piston class K	- - - - -	49.744 mm
Piston class L	49.705 mm	49.814 mm
Piston class M	49.775 mm	49.884 mm
Piston class N	49.845 mm	- - - - -

Piston Rings:
- Type   1 straight compression ring, 1 taper compression ring, 1 oil control ring. Upper rings of 2.5 litre turbo engines different

- Fitting direction   "TOP" visible from above

Piston Ring Thickness (1.9 litre):
- Upper rings   2.00 mm (turbo 3.5 mm)
- Centre rings   2.00 mm
- Oil control ring   3.00 mm

Piston Ring gaps (all engines):
- Upper and centre rings   0.20 – 0.40 mm
- Oil control rings   0.25 – 0.50 mm
- Gap arrangement   At 120° intervals

Piston Ring Identification – 2.5 litre without Turbo:
- Upper rings   Lemon yellow
- Centre rings   White/green
- Oil control rings   Brown

Piston Ring Identification – 2.5 litre with Turbo:
- Upper rings   Green
- Centre rings   Blue
- Oil control rings   Yellow/orange

Piston Pins (1.9 litre):
- Outer diameter – non-turbo   24.994 – 25.000 mm
- Outer diameter – Turbo   28.000 mm
- Length, all engines   71.70 – 72.00 mm

Connection Rods and Big End Bearings

Type	Forged steel, "I" section
Bearing shell material	Aluminium/tin
Connecting rod length, centre to centre	145.0 mm +/- 0.025 mm
Big end bearing bore	53.695 mm
Small end bore:	
- non-turbo	25.00 mm
- Turbo	28.00 mm
Big End Bearing Shell Thickness	
- Nominal	1.828 mm (2.5 litre = 1.818 mm)
- Repair size	1.978 mm (2.5 litre = 1.968 mm)

1.4.1.1. General

The pistons and connecting rods can only be replaced with the engine has been removed from the vehicle and the transmission disconnected from the engine.

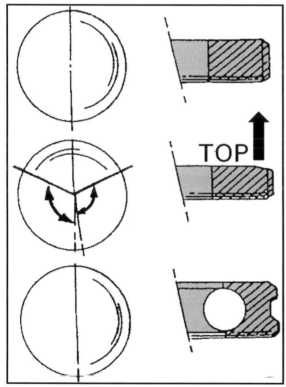

Fig. 1.73 – The arrangement of the piston rings. Note the fitting direction of the second ring and the arrangement of the ring gaps.

Each piston is fitted with two compression rings and one oil control ring. Fig. 1.73 shows a sectional view of a piston, together with the arrangement of the piston ring gaps. Note that the marking of the piston rings must be visible from above after installation.

The pistons must have a certain protrusion above the surface of the cylinder block. In the case of a 1.9 litre engine, a cylinder head gasket of a different thickness is selected to obtain the protrusion and all pistons have the same length. In the case of the 2.5 litre engine, pistons of different length are fitted to obtain the protrusion. The following information for the 2.5 litre engine are mainly given for reference, as it will be unlikely, that you replace the pistons yourself:

- The pistons of a "T9A" or "T8A" (THZ) engine must protrude 0.50 mm (plus or minus 0.05 mm). Pistons with three different heights are available. Pistons for a "T9A" engine (without turbo) have the letters "L", "M" or "N" in the piston crown. In the case of the "T8A" (Turbo), the letters "K", "L" or "M" are marked into the piston crown. It should also be noted that pistons for a non-turbo and turbo engine are different.

- The pistons of an engine with direct injection (DJ5 TED) must protrude 0.63 mm above the cylinder block surface. Again this dimension is obtained by fitting one of three different pistons. Pistons are marked with the letters "A", "B" and "C" in the piston crowns.

• The difference between the pistons of one engine must not exceed 0.10 mm.
• Only one cylinder head thickness is available, 1.6 mm or 1.4 mm in the case of the DJ5 TED engine.

1.4.1.2 Dismantling Pistons and Connecting Rods

No special tools are necessary to dismantle the pistons and connecting rods. Securing rings are fitted to hold the piston in position. Proceed as follows to dismantle. Fig. 1.74 shows an exploded view of the assembly.

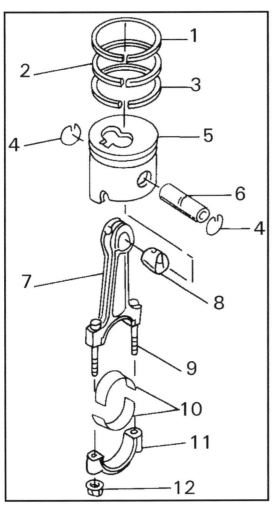

Fig. 1.74 – Exploded view of a piston and connecting rod assembly. Similar parts are used on all engines (pistons different on 1.9 and 2.5 litre engines).

1 Upper piston ring
2 Centre piston ring
3 Oil control ring
4 Piston pin retaining ring
5 Piston
6 Piston pin
7 Connecting rod
8 Big end bearing bush
9 Big end bearing bolt
10 Big end bearing shells
11 Big end bearing cap
12 Big end bearing cap nut

• Use a pair of piston ring pliers and remove the piston rings one after another from the crown end of the piston, as shown in Fig. 1.75. If no piston ring pliers are available, use three thin metal strips and slide the rings over the strips to remove them one by one. One of the strips must be placed underneath the piston ring ends to avoid scratches.
• Remove the securing rings out of the two piston pin bores. Either use a small screwdriver or a pair of circlip pliers for this operation.

Fig. 1.75 – Removal or installation of pistons rings.

• Use a stepped mandrel to drive out the piston pin. Hold the piston in one palm of the hand, whilst the pin is removed. If the piston has a tight fit, heat the piston in water.

Note: Pistons and connecting rods should only be separated if

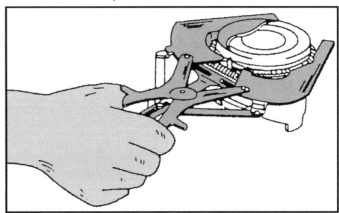

pistons or connecting rods must be replaced.

1.4.1.3. Checking Pistons and Connecting Rods

Thoroughly clean and check all parts. Signs of scratches or seizure or wear mean that the respective parts must be replaced.

*   One after the other insert each piston ring into the top of the cylinder bore (from where it was removed) and push it squarely into the bore, using an upside-down piston to do so, until the ring is inserted by approx. 15 – 20 mm. Insert a feeler gauge into the gap between the two ring ends and check that the gap obtained is not greater than specified in Section 1.4.1.0. Ring gaps cannot be adjusted and new rings must be fitted, if the gaps of any of the rings are greater. Fig. 1.76 demonstrates the check.

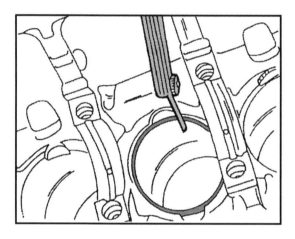

Fig. 1.76 – Checking piston ring gaps.

*   Measure the piston diameter with a micrometer. Apply the jaws of the micrometer at right angles to the piston pin bore at the bottom of the piston skirt. Various oversize pistons are available and we advise you to seek assistance from an engine shop, dealing with Citroen engines.
*   Check the piston pins and the bores in the pistons for wear. Piston pins must have a sliding fit in the pistons and connecting rod small ends, with the parts well oiled.

Fig. 1.77 – Correct installation of piston and connecting rod (1.9 litre).

1.4.1.4. Assembling Pistons and Connecting Rods

It is assumed that the parts have been checked as described in the last section and parts have been replaced if necessary.

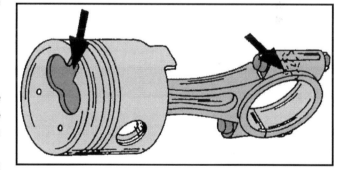

Lubricate the piston pin bores and the connecting rod small end bores and assemble the parts correctly, i.e. the cut-out in the piston bowl must be on the same side as the locating tabs of the connecting rod bearing shells, as shown in Fig. 1.77.

Fit one of the piston pin securing rings in to the piston pin bore. Check that the ring is engaged fully in its groove.

Insert the connecting rod into the piston, align the small end bore and the piston bore and insert the piston pin, using thumb pressure only. Check once more the correct relationship of piston and connecting rod and fit the second securing ring to the other side of the piston. Check the securing ring for proper fit.

Fit the piston rings over the pistons, using a pair of piston ring pliers, as shown in Fig. 1.75. The centre ring must be fitted so that the marking "Top" can be read from above after the rings have been fitted. If a piston ring compressor is not available, use three thin metal strips. Slide the rings to the level of the ring groove and then withdraw the strips. The ring will spring into the groove. Piston rings break easily and care should be taken.

Generously lubricate the piston rings and arrange the piston ring gaps in equal spacing around the outside of the piston skirt. Refer to Fig. 1.73. Arrange the gaps as shown.

Lubricate the pistons with engine oil and place the assemblies for installation in the cylinder block. A piston ring compressor is required to fit the pistons.

The installation of the pistons and connecting rods is described in detail in Section 1.3. Tightening torques are given at the end of this chapter.

1.4.2. CYLINDER BLOCK

The cylinder block consists of the crankcase and the actual block with the cylinder bores. This is the case with the 1.9 litre engines. The crankcase of a 2.5 litre engine is a separate part. Special attention should be given to the cylinder block at each major overhaul of the engine, irrespective of whether the bores have been re-machined or not. Thoroughly clean all cavities and passages and remove all traces of foreign matter from the joint faces. If any machining of the bores has taken place, it is essential that all swarf is removed before assembly of the engine takes place.

Measurement of the cylinder bores should be left to an engine shop, as they have the proper equipment to measure cylinder bores. It is, however, feasible to check the cylinder block face for distortion, in a similar manner as described for the cylinder head. The max. permissible distortion is 0.05 mm. As already mentioned, there is no provision to have the block surface re-machined.

1.4.3 CRANKSHAFT AND FLYWHEEL

1.4.3.0. Technical Data

Number of main journals	5, in separate housing in case of 2.5 litre engine	
Main Bearings:		
- Type	Steel type	
- Material	Aluminium-tin	

Main Bearing Diameter:	*1.9 litre*	*2.5 litre*
- Nominal diameter	60.000 mm	63.961 – 64.000 mm
- Repair size diameter	57.700 mm	63.681 – 63.700 mm
Crankpin Diameter:		
- Nominal diameter	50.000 mm	53.981 – 54.000 mm
- Repair size diameter	49.700 mm	53.681 – 53.700 mm
Crankshaft end float	0.07 – 0.32 mm	0.04 – 0.29 mm

Thickness of thrust washers:	
- 1.9 litre engine	2.305, 3 oversizes, in steps of 0.10 mm

Width of bearing journal No. 2 (end float control) – 2.5 Litre:	
- Nominal	27.60 – 27.65 mm
- Repair size 1	27.70 – 27.75 mm

- Repair size 2   27.80 – 27.85 mm

Thickness of Main Bearing Shells:
- Nominal thickness   1.842 mm (2.5 litre = 2.397 mm)
- Repair size thickness   1.992 mm (2.5 litre = 2.477 mm)

1.4.3.1. General

The removal of the crankshaft is described in Section 1.2. The crankshaft runs in five bearings, but in the case of the 2.5 litre engine in a separate housing. Main bearing and crankpin journals can be re-ground once, i.e. repair size bearing shells are available. Fig. 1.78 shows the component parts of a crankshaft as fitted to a 2.5 litre engine. Similar parts are used in the other engine, with the difference that two half thrust washers are fitted at the No. 2 bearing.

An oil seal is fitted to the front and rear ends of the crankshaft. The front seal is inserted into a removable cover. The rear oil seal is fitted to the crankcase and the rear main bearing cap.

1.4.3.2 Checking the Crankshaft End Float

Check the end float of the crankshaft before it is removed from the crankcase. The resulting valve can then be used to correct the end float during installation of the shaft, by fitting oversize thrust washers. Check the end float as follows:

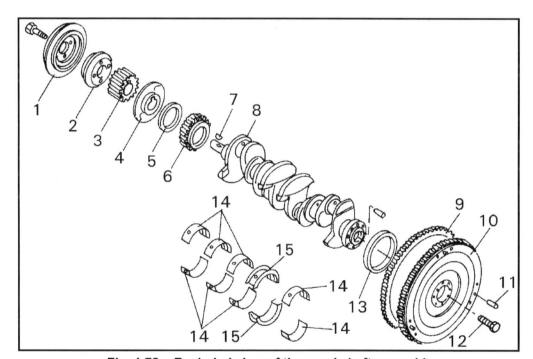

Fig. 1.78 – Exploded view of the crankshaft assembly.

1	Crankshaft pulley	6	Oil pump drive gear	11	Dowel pin
2	Pulley hub	7	Woodruff key	12	Flywheel bolt
3	Crankshaft timing gear	8	Crankshaft	13	Rear oil seal
4	Flanged plate	9	Starter ring gear	14	Plain shells
5	Front oil seal	10	Flywheel	15	Flanged shells

• Attach a dial gauge with a suitable bracket to the cylinder block end face, as already shown during the assembly of the engine and place the dial gauge stylus onto the shaft end. Push the crankshaft to one side, using a screwdriver and set the dial gauge to "Zero".

- Push the crankshaft into the other direction and read off the value on the dial gauge. Check that the end float is within the values given in Section 1.4.3.0. for the engine in question. If the end float is outside the upper limit, fit oversize thrust washers in the case of the 1.9 litre engine. The end float of the crankshaft of a 2.5 litre engine is adjusted by fitting flanged bearing shells (15, Fig. 1.78) at the bearing shown.

1.4.3.3   Crankshaft – Installation

The installation of the crankshaft has been described during the assembly of the engine. Always use two thrust washers of the same thickness.

The separate housing of a 2.5 litre engine is coated with sealing compound before it is fitted together with the bearing shells to the cylinder block. Tighten the bolts evenly to 2.0 kgm (14.5 ft.lb.) and from this position a further 60°.

1.4.3.4.   Rear Crankshaft Oil Seal – Replacement

The flywheel must be removed to replace the oil seal. A slipping clutch, for example, is a sign of a leaking oil seal.

To replace the oil seal without damaging any parts, screw a self-tapping screw into the outside of the seal and use a screwdriver as a lever to ease out the seal. Check the running area of the crankshaft for wear. If wear is visible, drive the new oil seal in a little further.

Coat the outside of the new seal with engine oil and the seal lip with grease and drive the seal into the rear bearing cap and the crankcase. Drive the seal in position until flush, or a little further if the crankshaft has shown signs of wear. Check that the oil seal is fitted evenly on its entire circumference.

1.4.3.5.   Front Crankshaft Oil Seal – Replacement

The front crankshaft oil seal is fitted to the oil pump flange and can be replaced with the engine fitted. The timing belt must be removed. Remove the old oil seal by screwing two self-tapping screws into the seal end face and pull it out with the help of a screwdriver and a pair of pliers.

Coat the lip of a new oil seal with a little M.P. grease and the outside with engine oil. Drive the seal into the cover until the outside is flush. Refit the removed parts.

1.4.4.   TIMING MECHANISM

The component parts of the timing mechanism can be removed with the engine fitted to the vehicle. The belt must be partially removed, i.e. from the camshaft gear, when the following operations are necessary:

- Removal and installation of the cylinder head.
- Removal and installation of the camshaft to adjust the valve clearances (1.9 litre engine only).
- Removal and installation of the oil pump drive chain or drive sprocket.
- Removal and installation of the water pump (1.9 litre engine) and the injection pump.

1.4.4.1. Removal and Installation of the Timing Belt

1.9 Litre Engine

Jack up the R.H. front of the vehicle, remove the front wheel and place a chassis stand underneath the body. Engage the highest gear to be able to rotate the engine during later operations. Disconnect the battery.

- Remove the wheel and remove the protector inside the front wheel arch.
- Slacken the drive belt at the front of the engine and remove it. See description in Section "Cooling System".

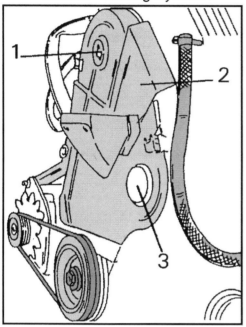

Fig. 1.79 – The three covers 1, 2 and 3 close off the front end of the engine.

- Refer to Fig. 1.79 and remove the timing belt cover. Withdraw the upper cover forwards and then upwards to remove it. Collect the fitted spacer sleeve.
- With the gear engaged, turn the wheel hub of the jacked-up front suspension until the piston of No. 1 cylinder is at the top dead centre position, i.e. the timing rod must be inserted into the flywheel/crankshaft (see Fig. 1.41).
- Obtain two M8 x 40 mm bolts. Insert one of the bolts at position (1) in Fig. 1.80 into the camshaft timing gear and one bolt at position (2) into the injection pump drive gear. Screw the bolts into the threads behind the respective gearwheel. The timing mechanism is now locked in position.

Fig. 1.80 – Details for the removal and installation of the timing belt.

1   Camshaft timing gear
2   Injection pump drive gear

- Slacken the bolt (2) and the nut (1) for the belt tensioning roller in Fig. 1.81. Insert the square of a 3/8 in. socket set extension into the square hole of the tensioning roller bracket and push the complete tensioning roller towards the outside, as shown in Fig. 1.22, to compress the spring of the automatic tensioner. Re-tighten the bolt (2) in Fig. 1.81 to lock the tensioning roller in the new position.
- With the gear engaged, slacken the crankshaft timing gear bolt in the centre of the pulley. Remove the crankshaft pulley from the end of the shaft. Either use two tyre levers or a universal two or three-arm puller to withdraw the pulley. The crankshaft

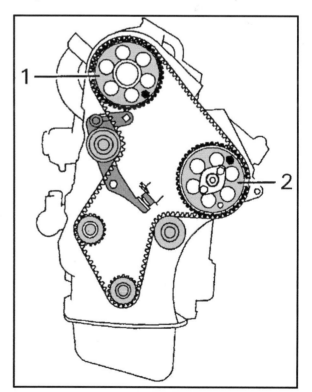

can also be held against rotation by inserting a tyre lever into the flywheel teeth. In this case remove the cover underneath the flywheel housing.

Engines

- Engage a chain or rope with the lifting bracket and lift the engine out of its mounting until just under tension. It is also possible to place a jack underneath the engine. Remove the engine mounting on the timing side.

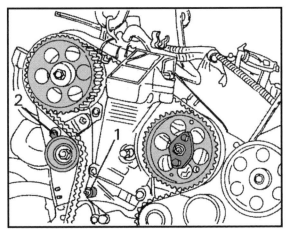

Fig. 1.81 – The nut (1) and the bolt (2) secure the tensioning roller for the automatic timing belt tensioning device.

Carefully slide the timing belt from the timing wheels, guide roller, tensioning roller and water pump. If necessary remove the crankshaft timing gearwheel from the end of the crankshaft, using two levers. This operation is only necessary when it is intended to replace the timing belt and the timing gears. Fig. 1.82 shows the parts in question.

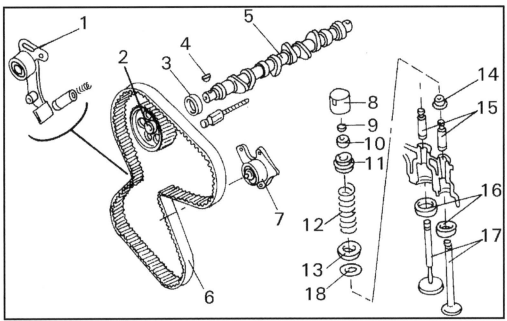

Fig. 1.82 – Timing mechanism and valves of a 1.9 litre engine.

1	Timing belt tensioner	7 Tensioning roller	13 Valve spring seat
2	Camshaft timing gear	8 Valve tappet	14 Valve stem oil seal
3	Oil seal	9 Valve adjusting shim	15 Valve guides
4	Woodruff key	10 Valve cotter halves	16 Valve seat inserts
5	Camshaft	11 Valve spring cup	17 Valves
6	Timing belt	12 Valve spring	18 Washer

The installation of the component parts is carried out as follows. It is assumed that the camshaft, crankshaft and injection pump drive gear are still in the locked position:

- Check that all parts in contact with the timing belt are free of grease or oil and that the belt tensioning roller is secured in the outer position. The two rollers (4) and (6) in Fig. 1.83 must rotate freely. The plunger (3) and the spring (7) must move freely in their housing.

- Refit the camshaft timing gear (if removed). Tighten the bolt to 4.5 kgm (32.5 ft.lb.).

- Turn the camshaft until the bolt (1) in Fig. 1.80 can be inserted through the timing gear and into the cylinder head. The camshaft is now in the timing position. Check that the timing bolt (2) is still in position in the injection pump drive and the timing rod is inserted into the flywheel.

•

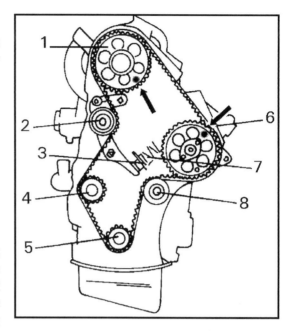

Fig. 1.83 – View of the fitted timing belt of a 1.9 litre engine. The arrows show where the locking bolts are inserted.

1 Camshaft timing gearwheel
2 Timing belt tensioner
3 Belt tensioner plunger
4 Water pump drive gear
5 Crankshaft timing gearwheel
6 Injection pump drive gear
7 Belt tensioner spring
8 Timing belt idler roller

• Fit the crankshaft timing gear. Check that the keys in the gearwheels are in the correct position. Screw the bolt with the washer into the end of the crankshaft to rotate the shaft during later operations.

• Fit the timing belt over the crankshaft timing gear (5), then over the centre idle roller (8) in Fig. 1.83, the injection pump drive gear (6) and finally over the camshaft timing gear (1). Tighten the belt and place on the opposite side over the water pump wheel (4) and behind the tensioning roller (2). Check that the belt has properly engaged with all gearwheels.

• Slacken the tensioning roller bracket to allow the roller to snap towards the inside and tighten the bolt (2) and nut (1) in Fig. 1.81.

• Remove the timing bolts from the gearwheels and the metal rod from the rear of the crankcase.

• Turn the crankshaft by at least two revolutions (apply a ring spanner to the fitted crankshaft gear bolt) in the direction of engine rotation to align the timing belt correctly. Then slacken the bolts (1) and the nut (2) in Fig. 1.81, allow the tensioning roller to push the timing belt towards the inside and tighten the nut and bolt to 1.8 kgm (14 ft.lb.).

• Turn the crankshaft by several turns and check the timing setting by inserting the timing bolts and the metal rod. If any of them cannot be inserted, re-adjust the timing as something is not right.

• Refit the three timing belt covers.

• Remove the bolt and washer from the crankshaft end. Coat the threads of the crankshaft pulley bolt with "Loctite". Fit the crankshaft pulley and insert the bolt. Prevent the crankshaft from rotation and tighten the bolt to 4.0 kgm (30 ft.lb.). From the end position tighten the bolt a further 60°.

• The remaining operations are carried out in reverse to the removal procedure. Fit and tighten the engine mounting; the bolts to 5.0 kgm (36 ft.lb.), the nuts to 8.0 kgm (58 ft.lb.). Fit and tension the belt for the auxiliary equipment and refit the cover to the flywheel housing.

2.5 Litre Engine – Partial Removal of Timing Belt

As already mentioned, the belt must be partially removed during the removal of the camshaft and the injection pump.

Engines

- Disconnect the negative battery cable, lift up the R.H. front wheel and place a chassis stand under the body on this side. Remove the wheel to improve the access to the various parts. Remove the protective shield underneath the vehicle and the panel inside the wheel arch. Engage 5th gear to turn the crankshaft later on.

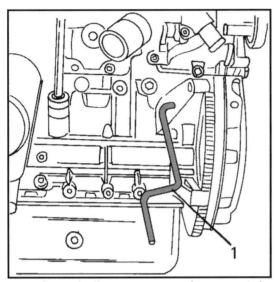

Fig. 1.84 – The metal rod (1) has a diameter of 8 mm and is inserted at the position shown (engages with a bore in the crankshaft).

- Remove the timing belt cover.
- Turn the hub of the removed wheel until the piston of No. 1 cylinder is at the top dead centre position in the compression stroke. In this position insert the locking rod as shown in Fig. 1.84. The illustration shows the special rod, which can, however, be substituted by an 8 mm bolt. The bore is behind the starter motor.

Obtain a bolt M7 x 60 mm long and screw it at position (1) in Fig. 1.85 into the camshaft timing gear. Lock the injection pump drive gear in a similar manner, using a metal rod, but note: **Bosch injection pump** = 9.5 mm diameter, **Lucas injection pump** = 6.0 mm diameter.

Fig. 1.85 – Camshaft and injection pump timing gears are fitted as shown.
1 Camshaft locking bolt (8 mm)
2 Pump drive gear locking pin (9.5 or 6 mm, depending on pump)
3 Camshaft timing gearwheel
4 Injection pump drive gear

The following operations are different, depending if camshaft or injection pump are removed:

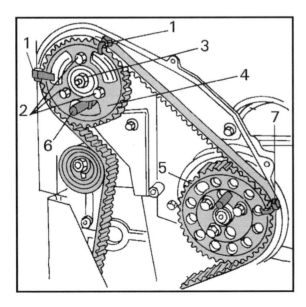

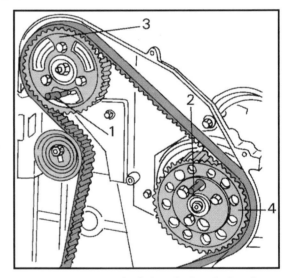

Fig. 1.86 – Removal of the timing belt when removing the camshaft.
1 Timing belt attached to timing gear
2 Camshaft gear bolts
3 Camshaft gear nut
4 Camshaft timing gear
5 Injection pump drive gear
6 Camshaft gear locking bolt
7 Pump gear attached to belt

Removal of the Camshaft

- Attach the timing belt in a suitable manner to the camshaft timing gear. In the workshop plastic clips are used, which are fitted over timing belt and timing gear. Otherwise use wire and tie the parts together.

- The removal is now carried out by referring to Fig. 1.86. Remove the nut (3) and slacken the three bolts (2). Withdraw the locking bolt (6) and withdraw the camshaft timing gearwheel. The timing belt must be held fully stretched, by pulling the camshaft timing gear upwards as shown in Fig. 1.87 after it has been removed. Attach the camshaft gearwheel in this position, using a piece of wire, to make sure it cannot disengage from the other wheels. A tight timing belt is very important.

- The camshaft can now be removed (see below).

Removal of the Injection Pump

- Attach the timing belt to the camshaft timing gearwheel and the injection pump drive gear as described above.

Fig. 1.87 – Pull the timing gears in the direction of the arrows and tie them up. The belt must be kept fully stretched.

- Refer to Fig. 1.88 to continue. Remove the three bolts (4) and withdraw the locking bolt (5). Withdraw the pump drive gear. Again keep the belt tight as described above, similar as shown in Fig. 1.87. Make sure that the belt cannot slip off the other timing wheels.

- The injection pump can now be removed.

Refit the timing belt as follows:

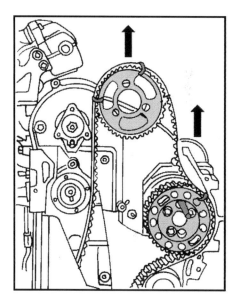

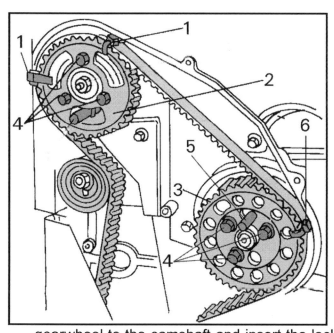

Fig. 1.88 – Removal of the timing belt during removal of the injection pump.
1   Belt attached to timing gear
2   Camshaft timing gear
3   Injection pump drive gear
4   Pump gear bolts
5   Pump gear locking rod
6   Timing belt attached to wheel

After the camshaft has been removed

- Fit the camshaft timing gearwheel to the camshaft and insert the locking rod (6) in Fig. 1.87. Fit the three bolts (2) and tighten them to 1.0 kgm (7 ft.lb.). Again tighten the bolts, but this time to 2.5 kgm (18 ft.lb.). Fit the nut (3) and tighten to 4.3 kgm (31 ft.lb.).

- Remove the timing belt from the timing gearwheels and the locking bolt out of the camshaft gearwheel, the injection pump drive gear and the flywheel. All other operations are carried out in reverse order to the removal procedure.

Engines

After the injection pump has been removed

Fit the injection pump gear to the pump hub and insert the locking bolt (5) in Fig. 1.88. Fit the three bolts (4) and tighten them to 1.0 kgm (7.2 ft.lb.). Again tighten the bolts, but this time to 2.5 kgm (18 ft.lb.).

- Remove the timing belt from the timing gearwheels and the locking bolt out of the camshaft gearwheel, the injection pump drive gear and the flywheel. All other operations are carried out in reverse order to the removal procedure.

During all operations

- Rotate the engine two complete turns in the direction of rotation and check that the timing belt is engaged properly.
- The next operation is critical, as the correct timing adjustment must be checked. When the lock bolt is inserted into the hole shown in Fig. 1.84, you must be able to insert the lock bolt into the camshaft gearwheel (1) and the injection pump gear (2) in Fig. 1.89. The inset at the bottom shows the correct and incorrect alignment. The belt must be completely removed, if the alignment cannot be obtained. If the alignment is correct, there is no need to tension the belt.

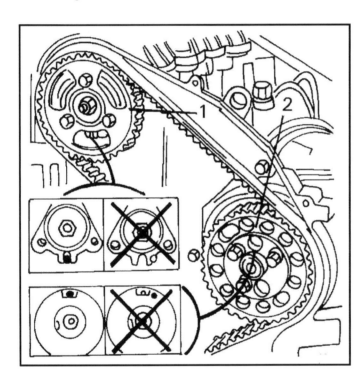

Fig. 1.89 – Checking the timing adjustment. The camshaft timing gearwheel (1) and the pump drive gear (2) must be in the position shown to insert the locking bolts.

2.5 Litre Engine – Timing Belt Replacement

Fig. 1.90 shows the component parts of the timing mechanism. We must point out that a checking instrument and a special wrench to adjust the timing belt tension is used in the workshop. The latter can, however, be substituted by a 7 mm square spanner.

Experienced mechanics may be able to adjust the belt tension without the tension checking gauge. Our advice is to read the following instructions before attempting any work described below.

- Disconnect the battery, jack up the R.H. side of the vehicle and remove the wheel to improve the access to the various parts. Remove the panel underneath the engine and the protective shield from inside the wheel arch. Engage the 5th gear to rotate the crankshaft later on.
- Remove the drive belt from the front of the engine.
- Remove the upper timing belt cover. Remove the four bolts in the centre of the crankshaft pulley and remove the pulley. The lower belt cover can now be removed.
- Obtain a bolt M7 x 60 mm long and screw it at position (1) in Fig. 1.85 into the camshaft timing gear. Lock the injection pump drive gear in a similar manner, using a metal rod, but note: **Bosch injection pump** = 9.5 mm diameter, **Lucas injection pump** = 6.0 mm diameter.

- Hold the camshaft timing gear against rotation and slacken the bolts (1) and (6) in Fig. 1.92 (see following page). Tighten bolts once more until they contact the surface and from this position slacken each bolt by 1/6 of a turn.

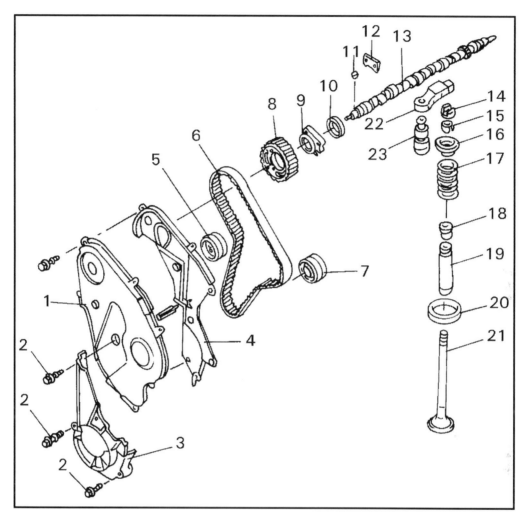

Fig. 1.90 – The timing gear parts of a 2.5 litre engine. The drive gear for the vacuum pump is integrated into the camshaft in the case of the engine with direct injection.

1 Upper timing belt cover	8 Camshaft timing gearwheel	15 Valve cotter halves
2 Bolts	9 Camshaft gearwheel hub	16 Valve spring cup
3 Lower timing belt cover	10 Oil seal	17 Valve spring
4 Rear timing belt cover	11 Woodruff key, camshaft	18 Valve stem oil seal
5 Belt tensioner roller	12 Camshaft keeper plate	19 Valve guide
6 Timing belt	13 Camshaft	20 Valve seat insert
7 Idler roller	14 Rocker lever seat	21 Valve

- Slacken the nut securing the timing belt tensioner and lift off the belt. If the old belt is to be refitted, mark the running direction of the belt into the outside, using a felt pen. A new belt requires the replacement of the tensioning roller and the idler roller.

The installation is carried out as follows:
- When the original belt is refitted, check that the two rollers can be rotated freely.
- Fit the belt in the order shown in Fig. 1.91: over the crankshaft gear (6), over the idler roller (7), over the injection pump gear (4), over the camshaft timing gear (2) and behind the tensioning roller (3). Timing gears (4) and (2) must be rotated to engage the belt properly.

Engines

Fig. 1.91 – View of the fitted timing belt from the front of the engine. Place the belt over the gearwheels as described in the text.

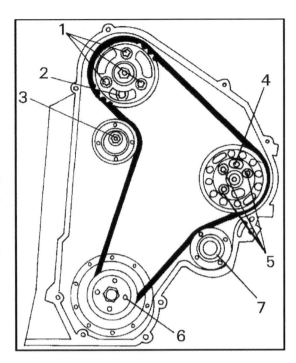

- The tension checking instrument (4) must now be placed between the camshaft and injection pump over the timing belt. First pre-tension the belt. To do this, insert the 7 mm square spanner (3) into the opening of the tensioner roller and rotate the roller until an indication of 8 kgm (new belt) or 5 kg (used belt) is obtained. If the instrument is used, you must obtain an indication of 107 or 80. Tighten the tensioning roller nut to 4.3 kgm (31 ft.lb.).

The belt tension is now checked:

- Tighten the bolts (1) and (6) in Fig. 1.92 to 1.0 kgm (7.2 ft.lb.) and then again to 2.5 kgm (18 ft.lb.).

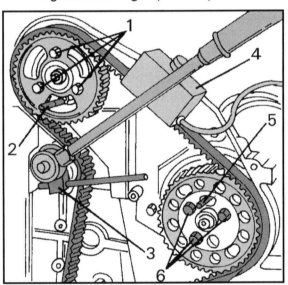

Fig. 1.92 – Details for the timing belt tension adjustment.

1   Camshaft gear bolts
2   Fitted locking bolt
3   Spanner for belt adjustment
4   Torque wrench
5   Fitted locking bolt
6   Injection pump gear bolts

- Remove all locking bolts, the checking instrument and the square spanner and rotate the crankshaft 10 times in the direction of rotation, until the metal rod can be inserted once more into the flywheel as shown in Fig. 1.84. Rotate the crankshaft very slowly, as your cannot turn it against the direction of rotation, when you passed the setting.

- Slacken the bolts (1) and (6) in Fig. 1.92 and re-tighten them until the contact the surface. From this position slacken them by 1/6 of a turn.

- Move the tensioning roller to fully slacken the belt and insert the locking bolt (2) and (5) into the two timing gears.

- Fit the tension checking instrument to the timing belt and adjust the tension as described above. Adjust a new belt to 30 kg (instrument reading 58) or a used belt to 25 kg (instrument reading 51). After the correct tension has been obtained, tighten the tensioner pulley nut to 4.3 kgm (31 ft.lb.).

- Tighten the bolts (1) and (6) in Fig. 1.92 with 1.0 kgm (7.2 ft.lb.) and then with 2.5 kgm (18 ft.lb.). Remove all tools and rotate the crankshaft by two complete revolutions.

- The next operation is critical, as the correct timing adjustment must be checked. When the lock bolt is inserted into the hole shown in Fig. 1.84, you must be able to insert the lock bolt into the camshaft gearwheel (1) and the injection pump gear (2) in Fig. 1.89. The inset at the bottom shows the correct and incorrect alignment.

The belt must be completely removed, if the alignment cannot be obtained. If the alignment is correct, there is no need to tension the belt.

1.4.4.2.   Removal and Installation of Camshaft

1.9 litre Engine

The camshaft can be removed with the engine fitted, as this may be necessary if you want to check the valve clearances.

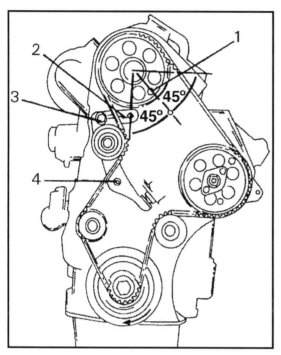

Fig. 1.93 – Position of the camshaft gearwheel when removing the camshaft (1.9 litre).

1	Inserted lock bolt
2	Square hole
3	Securing bolt
4	Securing nut

- Remove the cylinder head cover with all attached parts.
- Remove the upper and centre timing belt covers.
- Rotate the crankshaft into the hole for the locking bolt (1) in Fig. 1.93 is in the centre between the two holes in the cylinder head.
- Remove the vacuum pump or slacken the drive belt and remove it.
- Remove the two bolt (3) and nut (4) in Fig. 1.93.
- Insert the drive of a 3/8 in. Socket set into the square hole (2) in Fig. 1.93 and push the tensioning roller towards the outside until the spring is compressed. Tighten the bolt (3) in this position (the tensioning roller must not move).
- Carefully remove the belt and store it in a safe place.
- Mark the camshaft bearing caps with the bearing number and unscrew the cap screws.
- Lift out the camshaft. If necessary remove the valve adjusting shims and the tappets. Keep shims and tappets together as they are removed.

Install the camshaft as follows. Check and if necessary adjust the valve clearances as already described.

- Fit the valve tappets and the adjusting shims (well oiled). Remember, once in position they cannot be lifted, as the shim will be dislodged. If necessary remove the tappet completely and refit it with the shim.
- Lubricate the camshaft journals and place the camshaft into the bearing bores, so that the 4th and 6th cam (counting from the flywheel side) is resting against the respective cam.
- Coat the mounting face of the two outer covers with sealing compound and fit them to the cylinder head. Fit the remaining bearing caps and evenly tighten all bearing caps to 2.0 kgm (14.5 ft.lb.).
- Fit the two oil seals into the cylinder head ends.

Engines

- Refit the camshaft timing gear and fit and tighten the bolt (with washer) to 4.5 kgm (32.5 ft.lb.). Turn the camshaft by at least 2 revolutions and check the valve clearance once more (see Fig. 1.71). Corrections must be carried out now.
- Fit the vacuum pump. Two new "O" seals must be used. Tighten the bolts to 2.5 kgm (18 ft.lb.).
- All other operations are a reversal of the removal procedure. Refit the timing belt as described for the 1.9 litre engine.

2.5 Litre Engines

Certain differences must be noted when the camshaft of an engine with direct injection (DJ5 TED) is removed. The camshaft has also been modified around June 1995. See description below.

- Partially remove the timing belt as already described under "Removal of Camshaft".

Except Engine with Direct Injection

- Remove the nut securing the camshaft hub (item 9, Fig. 1.90) and the screw on the left. Before removal of the hub insert the locking bolt, shown later in Fig. 1.97 (a bolt of suitable diameter can be used).

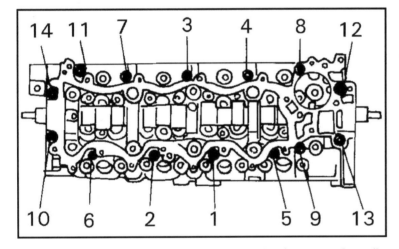

Fig. 1.94 – Tightening sequence for the camshaft housing bolts (except DJ5 TED engine with direct injection).

- Slacken the camshaft housing bolts in reverse order to the one shown in Fig. 1.94, remove the bolts and lift off the camshaft housing.
- Remove the two oil seals from each end of the camshaft housing, unscrew the keeper plate (item 21, Fig. 1.90) and withdraw the camshaft.

Fig. 1.95 – Disconnect the connections from the EGR system.

Engine with Direct Injection

- Remove the parts belonging to the exhaust gas recirculation system (EGR) in Fig. 1.95. To do this, disconnect the hose (1), slacken the clamp (2) of the EGR valve and withdraw the EGR valve (3).
- Remove the cylinder head cover.
- Remove the vacuum pump by referring to Fig. 1.96. Disconnect the quick fastener (1) from the pump, remove the bolts (2) and withdraw the pump (3).

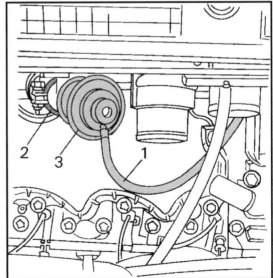

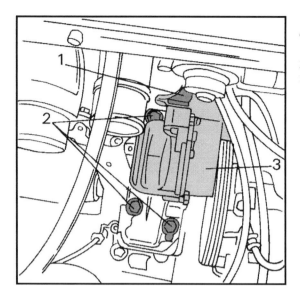

Fig. 1.96 – The vacuum pump of the DJ5 TED engine.
1   Quick fastener
2   Securing screws
3   Vacuum pump

* Remove the camshaft hub after locking it in position in relation to the camshaft. Again a special locking bolt is used, inserted as shown in Fig. 1.97. Unscrew the nut (1) in the centre of the hub, remove the washer and remove the hub (3).

* The camshaft housing is now removed. Refer to Fig. 1.98 and slacken the bolts in several stages, until they can be removed. Lift off the housing and withdraw the camshaft.

* Remove the water pump pulley.

Fig. 1.97 – Hub attachment to the camshaft. The locking bolt is inserted at the bottom.
1   Nut, note tightening torque
2   Washer
3   Hub
4   Inserted locking bolt

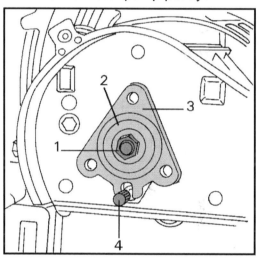

The installation is a reversal of the removal procedure, noting the differences between the two different engine types:

Except Engine with Direct Injection

* Thoroughly clean all gasket faces. The condition of the hydraulic compensating elements should be checked.

* Oil the camshaft bearing journals and insert the shaft into the camshaft housing. Fit the keeper plate and tighten the bolts (new) to 1.1 kgm (8 ft.lb.). Rotate the shaft a few times.

* Fit new oil seals into the cylinder head (use a suitable drift).

* Fit the camshaft hub as shown in Fig. 1.97 and insert the locking bolt. The hub is now removed and the bolt withdrawn. ***The camshaft must not be rotated until the camshaft housing is fitted to the head.***

* Coat the upper face of the cylinder head with sealing compound (Autojoint), lower the housing over the head and tighten the bolts in the order shown in Fig. 1.55 earlier in the manual. Tighten the bolts to 2.0 kgm (14.5 ft.lb.).

* The remaining installation is a reversal of the removal procedure. Relevant tightening torques are given in Section 1.5.

Engine with Direct Injection DJ5 TED

* Thoroughly clean all gasket faces. The condition of the hydraulic compensating elements should be checked. Oil the camshaft bearing journals and insert the shaft into the camshaft housing. Fit the keeper plate and tighten the bolts (new) to 1.1 kgm (8 ft.lb.). Rotate the shaft a few times and finally turn it to the position where the locking bolt in Fig. 1.97 can be inserted.

* Refit the water pump pulley. Tighten the pulley bolts to 4.3 kgm (31 ft.lb.).

Engines

- Fill the groove of the camshaft bearing housing with "Autojoint" sealing compound. Note the small bore on the drive end for the vacuum pump, which must not be filled with the compound.

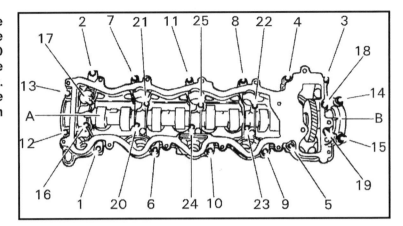

Fig. 1.98 – Slacken the camshaft housing in the order shown (DJ5 TED engine). The bolts are tightened in reverse order. The drive gear for the vacuum pump can be seen on the R.H. side.

A Camshaft
B Camshaft housing

- Fit the camshaft and fit the bolts. A seal is fitted underneath bolts (18) and (19) in Fig. 1.98. Tighten the bolts in the reverse order shown to 1.0 kgm (7.2 ft.lb.). Refit the oil seals after installation.
- Fit the camshaft hub, fit the washer and the nut and tighten the nut first to 1.1 kgm and then a further 50°.
- Fit a new vacuum pump seal, insert the pump and tighten the bolts (1.3 kgm). Re-connect the quick fasteners to the pump.
- All other operations are carried out in reverse order.

1.4.4.3   Engines with modified Camshaft

Up to May 1995 the drive gear for the vacuum pump is a part of the camshaft on the flywheel side of the engine. On later engines the drive gear is pushed over the end of the camshaft and must be fitted during installation of the shaft. The following differences should be noted:

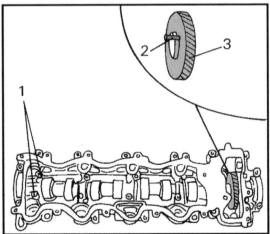

Fig. 1.99 – Arrangement of the separate vacuum pump drive gear.
1   Bolts, 1.2 kgm
2   Key for drive gear
3   Drive gear

- Insert the camshaft and push it as far as possible towards the timing side.
- Fit the drive pin (2) in Fig. 1.99 into the vacuum pump drive gear and fit the gearwheel and the camshaft stop as shown in the illustration.
- Clean the threads of the bolts (1), coat them with "Loctite" and evenly tighten the bolts to 1.2 kgm (8.5 ft.lb.).

The remaining installation is carried out by referring to Fig. 1.100. Fit the intermediate bush (1) onto the camshaft. The intermediate bush has a chamfer on one side and a groove (b). This end must face the drive gear side. Fit the pin (5) into the slot (a) of the camshaft (3) and fit a new "O" seal (4).

Fig. 1.100 – Fitting the vacuum pump drive gear (modified camshaft).
1 Intermediate bush
2 Drive gear
3 Camshaft
4 Oil seal
5 Key (pin)
a Slot in camshaft
b Groove in bush

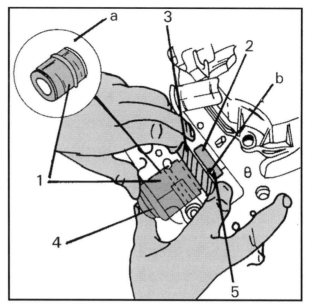

- Fit a new oil seal and the pulley. Coat the bolt with "Loctite", screw it into the camshaft and tighten it to 4.3 kgm (31 ft.lb.).

1.5   Tightening Torque Values – Engines

1.9 Litre Engine

Cylinder Head Bolts:
- 1st stage   2.0 kgm (14.5 ft.lb.)
- 2nd stage   6.0 kgm (43.5 ft.lb.)
- 3rd stage   Tighten by 180° (without turbo) or 220° (turbo)

Main Bearing caps – Without turbo   7.0 kgm (50.5 ft.lb.)

Main bearing caps – Turbo:
- 1st stage   1.5 kgm (11 ft.lb.)
- 2nd stage   60° angle-tightening

Connecting Rod Bearing Caps:
- 1st stage   2.0 kgm
- 2nd stage   70° angle-tightening

Flywheel bolts   5.0 kgm (36 ft.lb.)

Crankshaft pulley:
- 1st stage   4.0 kgm (30 ft.lb.)
- 2nd stage   60° angle-tightening

Injector to cylinder head   9.0 kgm (65 ft.lb.)
Oil splash jet to cylinder block   1.0 kgm (7.2 ft.lb.)
Timing belt tensioning roller   1.8 kgm (13 ft.lb.)
Timing belt idler roller   1.8 kgm (13 ft.lb.)
Oil cooler to cylinder block   6.5 kgm (47 ft.lb.)
Injection pump drive gear   5.0 kgm (36 ft.lb.)
Camshaft timing gearwheel   4.3 kgm (31 ft.lb.)
Oil pressure switch   3.0 kgm (22 ft.lb.)
Oil drain plug (sump)   3.0 kgm (22 ft.lb.)
Water drain plug (block)   2.5 kgm (18 ft.lb.)
Water pump   1.5 kgm (11 ft.lb.)
Cylinder head cover   0.8 kgm (6 ft.lb.)
Clutch bolts   2.0 kgm (14.5 ft.lb.)
Oil pump bolts   0.8 kgm (13 ft.lb.)

Engines

Lubrication pipe, turbo charger	Engine side 3.0 kgm (22 ft.lb.), turbo side 2.0 kgm (14.5 ft.lb.)
Injection pump, front	1.8 kgm (13 ft.lb.)
Injection pump, rear	2.0 kgm (14.5 ft.lb.)
Union nuts, injection pipes	2.5 kgm (18 ft.lb.)
L.H. Engine Mounting:	
- Nuts on side	1.8 kgm (13 ft.lb.)
- Nut in centre	3.5 kgm (25.5 ft.lb.)
R.H. engine mounting	4.5 kgm (32.5 ft.lb.)
Rear Engine Mounting:	
- Body side	5.5 kgm (40 ft.lb.)
- Engine side	3.5 kgm (25.5 ft.lb.)
Coolant inlet elbow	0.5 kgm, then 1.6 kgm
Glow plugs	2.5 kgm (18 ft.lb.)
Fuel filter bolt	1.5 kgm (11 ft.lb.)
Thermo switch	1.8 kgm (13 ft.lb.)
Exhaust Manifold:	
- Without turbo charger	3.0 kgm (22 ft.lb.)
- With turbo charger	2.5 kgm (18 ft.lb.)
Inlet manifold	2.0 kgm (14.5 ft.lb.)
Oil sump bolts	1.6 kgm (11.5 ft.lb.)

2.5 Litre Engine

Cylinder head bolts (see Fig. 1.50):	
- 1st stage	Tighten M12 bolts 1 to 14 to 5.0 kgm (36 ft.lb.)
- 2nd stage	Tighten M10 bolts to 15 to 22 to 3.5 kgm (25 ft.lb.)
- 3rd stage	Tighten all bolts to an angle of 120°, plus or minus 5°
Crankshaft Bearing Housing:	
- 1st stage	2.0 kgm (14.5 ft.lb.)
- 2nd stage	Angle-tighten 60°
Big End Bearing Caps:	
- 1st stage	2.0 kgm (14.5 ft.lb.)
- 2nd stage	Angle-tighten 65°
Flywheel bolts	5.0 kgm (36 ft.lb.)
Crankshaft pulley	2.0 kgm (14.5 ft.lb.)
Injectors to cylinder head	5.5 kgm (40 ft.lb.)
Oil splash jets to block	1.0 kgm (7.2 ft.lb.)
Tension roller bracket for timing belt	4.5 kgm (32.5 ft.lb.)
Centre nut of tensioning roller to water pump	2.0 kgm (14.5 ft.lb.)
Pulley to camshaft	4.3 kgm (31 ft.lb.)
Timing Gearwheel to Camshaft:	
- 1st stage	1.0 kgm (7.2 ft.lb.)
- 2nd stage	2.5 kgm (18 ft.lb.)
Camshaft housing to cylinder head	2.0 kgm (14.5 ft.lb.)
Camshaft keeper plate	1.1 kgm (8 ft.lb.)

Cylinder head cover	1.0 kgm (7.2 ft.lb.)
Oil cooler to cylinder block	6.5 kgm (47 ft.lb.)
Injection pump drive gear:	
- 1st stage	1.0 kgm (7.2 ft.lb.)
- 2nd stage	2.5 kgm (18 ft.lb.)
Oil pressure switch	3.0 kgm (22 ft.lb.)
Oil drain plug (sump)	3.0 kgm (22 ft.lb.)
Water drain plug (block)	2.5 kgm (18 ft.lb.)
Water pump	1.5 kgm (11 ft.lb.)
Water pump pulley	4.3 kgm (31 ft.lb.)
Cylinder head cover	1.0 kgm (7.2 ft.lb.)
Clutch bolts	2.0 kgm (14.5 ft.lb.)
Oil pump	9.9 kgm (7 ft.lb.)
Lubrication pipe, turbo charger:	
- Engine side	3.0 kgm (22 ft.lb.)
- Turbo side	1.0 kgm (7.2 ft.lb.), then 90° further
Injection pump, front and rear	2.0 kgm (14.5 ft.lb.)
Union nuts, injection pipes	2.5 kgm (18 ft.lb.)
Engine mountings, bolts	5.8 kgm (42 ft.lb.) – See Fig. 1.65
Engine mountings, nut	8.0 kgm (58 ft.lb.) – See Fig. 1.65
Glow plugs	2.5 kgm (18 ft.lb.), 2.0 kgm with Turbo
Thermo switch	1.8 kgm (13 ft.lb.)
Exhaust Manifold:	
- Without turbo charger	2.0 kgm (14.5 ft.lb.)
- With turbo charger	3.0 kgm (22 ft.lb.)
Inlet manifold	2.2 kgm (16 ft.lb.)
Bolt, water pump belt tension roller	2.0 kgm (14.5 ft.lb.)
Bolts, tensioning roller, auxiliary drive belt	2.0 kgm (14.5 ft.lb.)
Vacuum pump	1.5 kgm (11 ft.lb.)

1.6.   Lubrication System
1.6.0.   TECHNICAL DATA

Oil sump capacity	Refer to Pages 6 and 7
Oil type (recommended)	Total oil for diesel or turbo diesel engines (10W40 or 15W40)
Oil Pressure – 1.9 Litre Engines:	
- Min. oil pressure at idle speed:	
- Without turbo charger	2.2 bar (31.0 psi.)
- With turbo charger	2.4 bar (34 psi.)
- Oil pressure at 80° C and 4000 rpm:	
- 1.9 litre engine without turbo	4.6 bar (65 psi.)
- 1.9 litre with turbo	4.8 bar (68 psi.)
Oil Pressure – 2.5 Litre Engines:	
- Without turbo/with turbo – at 2000 rpm	3.6 bar (51 psi.)/3.0 bar (43 psi.)
- Without turbo/with turbo – at 4000 rpm	4.5 bar (64 psi)/3.5 bar (50 psi.)
- DJ5 TED engine – direct injection:	
- At 850 rpm	1.8 bar (26 psi.)
- At 2000 rpm	3.5 bar (50 psi.)

Lubrication System

- At 3000 rpm	4.0 bar (57 psi.)
- At 4000 rpm	4.4 bar (62 psi.)
Oil Filter:	
- Type	Replaceable filter cartridge
- Oil filter	Purflux LS 468 A or LS 520 C (Turbo)
- Changing intervals	Together with oil change or once a year (every 10,000 miles)

1.6.1.   GENERAL

An oil pump, driven by a separate chain from the crankshaft, is fitted to all engines and supplies the oil for the lubrication of all bearing points and moveable parts. Note the following:

- The bottom of the pistons are cooled by oil splash jets in the case of the 1.9 litre engine with turbo charger and all 2.5 litre engines. The jets are bolted to the cylinder block. Different jets are fitted to the 2.5 litre versions. The hydraulic valve clearance compensating elements of the 2.5 litre engines are also supplied with oil from the lubrication system.
- All engines have an oil cooler between the oil filter and the cylinder block.
- The oil filter of the two 2.5 litre engines (turbo and non-turbo) is the same. The oil filter for the two 1.9 litre versions is not the same. Replace the oil filter at every oil change.
- Note the oil capacity in the oil sump (pages 6 and 7).
- The oil pressure is different on all engines (see Section 1.6.0.).
- The oil sump of a 1.9 litre engine is either made of steel (without A/C system) or aluminium (with A/C system). The oil sump of all 2.5 litre engines is made of steel.

Fig. 1.101 shows a sectional view of the lubrication circuit of a 1.9 litre engine without turbo charger. Fig. 1.102 shows a side view of a 2.5 litre engine. Both illustrations show the location of the oil pump.

1.6.2.   OIL PUMP (and Oil Sump)

With 1.9 Litre Engine

The drive gear for the two diesel engines is not always the same. If the oil pump is replaced, quote the engine number. The oil pump can be replaced with the engine fitted.

- Lift up the front end of the vehicle (chassis stands) and remove the protective panel underneath the engine.
- Drain the engine oil into a suitable container. Slightly warm oil will drain easier.
- Unscrew the oil sump securing screws and lower the sump. A sticking oil pump can be carefully freed by tapping it with a plastic or rubber mallet. Do not insert a screwdriver into the joining faces. Note the differences between a steel sump and an aluminium sump (see dismantling procedures for the engine).
- To remove the oil pump refer to Section 1.2, covering the dismantling of the engine. The oil pump must be turned to disengage it from the drive chain.

Repair of the oil pump is not possible. Replace the pump if a low oil pressure is the reason for the pump removal. Only the pump suction filter can be replaced.

Check the oil pressure piston and the spring (the pump must be dismantled for this purpose). Clean out the piston bore and check for grooves or pitting. A sticking piston

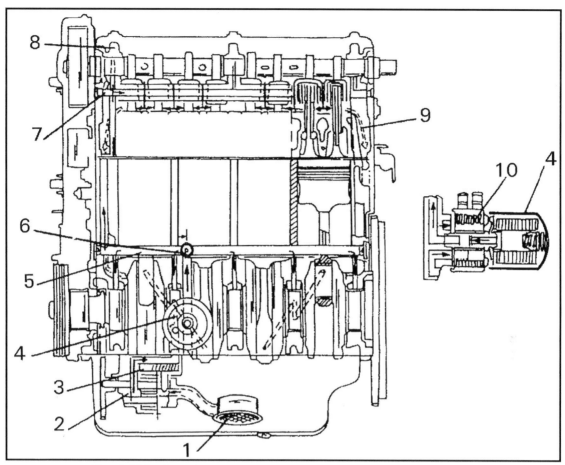

Fig. 1.101 – Lubrication circuit diagram of a 1.9 litre engine.

1 Oil suction filter
2 Oil pump
3 Oil pressure relief valve
4 By-pass valve (in filter)

5 Cylinder block oil gallery
6 Oil pressure switch
7 Oil bore in cylinder head
8 Camshaft bearings

9 Oil return
10 Oil cooler

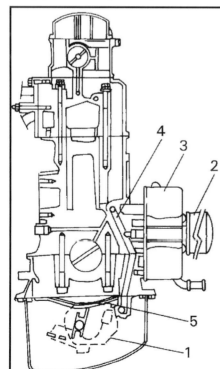

Fig. 1.102 – Sectional view of the 2.5 litre engine.
1   Oil pump
2   Oil filter
3   Oil cooler
4   Main oil gallery
5   Oil baffle plate

or one with excessive clearance can lead to oil pressure problems later on. Replace the piston, spring or the oil pump accordingly.

Before fitting the pump, clean the cylinder block face, without using sharp tools. Place the pump in the correct position, at the same time engaging it with the drive chain, and push it over the dowel sleeve. Tighten the bolts to 0.8 kgm. Refit the oil sump as described during the assembly of the engine.

Note the bolt length. Fit the oil sump drain plug and tighten to 3.0 kgm (22 ft.lb.). Fill the engine with the correct amount of oil.

Lubrication System

To make sure the pump has enough oil when the engine is started, disconnect the plug from the fuel shut-off valve on the injection pump and crank the engine (30 seconds) with the starter motor. Re-connect the cable plug and start the engine. Re-check the oil level after the engine has reached its operating temperature and if necessary correct.

2.5 Litre Engine

Sealing compound is required to fit the oil sump.

- Disconnect the battery. Lift up the front end of the vehicle (chassis stands) and remove the protective panel underneath the engine.
- Remove the R.H. drive shaft as described in the relevant section.
- Remove the covering panel underneath the flywheel housing.
- Drain the engine oil. Remember that the capacity of the sump is approx. 2 gallons (9 litres).

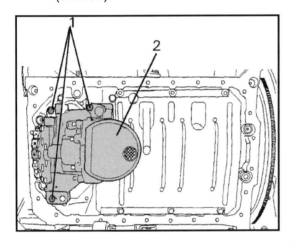

Fig. 1.103 – Remove the bolts (1) to remove the oil pump (2) – 2.5 litre engine.

- Remove the oil sump securing screws and lower the sump. Rock the sump to and fro if it is sticking.
- Remove the oil pump by referring to Fig. 1.103. Turn the oil pump slightly to disengage the chain.

The installation is a reversal of the removal procedure. Fig. 1.104 shows the component parts of the lubrication system. Fit the oil pump over the dowel sleeve, at the same

Fig. 1.104 – Oil sump and oil pump with filter and oil cooler of a 2.5 litre engine.

1 Oil dipstick
2 Oil dipstick guide tube
3 Oil filter
4 Oil filter threaded stud
5 Oil cooler
6 Oil pressure switch
7 Drive chain
8 Dowel pin
9 Relief valve piston
10 Spring
11 Spring guide
12 Oil pump housing
13 Cover with suction filter
14 Oil sump
15 Oil splash jet
16 Oil drain plug and gasket

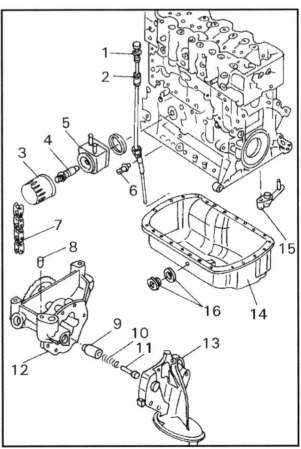

time engaging the drive chain. Tighten the bolts to 0.9 kgm (6.5 ft.lb.). Otherwise follow the instructions given for the installation of the oil pump for the 1.9 litre engine.

1.6.3. OIL FILTER

The oil filter has an integral by-pass valve and only a replacement filter with such a valve must be fitted (see Section 1.6.0.). To remove the filter, use a filter wrench to unscrew the filter. If none is available, try a piece of emery cloth. Place this around the outside of the filter, with the abrasive side towards the filter body, and with the two hands try to unscrew the filter.

Lubricate the seal of the new filter with engine oil and tighten the filter until it touches the cylinder block. From this position, and with the hands only, tighten the filter a further ¼ of a turn. Unscrew the filter once more and re-tighten it until it touches the cylinder block and now tighten it a further ½ to ¾ of a turn. These instructions must be followed to obtain a perfect seal. The fitting instructions are normally printed on a label, attached to the filter.

1.6.4. OIL PRESSURE

If a suitable adapter to screw into the thread for the oil pressure switch, is available, check the oil pressure as follows:

- Run the engine until the oil temperature has reached 80° C and then idle the engine for 5 minutes after the cooling fan has switched on.
- Switch off the engine, disconnect the plug from the oil pressure switch and screw the pressure gauge adapter into the thread normally taken by the switch. Location of switch: 1.9 litre engine = below the oil filter, 2.5 litre engine = on the R.H. side of the filter.
- Run the engine at idle speed and then at the speeds given in Section 1.6.0. Refer to the pressure to be obtained.
- If the oil pressure is below the values given, it may be necessary to carry out an oil change. Re-check the pressure. If the pressure is still low, the oil pump must be suspect and must be removed for further investigation.
- Remove the pressure gauge and fit the oil pressure switch with the copper washer. Tighten the switch to 3.4 kgm (25 ft.lb.) in the case of the 1.9 litre engine or 2.5 kgm (18 ft.lb.) in the case of the 2.5 litre engine.

1.7. Cooling System

1.7.0. Technical Data

Type of system	Sealed with expansion bottle. Oil cooler and fuel pre-heater connected to cooling system.
System capacity	Refer to Page 8
Water pump:	
- Type and drive – 1.9 litre	R.H. side of cylinder block, driven by timing belt from crankshaft. No repair possible
- Type and drive – 2.5 litre	Fitted to front of cylinder block, driven by separate belt from pulley on camshaft. Belt tension adjusted properly by means of special instrument
Radiator	Mounted at front of engine, below the lower, inner crossmember
Expansion tank	Plastic container, fitted to R.H. side of engine compartment. Opening pressure of cap 1.0 bar.

Cooling System

Anti-Freeze Content:
- Down to −15° C   28% anti-freeze
- Down to − 30° C   50% anti-freeze

Thermostat:
- 1.9 litre engine   Wax element in separate housing at front of cylinder head. Opening temperature 83°C

- 2.5 litre engine   Wax element. Two thermostats. Main thermostat in housing on water pump. Secondary thermostat underneath a cover in water outlet elbow on cylinder head.

- Opening Temperature – 2.5 Litre Engine:
  - Main thermostat   85°C, fully open at 100°C
  - Secondary thermostat   84°C, fully open at 88°C

Water Temperature Switch:
- Opening temperature – 1.9/2.5 litre   110°C/118°C
- Location   In thermostat housing

Electric Cooling Fan:
- Cutting-in/Cutting-out – 1st stage   88°C/83°C
- Cutting-in/Cutting out – 2nd stage   92°C/87°C

1.7.1.   DRAINING AND REFILLING

Two coolant drain plugs are fitted and both should be opened to drain the cooling system. A switch is used as a safeguard for overheating. The switch operates when the engine overheats and a warning light in the dashboard "blinks". Investigate the cause immediately, i.e. switch off the engine.

To drain the cooling system, remove the protective panel below the engine and unscrew the drain plug in the cylinder block and unscrew the plug at the bottom of the radiator. The expansion tank cap must be removed to facilitate the draining. The system is filled with anti-freeze and this can be collected if wanted. If it is intended to renew the anti-freeze, disconnect the lower radiator hose to drain the system, but catch as much of the anti-freeze as possible – **Avoid Pollution !** – dispose of the anti-freeze in responsible manner.

Prepare the anti-freeze mixture in accordance with the temperature you expect in your area. Manufacturers charts will give you the correct ratio, but remember that only an anti-freeze suitable for these engines must be used. Refer to Section 1.7.0 for general temperatures.

Refit the cylinder block and radiator drain plugs and make sure they are tight. Open the bleeder valve on the radiator (1.9 litre) or the on the coolant outlet housing at the bottom of the hose (2.5 litre).

Fill the coolant through the expansion tank opening and close the bleed screw as soon as only liquid, free of air bubbles, comes out of the bleeder screw hole and the coolant level is up to the "Max" mark on the expansion tank. *Do not run the engine with the bleeder screw slackened.*

Start the engine and run it at 1500 rpm. Wait until the thermostat has opened right up or the cooling fans have cut-in and then allow the engine to run approx. 1 minute at idle speed. Switch off the engine and fit the expansion tank cap. Allow the engine to cool down for at least 3 hours and re-check the coolant level. The coolant must be level with the "Max" mark. Otherwise correct. Take the opportunity to check the system for leaks.

1.7.2. RADIATOR – REMOVAL AND INSTALLATION

The removal and installation of the radiator is identical with the removal of the front panel of the engine, described during the removal of the engine. Smear the thread of the temperature switch with sealing compound (if removed) and screw the switch into the radiator. If the radiator has been replaced, transfer the rubber mountings to the new radiator. After installation fill the cooling system as described above.

1.7.3 WATER PUMP – REMOVAL AND INSTALLATION

The water pump cannot be repaired or serviced. If the pump is faulty or leaking, fit a new unit.

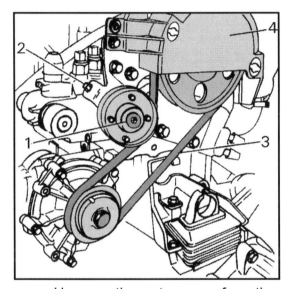

Fig. 1.105 – Removal and installation of the water pump (2.5 litre).
1   Nut, belt tensioner roller
2   Adjusting bolt, belt tension
3   Drive belt
4   Protective cover

The water pump of the 1.9 litre engine is located on the timing side of the engine and is driven by the timing belt, i.e. is hidden out of view. The pump can be removed with the engine fitted to the vehicle. The protection panel inside the wheel arch must be removed. Remove and refit the timing belt as described for the 1.9 litre engine to gain access to the water pump. Unscrew the water pump from the cylinder block.

Fig. 1.106 – Water pump – 2.5 litre engine.
1   Belt adjuster bolt
2   Belt pulley bracket
3   Belt tensioner roller
4   Drive belt, water pump
5   Gasket, water pump
6   Water pump housing
7   Gasket, thermostat housing cover
8   Thermostat housing cover
9   Water pump with pulley
10   Two-way elbow
11   Water pump bolts
12   Connecting to heater
13   Gasket
14   Connecting to lower radiator elbow
15   Connection to expansion tank

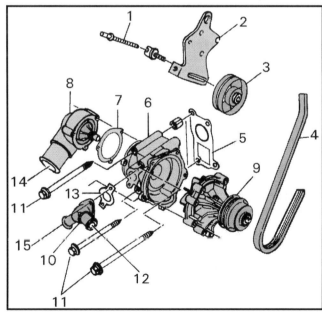

The water pump of the 2.5 litre engines is driven by means of a belt from a pulley on the camshaft. Note that a different pulley is used for turbo-charged and naturally aspirating engines. We must point out that the workshop uses a special instrument to measure the belt tension. Removal of the pump can be carried out by referring to Fig. 1.105:

Cooling System

- Disconnect the negative battery cable and remove the protective cover (4) over the pulley on the camshaft.
- Slacken the nut (1) in the centre of the tensioning roller and turn the bolt (2), until the belt (3) can be removed. Check that the roller can rotate freely. Otherwise replace it.
- Unscrew the water pump from the cylinder block. Fig. 1.106 shows a detailed view.
- Clean the cylinder head face and place a new gasket in position. Refit the pump.
- Place the drive belt (3) in Fig. 1.105 over the two pulleys, making sure that it rests well in the grooves.
- Adjust the belt tension by means of bolt (2). As the checking instrument is most probable not available, adjust the belt so that it can be deflected slightly. If you are not satisfied, have the tension checked in a workshop. If you have, however, some experience, there should be no problem to adjust the tension correctly. After adjustment tighten the nut (1) in the centre to 2.0 kgm (14.5 ft.lb.).
- Carry out all other operations in reverse order.

1.7.4 THERMOSTAT

1.9 Litre Engines

The thermostat is located inside the water elbow on the L.H. front of the cylinder head, below a cover. To remove the thermostat, drain the cooling system (Section 1.7.1.) and disconnect the hoses from the water outlet. One hose leads to the oil cooler, the other one to the lower radiator connection. Unscrew the cover from the thermostat housing and lift out the thermostat. A rubber sealing ring is inserted between cover and housing. Fig. 1.107 shows details.

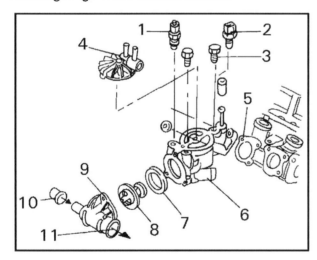

Fig. 1.107 – Thermostat – 1.9 litre
1 Thermo switch, overheating
2 Thermo switch (with turbo)
3 Plug (without turbo)
4 Pre-heater, fuel
5 Gasket, thermostat housing
6 Thermostat housing
7 Rubber sealing ring
8 Thermostat
9 Thermostat housing cover
10 Connection, oil cooler
11 Connection, radiator, top

2.5 Litre Engines

As already referred to in the technical data, two thermostats are used. The main thermostat is fitted inside a housing, as shown in Fig. 1.106. The secondary thermostat is underneath the water outlet elbow on the cylinder head. This is the elbow where the hoses leading to the expansion tank are connected. Fig. 1.108 shows how the thermostat is fitted.

To remove the thermostat, drain the cooling system and disconnect the hose or the hoses from the elbow after slackening the hose clips. Unscrew the cover in question and lift out the thermostat.

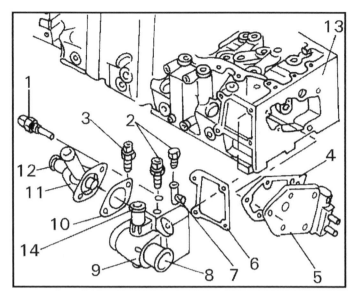

Fig. 1.108 – Secondary thermostat – 2.5 litre engine.

1 Sensor, temperature
2 Thermo switch
3 Thermo switch, overheating
4 Gasket
5 Pre-heater, fuel
6 Gasket, water elbow
7 Bleeder screw
8 Connection, radiator
9 Water outlet elbow
10 Gasket
11 Cover, secondary Thermostat
12 Connection, expansion tank
13 Cylinder head
14 Connection, heater

A thermostat cannot be repaired or adjusted and must be replaced if faulty. A thermostat can be tested by immersing it in a container of cool water and gradually raising the temperature to check that it opens properly. Suspend the thermostat on a piece of wire so that it does not touch the sides or the bottom of the container. A thermometer must be suspended in the same manner. The opening temperature is marked in the case and can be used as a guide during the test. The opening temperature and the "fully open" temperature is given in the Technical Data. A difference of 1° C is permissible in each case.

Use a new sealing ring when fitting the thermostat. Check the condition of the hose or hoses before connecting. Hoses are sometimes cut at the positions of the hose clips. In this connection also check the hose clips. Refill the cooling system.

If a new thermostat is fitted, take the vehicle on a run and check that the thermostat opens and closes as designed.

Fig. 1.109 – The radiator is removed from the vehicle as shown and can then be dismantled. The thermo switch (1) regulates the fan operation.

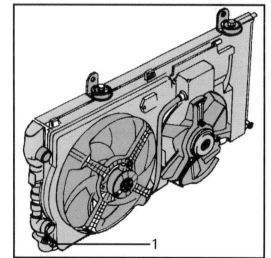

1.7.5. ANTI-FREEZE SOLUTION

The cooling system is filled with anti-freeze and the mixture should be left in the system throughout the year. If a fresh mixture is prepared, use anti-freeze and mix with water (50% anti-freeze; 50% water will protect the system down to −30° C). We advise you only to use the anti-freeze marketed by the relevant manufacturer, as the solution has been specially formulated for use with your engine. If the system is topped-up with plain water, remember that the anti-freeze solution will be diluted. It is always best to mix anti-freeze solution with water, even when topping up.

1.7.6. COOLING SYSTEM TEMPERATURE SWITCHES

Fan Temperature Switch: The switch is fitted to the rear of the lower radiator part, as shown in Fig. 1.109. The switch has the function to switch the cooling fans on and off in accordance with the coolant temperature.

Diesel Fuel Injection System

Coolant Temperature Switches: These switches are fitted into the thermostat housing. Removal and installation is straight forward. Check the sealing washer(s) when fitting the switch(es). The switches are tightened to 1.8 kgm (13 ft.lb.).

To replace the switch, drain the cooling system, withdraw the cable connector plug and unscrew the switch. The installation is a reversal of the removal procedure. Make sure that the sealing washer is in good condition. Refill the cooling system and check the proper operation of the fans.

1.8   Diesel Fuel Injection System

Absolute cleanliness is essential during any repair or work on the diesel fuel injection system, irrespective of the nature of the work in question. Thoroughly clean union nuts before unscrewing any of the injection pipes.

The fuel injection pump cannot be repaired or overhauled and an exchange pump or a new pump must be fitted in case of malfunction or damage. A Bosch injection pump is fitted to all 1.9 litre engines, but a different type is used for engines with and without turbo charger operation. The pump is located at the L.H. side at the front of the engine and driven by the timing belt.

Different injection pumps are fitted to the 2.5 litre engine. An engine without turbo charger is fitted with a Bosch pump, an engine with turbo charger has a Lucas pump. The pump is located on the R.H. side at the front of the engine and driven by the timing belt. The engine with direct injection (DJ5 TED) is also fitted with a Bosch pump.

The adjustment of the injection timing and also the removal and installation of the injection pump require certain special tools. This and the fact that the operations to remove the pump on engines with and without turbo charger and for Bosch and Lucas pumps are completely different, you will have the pump exchanged at your dealer, if this is necessary in the life time of the vehicle.

Diesel engines either operate with indirect injection or direct engine. Most diesel engines covered in this manual operate with indirect injection, i.e. the fuel is injected into a pre-chamber in the cylinder head which is in connection with the combustion chamber. The combustion is initiated in the pre-chamber and the resulting pressure increase directs the burning fuel particles into the main combustion chamber, where it is fully burnt. The DJ5 TED engine (2.5 litre) on the other hand has a direct injection, i.e. the fuel is injected into the cylinders and immediately burnt.

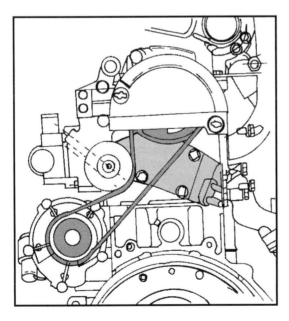

Fig. 1.110 – The fuel pre-heater of a 2.5 litre engine is fitted to the engine as shown on the cylinder head and connected to the fuel filter.

Fuel Filter and Fuel Pre-heater

The fuel pre-heater of a 1.9 litre engine is fitted to the upper side of the thermostat housing, into the fuel feed between fuel tank and fuel filter. The fuel is heated by the engine cooling system. A thermostatic element controls the quantity of the fuel to be heated. If the temperature is below 15° C, the temperature element lifts off his seat. The fuel is heated by the coolant before it flows to the fuel filter. As the temperature rises to between 15° and 35°, the thermostatic valve is only partially open. Only part of the fuel flows through the pre-heater, the remaining fuel is directed without pre-heating to the fuel filter. If the temperature has increased to 35° C, the thermostatic valve remains in its seat and the fuel flows directly to the fuel filter, without being pre-heated.

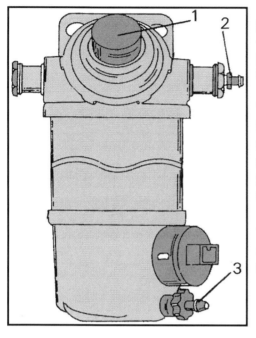

Fig. 1.111 – View of the fuel filter.
1   Priming pump button
2   Bleeding screw
3   Drain plug

The pre-heater of a 2.5 litre engine is fitted at the position shown in Fig. 1.110 on the L.H. side of the engine. The operation is similar to the above description, with the difference that the partial pre-heating takes place between 15° C and 25° C and stops at a temperature of 25° C.

The fuel filter is fitted with a replaceable filter cartridge and can be found behind the air cleaner and has the shape shown in Fig. 1.111.

1.8.0.   PRECAUTIONS WHEN WORKING ON DIESEL FUEL INJECTION SYSTEMS

Whenever repairs are carried out on a diesel injection system, whatever the extent, observe the greatest cleanliness, apart from the following points:

- Only carry out work on diesel injection systems under the cleanest of conditions. Work in the open air should be carried out when there is no wind, to prevent dust from entering the open connections.
- Before removal of union nuts, clean around it with a clean cloth.
- Removed parts must only be deposited on a clean bench or table and must be covered with a sheet of plastic or paper. Never use fluffy rags to clean parts.
- All open or partially dismantled parts of the injection system must be fully covered or kept in a cardboard box, if the repair is not carried out immediately. Check the parts for cleanliness before installation.
- Never use an airline to clean the exterior of the engine, when connections of the injection system are open.
- Take care not to allow diesel fuel in contact with rubber hoses or other rubber parts. Immediately clean such a hose, if should happen accidentally.

1.8.1.   FUEL FILTER

The fuel filter should be replaced every 20,000 miles when the engine has a turbo charger or every 40,000 miles without one, but must be drained approximately every 6,000 miles to empty the water collected through condensation.

1.8.1.0.   Filter Replacement

- Disconnect the battery and remove the complete air cleaner.

Diesel Fuel Injection System

- Place a small container underneath the filter and open the bleeding screw (2) in Fig. 1.111. Open the drain plug (3) at the bottom of the filter housing and allow the fuel to drain into the container.
- Remove the filter securing bolt at the upper end of the filter and lower the filter housing together with the filter element towards the bottom. Remove all sealing rings (always replace them). The element can be pulled out of the filter housing.
- Clean the filter housing and insert the new element into the housing. Place the filter housing with the new sealing rings against the filter bracket and fit and tighten the bolt.
- Tighten the drain plug at the bottom of the filter housing, fit the air cleaner and re-connect the battery. Bleed the system as described below.

1.8.1.1. Bleeding the Fuel System

- Open the bleed screw (2) in Fig. 1.111, next to the hand priming button.
- Place a small hose over the connection of the bleeding screw and hold the hose into a small container.
- Operate the priming pump button in Fig. 1.111, until only diesel fuel, free from air bubbles drains into the container.
- Close the bleeding screw and withdraw the hose. Remove the container.
- Start the engine and allow it to idle to stabilise the fuel feed.

1.8.1.2. Draining the Water in the Fuel Filter

Note: The water should be drained from the fuel filter every time the engine oil is changed. The system must be bled as described above after the water has been removed.

- Remove the complete air cleaner.

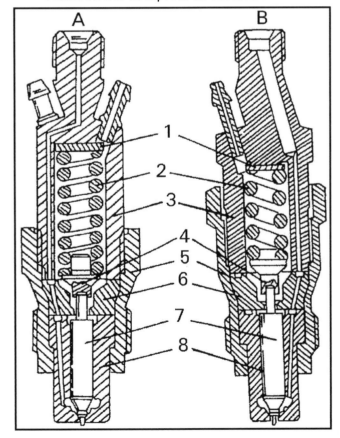

Fig. 1.112 – Sectional view of a Lucas injector (A) and Bosch injector (B).
1   Adjusting shim
2   Spring
3   Injector holder
4   Plunger
5   Hexagon
6   Spacer
7   Injector needle
8   Injector body

- Open the bleeding screw in Fig. 1.111 in the side of the fuel filter.

- Place a suitable container underneath the filter housing and unscrew the plug (3) at the bottom of the filter housing. Allow the water/fuel to drain off until only clean diesel fuel is running out (approx. 100 cc). Then close the drain plug. Bleed the system as described above.

1.8.2. INJECTOR HOLDERS AND INJECTORS
1.8.2.1. Removal and Installation

Before removing an injector holder or injector remember that parts of different manufacturers cannot be interchanged. Fig. 1.112 shows the difference between Lucas and Bosch injectors, which can also be recognised on their connections. The injectors for the direct injection engine are completely different, as they are not screwed into the cylinder head.

Fig. 1.113 –View of a fitted injector.
1 Copper washer
2 Flame-arrester washer
3 Injector pipe union nut
4 Injector holder
5 27 mm hexagon
6 Glow plug
7 Glow plug hexagon

Injectors are fairly hidden and parts must be removed to gain access. The injectors are located next to the glow plugs in the cylinder head, as shown in Fig. 1.113.

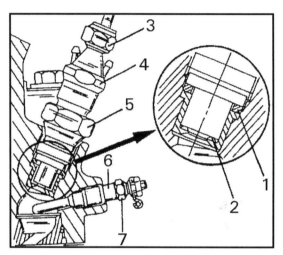

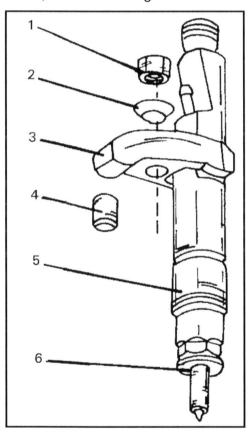

Fig. 1.114 – View of an injector is fitted to the DJ5 TED engine.
1 Securing nut
2 Washers
3 Securing flange
4 Guide sleeve
5 Injector
6 Sealing washer

Except DJ5 TED Engine
• Disconnect the battery negative cable.

Disconnect the fuel injection pipe. A ring spanner with a cut-out should be used for this operation. Carefully push the pipe to one side. Also withdraw the spill hose from the injector.
• Unscrew the injector holder. Either a 27 mm box spanner or the special tool 7007-T is used for this operation. Remove the flame arrester washer and the copper washer from the injector holder. Both must be replaced during installation.

The installation is a reversal of the removal procedure. Fit the flame arrester washer (2) in Fig. 1.113 with the curved face towards the top and fit the new copper washer (1). Tighten the injector holder to 5.5 kgm (2.5 litre engine) or 9.0 kgm (1.9 litre engine) with the tool mentioned above. Tighten the injector pipe union nut to 2.0 kgm (14.5 ft.lb.). As already mentioned, the fuel system must be bled after installation.

D5J TED Engine (direct injection)
The attachment of the injectors is different and can be seen in Fig. 1.114, the injectors are not screwed into the cylinder head, but pushed into the head and attached by means of a nut. Remove as follows:

Turbo Charger

- Disconnect the battery negative cable.
- Disconnect the two hoses below one of the wiper arms and the spill pipe.
- Remove the injector pipe as described above. Remove the nut (1) in Fig. 1.114 and take off the washer (2). Withdraw the injector out of the cylinder head. Note the sealing ring (6). The sleeve (4) remains in position.

The installation is a reversal of the removal procedure. Always replace the sealing washer (6). Tighten the securing nut and the injector pipe union nut to 2.5 kgm (18 ft.lb.).

1.8.2.2.   Injector Repairs

The injection pressure of the injectors should only be tested in a specialist shop. Never attempt to carry out this operation yourself. Injectors are sometimes changed. If one is replaced, make sure the correct injector is installed. Injectors are marked with a colour mark, which can be seen on the fitted injector. There are, however, injectors without colour marks.

To find a faulty injector, unscrew the union nuts one after the other at the injector connection and start the engine. Run the engine at increased speed. If the engine noise does not change after a certain injector pipe has been disconnected, the faulty injector has been found.

1.8.3.   GLOW PLUGS

The glow plugs receive electrical current when the ignition switch is turned to the glow position. Certain engines have a pre-glow and an after-glow function. A glow plug control unit is fitted to the bulkhead, below the battery. The control unit supplies the glow plugs and the glow plug warning light with current, as soon as the ignition key is turned, if the coolant temperature is less than 60° C. The current feed is interrupted after a certain period, as regulated by the control unit.

After-glow means that the glow plugs are still heating the fuel mixture after the engine has started, as soon as the ignition key is released.

Because of the high temperatures it is quite possible that one of the glow plugs burns out. Glow plugs can also be damaged through faulty injectors, wrong injection times and low injection pressure. Plugs are not the same for all engines.

Glow plugs are fairly hidden and certain parts must be removed to gain access. Remove the nuts from the ends of the plugs and unscrew the plug in question. A socket with extension and ratchet should be used to remove the plugs. Tighten the new plug to 2.0 kgm (14.5 ft.lb.). Do not overtighten the cable connection nut.

1.8.4.   INJECTION PUMP ADJUSTMENTS

We do not advise to carry out any adjustments on the injection pump, irrespective of the system fitted. Adjustments are not the same on the two
Bosch systems (1.9 litre engine and 2.5 litre engine without turbo charger) and the Lucas system. The following adjustments are possible, but must be carried out in a certain order: throttle operation, idle speed adjustment, stall speed adjustment, fast idle speed adjustment, throttle damper adjustment (not all engines). If any of the given adjustments are not satisfactory, see a workshop dealing with Bosch or Lucas injection systems or your dealer.

1.8.5.   TURBO CHARGER

The removal and installation of the turbo charger is an extensive operation. The following description refers to the 1.9 litre and 2.5 litre engine under different headings.

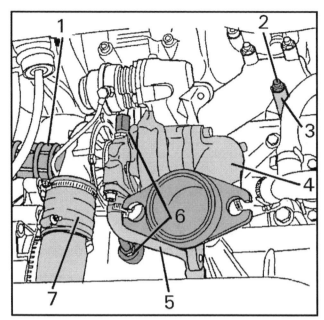

Fig. 1.115 – Details for the removal and installation of the turbo charger (1.9 litre engine).

1	Air intake hose
2	Securing nuts
3	Spacer sleeves
4	Turbo charger
5	Oil return pipe
6	Oil feed pipe
7	Air outlet hose

1.9 Litre Engine

• Disconnect the negative battery cable and jack up the front end of the vehicle. Remove the protective panel underneath the engine compartment.

• Disconnect the exhaust pipe from its flange.

• Refer to Fig. 1.115 and disconnect the following items: The air intake hose (1), the connection of the air outlet (7), the oil return hose (5), the two union nuts of the oil feed pipe (6), the oil filter, the nuts (2) together with the spacer sleeve (3) and the turbo charger (4) together with the exhaust manifold.

Carry out the following checks before installation:

• Check the air cleaner system and all connections for good condition.

• Change the engine oil and the oil filter.

• Make sure that the oil circuit and the union nuts are clean. Use new sealing rings where necessary. Use only the bolts specified for the turbo charger, as these must be heat-resistant.

• Make sure that the air intake hoses and the exhaust manifold are free of foreign matter.

Install as follows:

• Insert the turbo charger into the engine compartment and fit a new filter to the oil feed pipe union nut (6). Tighten the nut to 3.0 kgm (22 ft.lb.).

• Set the turbo charger into the correct position and fit as follows: Fit the nuts (2) with the spacer sleeves (3), the oil return hose (5), the air intake hose (1) and the connection of the air outlet hose (7). Tighten the nuts to 5.5 kgm (40 ft.lb.).

• Refit the exhaust pipe. All other operations are carried out in reverse order.

After the vehicle has been lowered to the ground, re-connect the battery and proceed as follows:

• Withdraw the connector plug from the cut-off solenoid switch on the injection pump and crank the engine until the oil warning light is extinguished.

• Re-connect the connector plug and start the engine. Allow the engine to idle for at least 30 seconds before increasing the engine speed.

• After a while, check all connections for leaks.

2.5 Litre Engine

The removal and installation of the turbo charger in the case of the original 2.5 litre engine is more or less the same as described above for the 1.9 litre engine. The turbo charger securing nuts are only tightened to 2.0 kgm (14.5 ft.lb.). Different operations are necessary on the DJ5 TED engine (direct injection). In this case remove the parts shown in Fig. 1.116. Then remove the exhaust manifold nuts and lift out the manifold

Turbo Charger

together with the turbo charger. Separate the manifold from the turbo charger and remove the latter from the engine sub-frame.

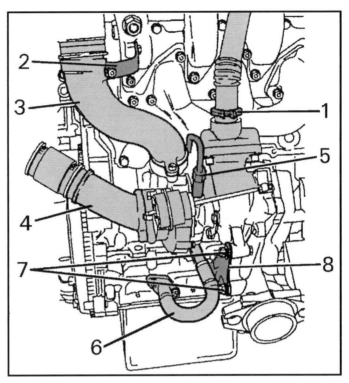

Fig. 1.116 – Details for the removal and installation of the turbo charger (2.5 litre engine with direct injection).

1   Mounting clamp
2   Bracket
3   Air outlet hose
4   Air suction hose
5   Oil feed pipe
6   Oil return pipe
7   Nuts and bolts
8   Securing flange on block

The installation is a reversal of the removal procedure. Note the tightening torques: Manifold to turbo charger 2.5 kgm (18 ft.lb.), exhaust manifold nuts 2.0 kgm (14.5 ft.lb.), flange (8) in Fig. 1.116 to cylinder block 2.0 kgm (14.5 ft.lb.), nuts (7) to 3.0 kgm (22 ft.lb.).

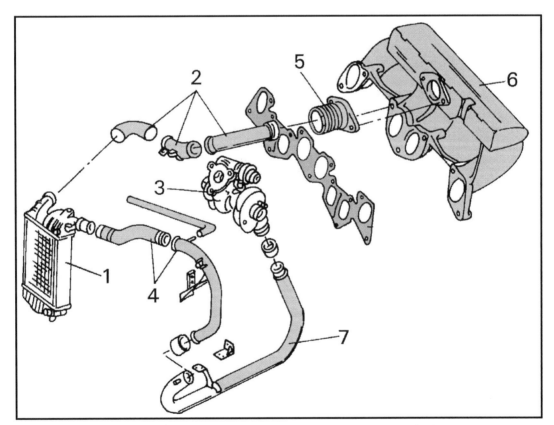

Fig. 1.117 – Intercooler installation (1.9 litre engine).

1 Intercooler
2 Hose connection
3 Turbo charger
4 Hose, cooler to charger
5 Connecting flange
6 Inlet manifold
7 Hose to turbo charger

1.8.6. CHARGE AIR COOLER (INTERCOOLER)

Fitted to the turbo engine only. The cooler reduces the air temperature before it enters the turbo charger. The component parts of the installation in the case of a 1.9 litre engine is shown in Fig. 1.117. To remove the cooler, remove the radiator grille, the R.H. front indicator lamp and the headlamp, depending on the model. Other parts obstructing the removal must also be removed or disconnected, before the cooler is taken out. To lift out the cooler, push it first against the engine and then lift it out towards the top.

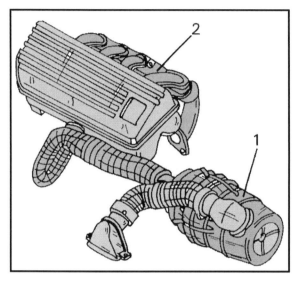

Fig. 1.119 – The air intake circuit of a 1.9 litre engine with turbo charger.
1 Inlet manifold
2 Turbo charger
3 Air cleaner
4 Intercooler

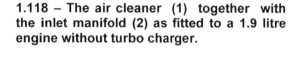

1.118 – The air cleaner (1) together with the inlet manifold (2) as fitted to a 1.9 litre engine without turbo charger.

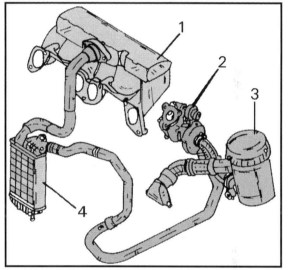

Fig. 1.120 – The inlet manifold (1) and the air cleaner (2) of a 2.5 litre engine without turbo charger.

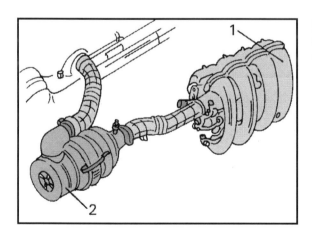

Fig. 1.121 – Air cleaner installation, 2.5 litre engine with turbo charger.
1 Inlet manifold
2 Turbo charger
3 Air cleaner

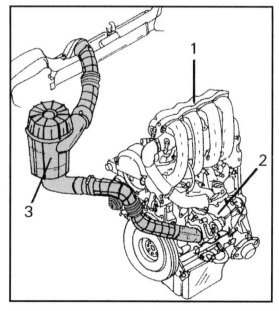

1.8.7.   AIR CLEANER

The air cleaner is fitted with a dry paper element and is fitted to the L.H. side of the inner wing panel. Different installations are used with the different engines. Figs. 1.118 to 1.121 show various air cleaners, but we would like to point out that not all engines are shown. A Purflux A595 filter element is, however, used in all air cleaners. The air cleaner element should be changed every 40,000 miles in the case of a naturally aspirating engine or every 20,000 miles in the case of a turbo charged engine.

2.   CLUTCH

The operation of the clutch is not the same on all models, as it depends on the gearbox in the vehicle. The clutch of a vehicle with MG5TE gearbox, the clutch release lever is "pulled", with a ME5TU gearbox it is "pushed". The differences between the two types can be seen in Figs. 2.1 and 2.2.

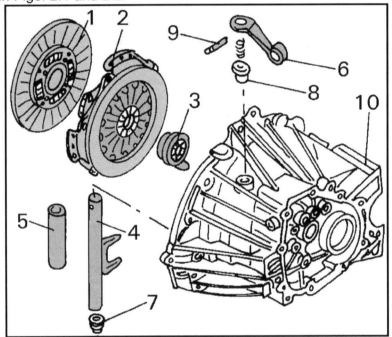

Fig. 2.1 - View of the clutch unit (ME5TU gearbox, "push" type release).

1 Driven plate	6 Clutch release lever
2 Clutch pressure plate	7 Release shaft bush
3 Clutch release bearing	8 Release shaft bush
4 Clutch release shaft	9 Clamp bolt
5 Bearing bush	10 Gearbox

2.0.   Technical Data

Type	Single plate, dry clutch with diaphragm spring.
Clutch operation	By clutch cable
Pedal adjustment	At release lever
Clutch release bearing	Sealed ball-type bearing in constant contact with the clutch plate. "Pulled" or "pushed" as mentioned above.

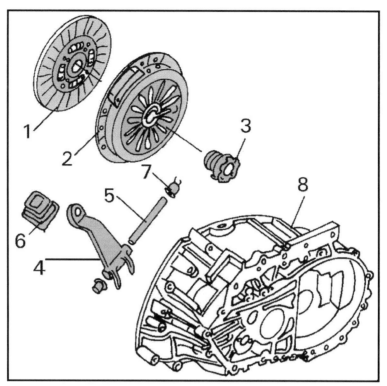

Fig. 2.2 - View of the clutch unit (MG5TU gearbox, "pull" type release).

1 Clutch driven plate   5 Clutch release shaft
2 Clutch pressure plate   6 Rubber dust cap
3 Clutch release bearing   7 Release shaft bushes
4 Clutch release lever   8 Gearbox

Clutch Type Fitted:

- 1.9 litre, all models before July 1994	235 CP 5650
- 1.9 litre, all models after July 1994	235 CP 5660, different driven plate
- 2.5 litre with MG5TU gearbox, before July 1994	242 DT 5800
- 2.5 litre, from July 1994	235 CP 5800
- 2.5 litre, with turbo charger	242 DT 5800

Clutch Diameter:

- 1.9 litre	228.6 mm
- 2.5 litre	228.6 mm
- 2.5 litre turbo-charged	242.0 mm

Colour of Torsion Springs in Driven Plate:

- 235 CP 5650 (before July 1994)	2 x dark brown, 2 x yellow, 2 x red
- 235 CP 5650 (from July 1994)	2 x black/pink, 2 x yellow, 2 x beige
- 235 CP 5800	2 x black/pink, 2 x yellow, 2 x beige
- 242 DT 5800 (before July 1994)	2 x dark brown, 2 x yellow, 2 x red
- 242 DT 5800 (after July 1994)	2 x red, 2 x light blue, 2 x silver-grey, 2 x blue

Clutch linings	F202

Clutch

2.1 Clutch Unit

2.1.0. CHECKING THE CLUTCH OPERATION

The clutch can be checked for proper operation when fitted to the vehicle. To do this, proceed as follows:

• Start the engine and allow to idle. Depress the clutch pedal and wait approx. 3 secs. Engage the reverse gear. If grating noises can be heard from the transmission, it can be assumed the clutch or driven plate needs replacement, as the driven plate no longer connects the clutch pressure plate with the flywheel.

• To check the clutch for signs of slipping, drive the vehicle until the clutch and transmission have reached operating temperature. Stop the vehicle, firmly apply the handbrake and engage the 3rd gear. Keep the clutch pedal fully depressed and accelerate the engine to approx. 3000 - 4000 rpm. Release the clutch pedal suddenly. The clutch operates satisfactorily if the engine stalls immediately.

2.1.1 REMOVAL AND INSTALLATION

The gearbox or the engine and the gearbox must be removed to replace the clutch plate and/or the driven plate. The following description refers to the removal when the gearbox has been removed, which is generally the case.

• Mark the clutch cover and the flywheel to ensure correct re-assembly, if the parts are refitted. Remove the clutch bolts carefully. The engine must be prevented from rotating when the bolts are slackened. Otherwise use a ring spanner and place it over the bolt heads and hit the spanner with a short sharp blow to loosen the bolts.

• Remove the clutch. If a MG5TE gearbox is fitted, you will find the clutch release bearing attached to the clutch plate as shown in Fig. 2.3. Remove the driven plate. Do not allow grease or oil to contaminate the lining faces or any other part, if there is a chance that the parts can be re-used. Make a note which way the driven plate is fitted.

Fig. 2.3 – The clutch release bearing is fitted to the clutch diaphragm spring as shown.

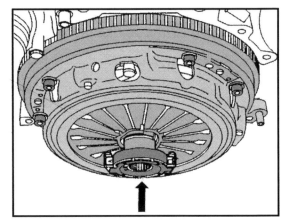

• Clean the inside of the flywheel and check the friction face for wear. If the clutch linings have worn down to the height of the rivet heads, there is a possibility that the rivet heads have scored the flywheel. Replace the flywheel if necessary, but remember that new flywheel bolts must be used. Flywheels can be re-ground to a certain dimension, but only your dealer will be able to advise you.

The installation is a reversal of the removal procedure. The installation requires normally the use of an alignment mandrel, which is inserted as shown in Fig. 2.4. If this is not available, a spare clutch shaft can also be used. If neither of the above is available and tools cannot be obtained, it is possible to line-up the clutch disc in the inside of the flywheel by inserting a drift of the diameter of the spline bore. Tool hire companies normally have sets of alignment mandrels and one of them will fit your driven plate.

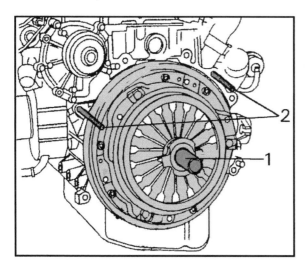

Fig. 2.4 – Fit the centring mandrel (1) into the driven plate when the bolts are tightened. Two studs are screwed into the cylinder block flange to guide the transmission during installation.

Offer up the clutch assembly to the flywheel and centre the disc by inserting the mandrel into the flywheel bearing and the splines. Tighten the bolts carefully, a little at a time, working in a diagonal manner, to a final torque setting of 2.0 kgm (14.5 ft.lb.).

Coat the clutch drive shaft and the outer face of the release bearing with a little Molykote BR2 grease (graphite grease) and refit the gearbox to the engine. Finally adjust the clutch pedal clearance as described later on.

2.2   Servicing

The cover assembly - pressure plate and diaphragm spring - must not be dismantled. Replace if necessary with a complete assembly, but make sure to quote the year of manufacture and the chassis number.

Fig. 2.5 – Checking a clutch driven plate for run-out between the centres of a lathe.

Inspect the driven plate and the linings, replacing the complete plate, if the lining material is worn down to the rivet heads. Again specify the engine type and the model year, as different driven plates and clutch units are used. A driven plate with the linings contaminated with oil cannot be cleaned successfully and should also be replaced. All rivets should be tight and the torsion springs should be sound and unbroken. Also check the condition of the driven plate splines. Clamp the driven plate between the centres of a lathe and apply a dial gauge to the outside of the plate as shown in Fig. 2.5. Slowly rotate the disc and read off the dial gauge indication. Of more than 0.5 mm is indicated, fit a new disc.

Fig. 2.6 – Checking the clutch pressure plate for distortion or wear at the inner edge.

Place a straight edge (steel ruler) over the friction face of the clutch unit and insert feeler gauges between the ruler and the surface. If the gap at the innermost spot on the friction face is no more than 0.3 mm, the plate can be re-used. Fig. 2.6 shows the check.

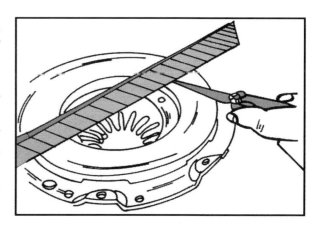

Clutch

2.2.1 CLUTCH RELEASE BEARING

The transmission must be removed to replace the clutch release bearing. Remove the release bearing from the inside of the gearbox bell housing and withdraw towards the front of the shaft. Refer to Fig. 2.3 when a release bearing of an MG5TU gearbox is dealt with. The bearing is attached to the clutch unit and we recommend that you can try to have it fitted in a workshop as special tools are necessary to remove the bearing, which is secured by a circlip. The release bearing is of the sealed type and must not be placed in any solvent.

The installation of a standard bearing is a reversal of the removal procedure. Coat the shaft and the bearing sleeve with Molykote BR2 grease. Grease the two sides of the release fork with M.P. grease. The release bearing should always be replaced at the same time as the clutch unit. It may, therefore, be possible to have the release bearing fitted where you buy the clutch unit.

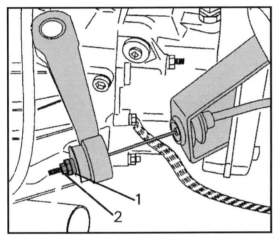

Fig. 2.7 – Details for the clutch pedal adjustment when the clutch release lever is "pushed".
1   Adjusting nut
2   Locknut

2.3 Clutch Cable Replacement

As already mentioned, the clutch release lever can either be "pulled" or "pushed". The removal and installation is, however, the same on both types. Figs. 2.7 and 2.8 show the attachment of the cable on the release lever on the two gearboxes. The other side of the cable is connected to the clutch pedal. Fig. 2.9 shows the complete mechanism. Proceed as follows:

Fig. 2.8 – Details for the clutch pedal adjustment when the clutch release lever is "pulled".
1   Adjusting nut
2   Locknut

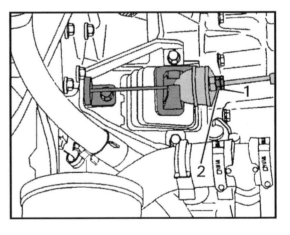

- Disconnect the battery and place the front end of the vehicle on chassis stands. Remove the protective shield underneath the front of the vehicle.

- Unscrew the nut from the outside of the clutch release lever (Figs. 2.7 and 2.8). The nut is locked, i.e. 2 flat spanners are required.

- Pull the cable away from the gearbox until the outer sleeve is free. Depending on the type disconnect the cable from the release lever and the bracket.

- Remove the lower trim on the drivers side to gain access to the clutch pedal. Pull the clutch pedal upwards until the cable can be disengaged. Direct the clutch cable end upwards and disengage it. Extract the clutch cable from the body panel from underneath the vehicle.

The installation is a reversal of the removal procedure. The clutch pedal play must be adjusted as described below after the cable has been fitted.

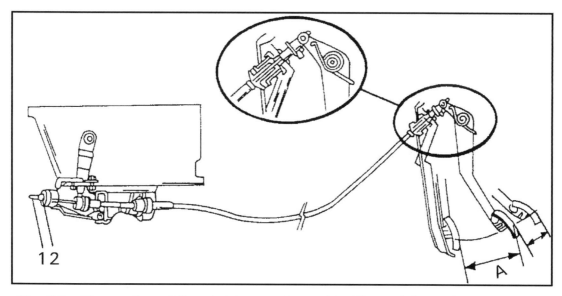

Fig. 2.9 – The routing of the clutch operating cable. The pedal travel is shown with "A".

1 Adjusting nut   2 Locknut

2.4   Clutch Pedal Adjustment

First ensure the type of clutch cable arrangement (gearbox) fitted to the vehicle, as the adjustment is not the same on all vehicles. As the clutch release bearing is in constant contact with the diaphragm spring, only the clutch pedal needs adjustment. Proceed as follows:

•   Check that the clutch pedal is at the same height as the brake pedal.

•   In the case of the "push" type, shown in Fig. 2.7, slacken the locknut (2) and rotate the adjusting nut (1) until both pedals have the same height. Tightening the nut will lift the pedal. Re-tighten the locknut and measure the pedal travel as described below.

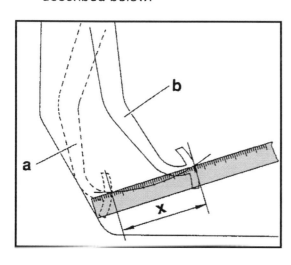

Fig. 2.10 – Measuring the pedal travel. Bring the pedal into position "a" and then into position "b". The difference is the clutch pedal travel, referred to in the text.

•   In the case of the "pull" type arrangement, refer to Fig. 2.8, slacken the locknut (1) and rotate the adjusting nut (2) until both pedals have the same height. Tightening the nut will lift the pedal. Re-tighten the locknut and measure the pedal travel as described below.

•   Push the pedal fully to the floor and apply a ruler as shown in Fig. 2.10. Release the pedal and measure dimension "X" as shown. This is also dimension "A" in Fig. 2.9. The pedal travel should be 180 mm, with a tolerance of 3 mm plus or minus. It must never be less.

2.5   Clutch – Tightening Torques

Flywheel to crankshaft   5.0 kgm (36 ft.lb.)

Gearbox

Gearbox to engine	6.0 kgm (43 ft.lb.)
Clutch to flywheel	2.0 kgm (14.5 ft.lb.)

3. GEARBOX

3.0. Technical Data

Type

5-speed transmission together with final drive in one housing. Fitted gearbox type depends on engine.

ME5TU Gearbox

Identification

All transmissions have a number, commencing with "20KE". The two end numbers are different and indicate the engine and carrying capacity. The following gearboxes are fitted to 10Q and 14Q vehicles:

2.5 litre engine, DJ5-T9A	from Feb. 1994
1.9 litre engine, D9B, without turbo charger	from Feb. 1994
1.9 litre engine, D8C/DHX, turbo charger	from Feb. 1994
2.5 litre engine, DJ5-T9B, without turbo charger	from July 1994
1.9 litre engine, D9B, without turbo charger	from July 1994
1.9 litre engine, D8C/DHX, turbo charger	from July 1994

Gearbox Ratios:

- 1st gear	3.727 : 1
- 2nd gear	1.944 : 1
- 3rd gear	1.250 : 1 or 1.320 : 1
- 4th gear	0.880 : 1 or 0.969 : 1
- 5th gear	0.674 : 1, 1.077 : 1 or 0.814 : 1
- Reverse gear	2.000 : 1 or 3.154 : 1
Final drive ratio	5.61 : 1 or 4.470 : 1

Lubrication Oil

Filling capacity	1.85 litres
Oil change intervals	Every 40,000 miles
Recommended Oil	Total gearbox oil

MG5TU Gearbox

Identification

All transmissions have a number, commencing with "20KM". The two end numbers are different and indicate the engine and carrying capacity. Only fitted to models 14Q and 18Q with 2.5 litre engine. The following gearboxes are fitted to 10Q, 14Q and 18Q vehicles, but note that some gearbox codes have changed:

2.5 litre engine, DJ5-T9A, without turbo charger   Model 18Q
2.5 litre engine, DJ5T-T8A, turbo charger   Model 14Q
2.5 litre engine, DJ5T-T8A, turbo charger   Model 10Q
2.5 litre engine, DJ5T-T8A, turbo charger   Model 18Q
2.5 litre engine, DJ5T-THZ, turbo charger   Model 18Q
2.5 litre engine, DJ5TED-THX, turbo charger   Different models

Gearbox Ratios:

- 1st gear	3.727 : 1
- 2nd gear	1.952 : 1
- 3rd gear	1.281 : 1
- 4th gear	0.953 : 1 or 0.884 : 1
- 5th gear	0.717 : 1
- Reverse gear	4.417 : 1
Final drive ratio	6.251 : 1, 5.231 : 1, 5.917 : 1 or 6.349 : 1

Lubrication Oil

Filling capacity:	
- With 1.9 litre engine	2.5 litres
- With 2.5 litre engine	2.75 litres
Oil change intervals	Every 40,000 miles
Recommended Oil	Total gearbox oil

Note: A type identification plate is fitted to the top of the transmission at the location shown in Fig. 3.1, in this case shown for the ME5TU transmission.

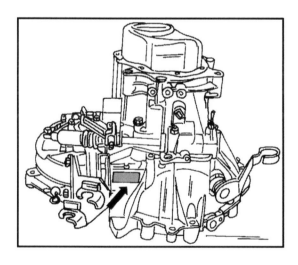

Fig. 3.1 - The arrow shows where the type identification plate is fitted.

On the other transmission, the plate is situated at a similar position, with the difference that the clutch release lever is on the opposite side. The plate shows the important details of the gearbox, including the two end numbers. The differences between the two transmissions are internally.

3.1   Gearbox - Removal and Installation

Although there are some differences during the removal and installation of the two gearboxes, all models are covered below. The transmission is removed without the engine. Note the following before commencing removal:

- There are two oil drain plugs fitted to the ME5TU gearbox, one in the actual transmission housing and one in the final drive housing (differential housing).
- The MG5TE gearbox has one oil drain plug, situated at the bottom of the transmission.

Remove the transmission as follows:

Gearbox

- Disconnect the negative battery cable.
- Remove the protective panel underneath the front of the vehicle.
- Drain the gear box oil (see last page and description later on).
- Slacken the wheel bolts and the drive shaft nuts as explained during the removal of the drive shafts, place the front end of the vehicle on chassis stands and remove the wheels. The two drive shafts are now removed as described in Section 4.1.
- Remove the air cleaner together with the air intake hoses. In the case of a turbocharged engine remove the hose/pipe connections between the turbo charger and the intercooler (charge air cooler).

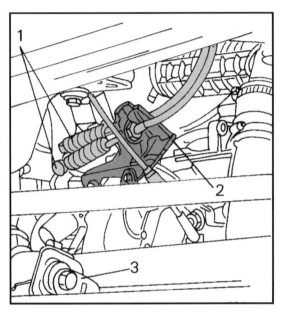

Fig. 3.2 - The attachment of the gearchange cables on the transmission.

1	Gearchange cables
2	Cable abutment bracket
3	Torque strut

- Disconnect the clutch cable as already described.
- Unscrew the battery earth cable.
- Separate the front exhaust pipe from the exhaust manifold flange. Use a piece of wire and tie the pipe to the bottom of the vehicle.

Disconnect the speedometer drive cable and pull it out of the gearbox.

The following operations are carried out by referring to Fig. 3.2. Remove the two gearchange cables (1), unscrew the bracket (2) and separate the torque strut (3).

- Remove the protective panel underneath the flywheel housing. Disconnect the cables from the starter motor and remove the starter motor.
- Disconnect the cables from the reversing light switch.

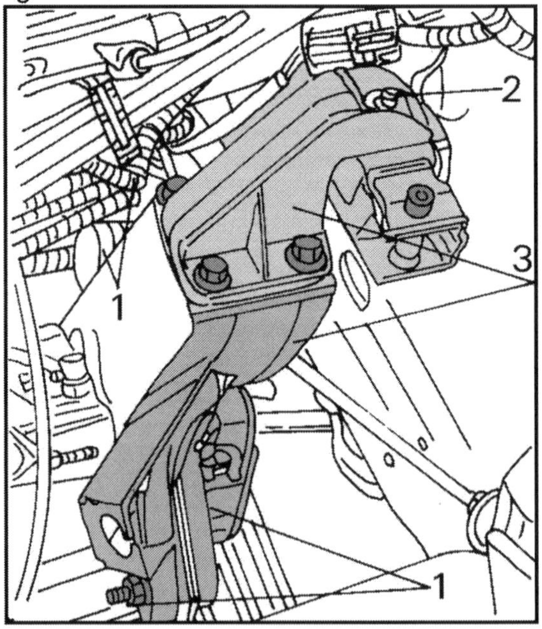

Fig. 3.3 - The gearbox mounting.

1	Bolts, 5.0 kgm
2	Nut, 9.0 kgm
3	Mounting

- Attach the engine to a suitable hand crane or hoist, using ropes or chains and lift the assembly until you can feel that it is under tension. It is also possible to place a hydraulic jack underneath the engine (wooden plank between jack and oil sump) to lift the power unit. Place a mobile jack under the transmission to support the transmission from below in preparation for the next operation.
- Remove the gearbox mounting by referring to Fig. 3.3. First remove the four bolts (1) and then the nut (2).

Check that the engine is supported by the jack or the hoist and remove the two parts of the gearbox mounting.

- Remove the bolts between engine and gearbox at the top and bottom, after checking that the gearbox is well supported on the jack.
- Withdraw the gearbox from the engine. A helper is required to keep the gearbox on the jack and to guide it out.

The installation is a reversal of the removal procedure, noting the following points:

- Coat the clutch shaft splines and the guide sleeve for the clutch release bearing with a little graphited grease. Check that the clutch release fork is resting against the release bearing.
- To facilitate the installation of the gearbox, prepare two studs with suitable thread. Cut a slot for a screwdriver into one end and screw the studs at the top on the right-hand side and at the bottom on the left-hand side into the engine mounting flange.
- Lift the engine in position on the jack and guide the clutch shaft into the clutch driven plate. Push the gearbox against the engine and over the two studs. Fit some of the bolts and tighten them until the gap between gearbox and engine is nearly closed. Finally unscrew the two studs and replace with the remaining bolts. Tighten all bolts evenly to 6.0 kgm (43 ft.lb.).
- Fit the gearbox mounting with reference to Fig. 3.3. Tighten bolts (1) to 5.0 kgm (36.5 ft.lb.) and the nut (2) to 8.0 kgm (58 ft.lb.).
- Tighten the torque strut (3) in Fig. 3.2 with 9.0 kgm (65 ft.lb.).
- Refit the drive shafts as described in Section 4.1, connect the clutch cable and finally refill the gearbox with oil.

Models with four-wheel drive

The removal is carried out in a similar manner, with the difference that the propeller shaft must be disconnected at the rear of the gearbox.

3.2   Gearbox Repairs

Many special tools are required to dismantle, assemble and adjust the transmission. Additionally there are of course two transmissions to be considered. The only operation we recommend is the replacement of the oil seals in each side of the transmission, which is described in the section dealing with the drive shafts.

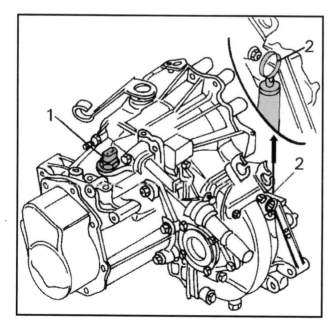

Fig. 3.4 - On the ME5TU gearbox the reversing light switch (1) is used to fill the gearbox. The oil dipstick (2) is used for the oil level check.

A damaged or faulty gearbox should be taken to a workshop for overhaul or try to obtain an exchange gearbox. In this case, you will need the usual chassis number, model year, model, etc. to ensure that the correct gearbox is fitted.

3.3   Gearbox Oil Level and Oil Change

Only the interval to change the gearbox oil is the same on the two gearbox types, i.e. the oil should be changed

Gearbox

every 40,000 miles. When changing the oil and also when checking the oil level, proceed as follows for the two gearbox types.

ME5TU Gearbox

This gearbox has an oil drain plug in the actual gearbox housing and one in the final drive housing. Both plugs are located next to each other at the bottom of the transmission housing, just below the drive shaft exit on the cover side of the gearbox. To check the oil level, an oil dipstick is fitted at the position (2) in Fig. 3.4 into the final drive housing. Checking is simple. Withdraw the dipstick and read off the oil level. Correct the oil level as described below.

Change the gearbox oil as follows:

*   Unscrew the two drain plugs and allow the gearbox oil to drain into a suitable container (capacity approx. 5 pints). Warm gearbox oil will drain easier. Clean and refit the plugs after the gearbox is empty.

*   Fill the gearbox with the recommended oil (SAE 75W/80W). The reversing light switch (1) in Fig. 3.4 must be removed to fill the gearbox (first disconnect the cable). Use a funnel and fill the gearbox until the level remains steady. An empty gearbox will take 1.85 litres. After a while re-check the level with the dipstick and refit the switch if all is well. Do not forget the cable.

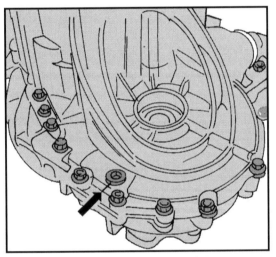

Fig. 3.5 - The arrow shows where the oil drain plug of a MG5TU gearbox is located.

MG5TU Gearbox

Only one drain plug is fitted to the bottom of the gearbox, at the position shown in Fig. 3.5. An oil level checking/filler plug is fitted, but the gearbox has been modified since its introduction. Originally fitted gearboxes have an oil dipstick at the position shown in Fig. 3.6, secured by a screw. To check the oil level unscrew the dipstick and pull it out. Read off the oil level and correct if necessary. Later a plug with a square opening is fitted below the drive shaft exit in the gearbox. To check the oil level, unscrew the plug with a square wrench and check that the oil is at the lower edge of the plug opening. Correct the oil level. An oil can, filled with oil is recommended.

Fig. 3.6 - Oil dipstick and filler opening (1) of a MG5TU gearbox on early gearboxes. Later gearboxes have a plug in the side of the transmission.

The oil change is carried out as described for the other gearbox. Fill the gearbox with a funnel if the arrangement shown in Fig. 3.6 is encountered or with the oil can mentioned above on later versions. The gearbox will take approx. 2.75 litres, a little less if a 1.9 litre engine is fitted.

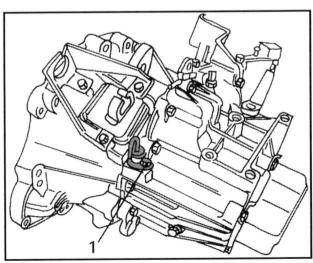

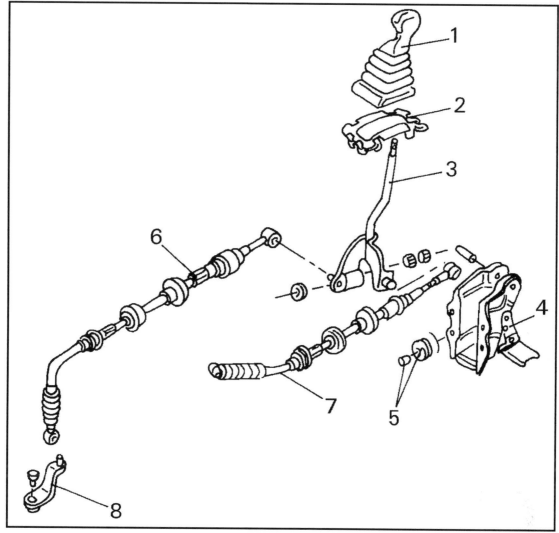

Fig. 3.7 - The component parts of the gearchange mechanism.

1 Gearchange lever
2 Gearchange lever bearing
3 Gear change lever
4 Cable bracket ("2" in Fig. 3.2)

5 Elastic mounting
6 Gear change cable
7 Gear selector cable
8 Lever on gearbox

3.4   The Gearchange

The gearchange is actuated by means of cables, one selector cable and one gearchange cable. The cables can be recognised on the ball joint connections; the gear change cable has the larger ball joint. Only the selector cable can be adjusted.

Fig. 3.7 on the previous page shows the arrangement of the gearchange elements.

The removal and installation of the cables is fairly easy. The cables are secured on the side of the gearbox and the gear lever with "C" shaped clips on a bracket. Fig. 3.8 shows the two cables together with the fitted dimensions.

After a cable has been replaced, adjust the gearchange mechanism as described below. A steel ruler is required for the adjustment.

- Place the gear change lever into the neutral position and check if the dimension between the arrows in Fig. 3.9 is exactly 304 mm.

- If necessary, disconnect the ball joint connection (1) in Fig. 3.8, slacken the locknut at the cable end and turn the end piece until the dimension is obtained.

Gearbox

Several attempts will be necessary to achieve success. Tighten the locknut after adjustment.

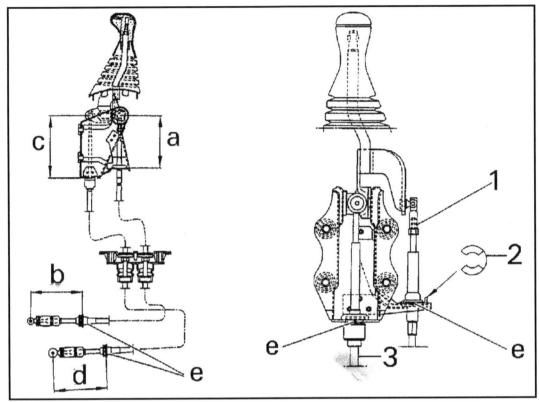

Fig. 3.8 - Cable gearchange together with the adjusting dimensions.
1 Gear selector cable (adjustable)
2 Securing clip
3 Gear change cable (not adjustable)
a 123 +/- 5 mm (adjustable)
b 123 +/- 1.5 mm
c 140 +/- 1.5 mm
d 129 +/- 1.5 mm (adjustable)
e Cable attachment (2 clips)

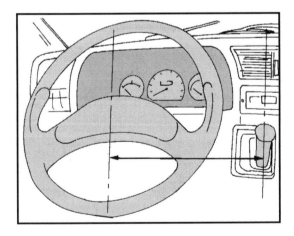

Fig. 3.9 - The dimension is measured between the arrows. The correct dimension is 304 mm.

If one or the other cable is replaced, adjust it to the correct dimension before installation. Refer to Fig. 3.10 and follow the given dimensions. Measure between the arrows.

3.5   Gearbox - Tightening Torque Values

Drive shaft Nuts:
- Models 10Q and 14Q   45.0 kgm (324 ft.lb.)
- Model 18Q   50.0 kgm (360 ft.lb.)

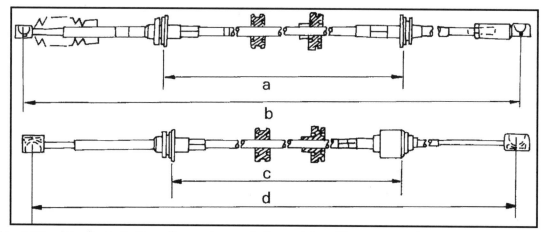

Fig. 3.10 - The installation dimensions of the cables. The upper view shows the selector cable, the lower view the gear change cable.

    a 750 mm +/- 2 mm   c 690 mm +/- 2 mm
    b 996 mm +/- 7 mm   d 963 mm +/- 3 mm

Wheel Bolts:
- Models 10Q and 14Q   16.0 kgm (115.5 ft.lb.)
- Model 18Q   18.0 kgm (130 ft.lb.)

Nut of Lower Suspension Arm Ball Joint:
- Models 10Q and 14Q   13.0 kgm (94 ft.lb.)
- Model 18Q   24.0 kgm (173 ft.lb.)
Track rod ball joint to steering lever   7.0 kgm (50.5 ft.lb.)
Intermediate bearing locking nuts   1.0 kgm (7.2 ft.lb.)
Brake caliper to steering knuckle   21.0 kgm (151 ft.lb.)
Brake caliper guide bolts   3.5 kgm (25 ft.lb.)

4. DRIVE SHAFTS

Note: Observe the different tightening torques applicable to the wheel bolts.

The L.H. and R.H. drive shafts are of different length. Drive shafts always look the same. When a new shaft is purchased, make sure you ask for the correct shaft. The following notes will help you with identification. "Loctite" thread locking compound will be required for the installation if the shaft.

The fitted gearbox is also responsible for the type of drive shaft and the outer diameter of the CV joint on the transmission side (86 mm in the case of a ME5TE gearbox or 92 mm in the case of a MG5TE gearbox) and on the wheel side (100 mm in the case of the ME5TE gearbox or 113 mm in the case of the MG5TE gearbox). The shafts are identified with a code in order to allocate the correct shaft to the vehicle. We therefore recommend to take the old shaft to the spare part counter to obtain the correct shaft.

Finally we must add, that the CV joints of the two shafts are different. A ball-type CV joint is fitted to the wheel side. A tri-axe Rzeppa joint is fitted on the gearbox side of all models.

Drive Shafts

An intermediate bearing is used to locate the R.H. drive shaft. The nut at the end of the shaft is tightened with a very high torque (again not the same on all models) and is subsequently secured in position by peening the shoulder of the nut into a groove in the shaft.

4.0.   Technical Data

Type   See above
Intermediate bearing dimensions   35 x 62 x 16 mm

Fitted Joints:	Identification L.H. Side	Identification R.H. Side
- ME5TU gearbox, 10Q/14Q, without ABS	8JN18	8JN19
- ME5TU gearbox, 10Q/14Q, with ABS	8JN12	8JN13
- MG5TU gearbox, 10Q/14Q, without ABS	8JN20	8JN21
- MG5TU gearbox, 18Q, without ABS	8JN18	8JN17
- MG5TE gearbox, 10Q/14Q, with ABS	8JN14	8JN15
- MG5TE gearbox, 18Q, with ABS	8JN10	8JN11

Diameter of CV joint, gearbox side:
- With ME5TU gearbox   86 mm
- With MG5TE gearbox   92 mm
Diameter of CV joint, wheel side:
- With ME5TE gearbox   100 mm
- With MG5TE gearbox   100 or 113 mm

Diameter of Axle Stump:
- With ME5TE gearbox   30 mm
- With MG5TE gearbox   30 mm (Q10/Q14) or 35 mm (Q18)

Lubrication grease   Total Multis Grease (G8)

4.1.   Removal and Installation

It should be noted that the oil seal for the drive shaft in the gearbox housing must be replaced, if a shaft is removed, irrespective what type of repairs are carried out. A suitable mandrel is therefore required to fit the new seal. Also note the following:

- The nut for the lower suspension ball joint has a different torque setting within the vehicle range.
- A 50 mm socket is required to slacken and tighten the axle shaft nut, but again a different size may be required, depending on the model.
- The tightening torque of the drive shaft nut is very high. *Never try to slacken or tighten the nut when the vehicle is on chassis stands.*

Remove a shaft as follows:
- Disconnect the battery earth cable.
- Apply the handbrake and engage first gear.
- Slacken the wheel bolts. Do not lift the vehicle at this stage.
- Remove the hub grease cap, using a small chisel or a strong screwdriver. If difficulties are experienced remove the wheel to remove the cap, but refit the wheel and lower the vehicle before the next operation.
- Slacken the drive shaft nut. The vehicle can now be placed on chassis stands and the nut removed from the shaft end.

- Partially drain the gearbox oil. Depending on the transmission one or two drain plugs must be removed. Allow about 1 litre of oil to drain in a suitable container. This will prevent oil from running out of the gearbox opening. If required, drain the gearbox completely.
- Remove the track rod ball joint nut and separate the joint from the lever on the steering knuckle (refer to Chapter "Steering").
- Remove the nut securing the suspension ball joint and separate the joint in the manner shown in Fig. 4.1.

The remaining removal depends on the side in question:

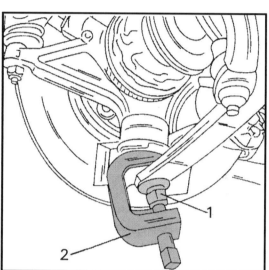

Fig. 4.1 – Separating the suspension ball joint at the bottom of the steering knuckle with a ball joint puller (2). The nut (1) can remain on the stud to protect the thread.

L.H. Drive Shaft

- Pull the steering knuckle towards the outside until the shaft is free of the wheel hub. The shaft can now be pulled out of the gearbox.

R.H. Drive Shaft

- Pull the steering knuckle towards the outside until the shaft is free of the wheel hub.

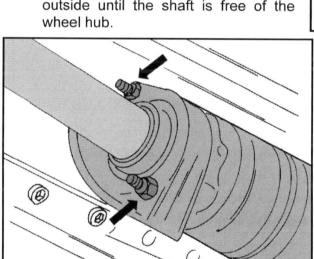

Fig. 4.2 – The arrows show where the support bearing for the R.H. drive shaft is attached. After removal of the nuts, rotate the bolt heads as described.

- Remove the two nuts in Fig. 4.2 and turn the bolt heads by a quarter of a turn from its original position. The shaft can now be removed.

Both Shafts

- Pull the wheel at the bottom towards the outside until the shaft is free from the inside of the wheel hub. When the shaft is free, remove it from the gearbox opening.
- The oil seal in the gearbox opening should be replaced. Oil leaks are possible if this precaution is ignored.

The installation of the drive shaft is carried out as follows:

- Clean the surrounding of the gearbox opening and drive a new oil seal into position until the outside is flush. The oil seal lip should be coated with gearbox oil. Take care not to damage the seal.
- Insert the installation sleeve, normally supplied with the new seal, into the differential opening as shown in Fig. 4.3 and slide the inner end of the shaft into the gearbox, engaging the splines on shaft and differential side gear. After the shaft is in position, grip the "ears" of the sleeve and withdraw it.

Drive Shafts

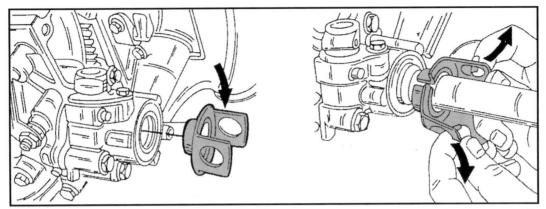

Fig. 4.3 – Fitting the installation sleeve in the L.H. view and removal of the sleeve after installation of the shaft in the R.H. view.

- If both shafts have been removed, carry out the same operations on the other side.

The remaining installation is different for the two shafts.

L.H. Shaft

- Pull the knuckle towards the outside as far as it will go and insert the shaft end into the steering knuckle.
- Push the steering knuckle towards the inside until the shaft end protrudes from the wheel hub. Fit the suspension ball joint and the track rod ball joint as described below.

R.H. Shaft

- Lubricate the outer bearing race and the oil seal of the intermediate bearing with grease and engage the drive shaft with the intermediate bearing. Bring the bearing in the correct position and insert the drive shaft into the differential side gear and the wheel hub. When in position, rotate the bolt heads by a quarter of a turn against the outer bearing race. Tighten the two securing nuts to 1 kgm (7 ft.lb.).

Fig. 4.4 – Always replace the two nuts (1) and (2). Note the tightening torque of nut (2) is not the same on all models.

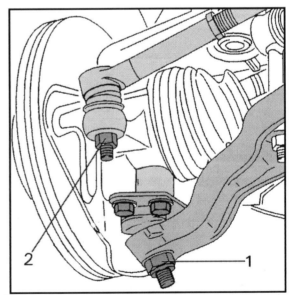

Both Shafts

- Fit the ball joint stud of the lower joint (2) in Fig. 4.4 into the steering knuckle and fit a *new* nut. Tighten the nut to the correct torque, depending on the fitted shaft. If the shaft end has a diameter of 30 mm, tighten the nut to 13 kgm (94 ft.lb.), if the diameter is 35 mm, tighten the nut to 24 kgm (173 ft.lb.). The latter shafts are fitted to models 18Q.
- Insert the track rod ball joint stud (1) in Fig. 4.4 into the steering lever and fit and tighten a *new* nut to 7.0 kgm (50 ft.lb.).
- Coat the drive shaft thread with "Loctite" and screw a ***new*** nut onto the shaft as far as it will go, without the final tightening.

- Fit the wheel and lower the vehicle onto the ground. Apply the handbrake. Tighten the drive shaft nut with a 50 mm socket. Again the drive shaft diameter is used to apply the torque. Either tighten to 45 kgm (32.5 ft.lb.), if the diameter is 30 mm or 50 kgm (360 ft.lb.), if the diameter is 35 mm.
- After the nut is tightened, use a blunt chisel and peen the nut shoulder into the shaft. The chisel must be applied vertically from above to avoid slackening of the nut.
- Fit a new grease cap.
- Tighten the wheel bolts (note the torque setting).
- Fill the gearbox with oil or correct the oil level, if the oil has only been drained partially.

4.2   Drive Shaft Repairs

Drive shaft repairs are always difficult, if the CV joint is worn or if the rubber gaiter is torn, we recommend taking the drive shaft to a workshop and having it overhauled or fit a new shaft. If dirt has entered through a torn rubber gaiter, it will have entered the CV joint, requiring the dismantling and the greasing of the latter.

4.3   Replacing the Support Bearing

The bearing can be replaced after removal of the R.H. shaft. Remove the bearing bracket from the cylinder block. If the bearing has not come off together with the drive shaft, remove it together with the oil seal from the bearing bracket. Fit the new bearing and the oil seal, refit the bearing bracket to the cylinder block and refit the drive shaft. The bearing must be greased with M.P. grease.

A different bearing bracket is used, depending which type of transmission is fitted. Fig. 4.5 shows an exploded view of the shaft for reference.

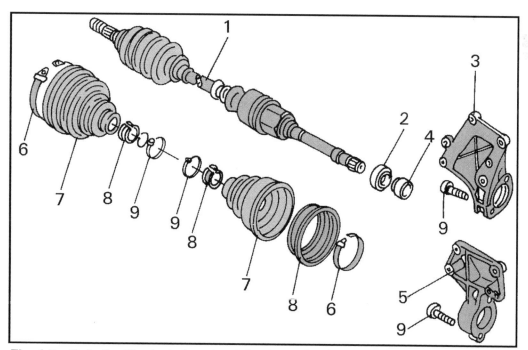

Fig. 4.5 – Only the illustrated parts of the drive shaft should be replaced.

1 R.H. drive shaft	5 Support bearing bracket (ME5TU)
2 Ball bearing	6 Large gaiter clip
3 Support bracket, MG5TU	7 Rubber gaiter
4 Bearing spacer	8 Sleeve for gaiter
	9 Bolt, 1.0 kgm

Front Axle and Front Suspension

Fig. 4.6 – Sectional view of the support bearing attachment (R.H. shaft).

1   Nuts, 1.0 kgm

2   Bolt heads

The nuts securing the outer bearing race are tightened to 1.0 kgm (7.2 ft.lb.). Fig. 4.6 shows a sectional view of the support bearing. The illustration shows the bolt heads in the locked position, after they have been rotated by a quarter of a turn.

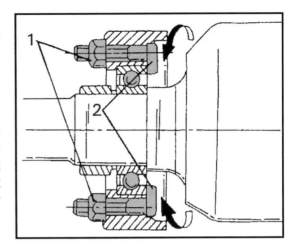

4.4   Drive Shafts - Tightening Torque Values

Drive shaft Nuts:

- Models 10Q and 14Q   45.0 kgm (324 ft.lb.)
- Model 18Q   50.0 kgm (360 ft.lb.)

Wheel Bolts:

- Models 10Q and 14Q   16.0 kgm (115.5 ft.lb.)
- Model 18Q   18.0 kgm (130 ft.lb.)

Nut of Lower Suspension Arm Ball Joint:

- Models 10Q and 14Q   13.0 kgm (94 ft.lb.)
- Model 18Q   24.0 kgm (173 ft.lb.)

Track rod ball joint to steering lever   7.0 kgm (50.5 ft.lb.)

Intermediate bearing locking nuts   1.0 kgm (7.2 ft.lb.)

Brake caliper to steering knuckle   21.0 kgm (151 ft.lb.)

Brake caliper guide bolts   3.5 kgm (25 ft.lb.)

5   FRONT AXLE AND FRONT SUSPENSION

5.0.   Technical Data

Type

Independent suspension with McPherson spring struts, lower suspension arms, integral shock absorbers, coil springs. With stabiliser bar, depending on model. Stabiliser bar mounting: Mounting clamps and rubber bushes, bolted to crossmember and connected to suspension arms with links.

Front springs

Colour coded. Only fit springs with original colour code. 1st marking denotes vehicle model, 2nd marking refers to weight category. Vehicle model and model year must be quoted when fitting new springs.

Stabiliser bar (if fitted)	24 mm ((0.95-in.) diameter. Fitted to models 18Q and 10Q/14Q with turbo diesel engine.
Shock Absorber identification:	
Models 10Q/14Q	Black marking
Model 18Q	Blue marking

Wheel Alignment

Caster, not adjustable:	1° +/- 30'
Camber, not adjustable	0° +/- 30'
Toe-in, adjustable	0 +/- 1 mm (0 +/- 0.04 in.)
Checking conditions	Tyre pressures correct, vehicle empty

Front Wheel Bearings

Type	Wheel hub with two taper roller bearings, pressed into steering knuckle
End float of bearings	0.02 - 0.10 mm (0.008 - 0.004 in.)
Means of adjustment	Spacer sleeves between 21.29 and 21.97 mm, available in various sizes, in steps of 0.04 mm between sizes.

5.1. Regular Maintenance Operations

The suspension ball joints between the suspension arms and the wheel bearing housings, also known as steering knuckles, require no maintenance. Rubber dust caps prevent the entry of dirt or moisture. Entry of dust has a grinding effect, entry of moisture leads eventually to rust formation. During regular maintenance work, you can check the ball joints as follows:

• Place the front of the vehicle on chassis stands and turn the steering wheel into full lock.

• Check the rubber dust caps on both sides for cuts or other damage. A damaged dust cap must be replaced by fitting a new ball joint. Apart from the fact that the dust caps cannot be replaced individually, there is the possibility that dirt has already entered the joint, thereby leading to wear.

Shock Absorbers and Spring Struts

In section 5.2.1 you will find certain instructions how to check shock absorbers. Follow the advice.

5.2 Front Spring Struts
5.2.0 REMOVAL

The following text describes the removal of the complete spring strut without the suspension arms and the drive shaft. The coil spring must be compressed before a spring strut can be dismantled. The wheel can remain on the hub or is removed to improve access to the various mounting points.

• Apply the handbrake, engage 1st gear and slacken the wheel bolts.

• Place the front end of the vehicle on chassis stands and remove the front wheel. Place a mobile jack loosely underneath the front axle unit.

• Inside the vehicle remove the lower part of the dashboard on the side in question. Remove the sound-proofing material and the earth lead and unscrew the three bolts in Fig. 5.1.

Front Axle and Front Suspension

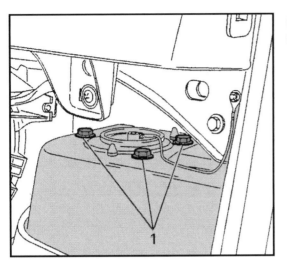

Fig. 5.1 – The three bolts (1) retain the upper spring strut bearing to the body panel.

- Refer to Fig. 5.2 and remove the four bolts indicated by the arrows.

- Slowly lower the jack until the upper end of the spring strut is free of the body panel and release the strut from the steering knuckle. Withdraw the complete strut towards the rear. *Under no circumstances remove the nut in the centre of the spring strut, as it would "explode".* If the spring strut is to be dismantled, you can slacken the nut, but re-tighten it again before the strut is removed. The steering knuckle and the suspension arm remain in the vehicle.

Fig. 5.2 – The four bolts (1) secure the spring strut to the steering knuckle. Steering knuckle, suspension arm, etc. remain in the vehicle when the spring strut is removed.

5.2.1.　DISMANTLING

Only the coil spring, the complete spring strut, the spring strut bearing and the sundry parts can be replaced. The spring strut cannot be dismantled. Never try to dismantle a spring strut, without compressing the spring first. Fig. 5.3 shows a compressor as used in the workshop. A similar tool, available from tool hire companies for example, is suitable as long as the hooks can be placed over four or five spring coils.

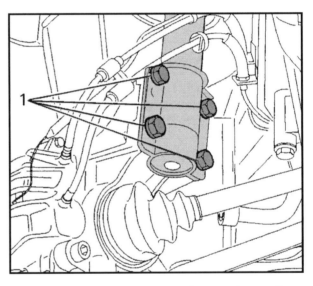

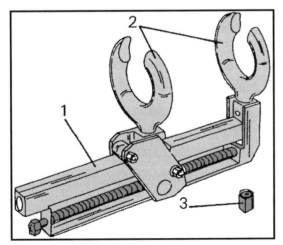

Fig. 5.3 – Special spring compressor for the dismantling of a front spring strut.
1　Compressor body
2　Claws
3　Nut

- Clamp the spring strut into a vice and fit the spring compressor. Fig. 5.4 shows the use of the spring compressor shown in Fig. 5.3. Make absolutely sure that the coils are securely retained in the compressor. Tighten the spring compressor until the spring can be rotated freely between the spring seats.

- Insert an Allen key into the end of the piston rod and slacken the piston rod nut (if not already slackened), using a flat or ring spanner of suitable size. Fully unscrew the nut and remove the upper spring strut bearing, the spacer, the needle thrust bearing, the upper spring seat and the coil spring. Remove the rubber rebound stop from the end of the piston rod and the strut from the compressed spring. The fitting order of the various parts is shown in Fig. 5.5.

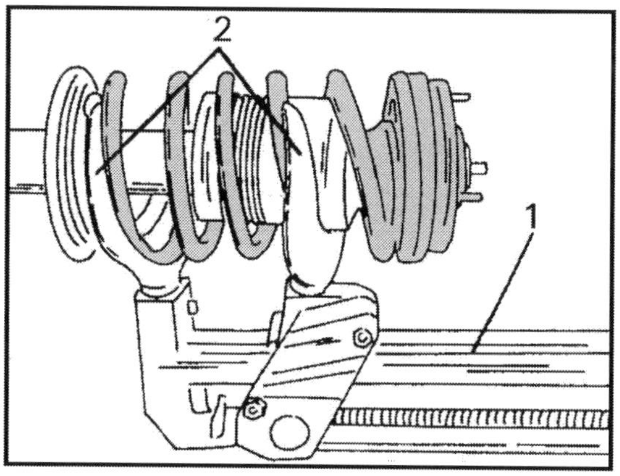

Fig. 5.4 – The spring compressor (1) can be clamped into a vice. The claws (2) are placed around the coils of the spring.

The rebound stop, the rubber protector, the needle thrust bearing and the spring strut bearing must be replaced if no longer in good condition. Take care not to damage the smooth surface of the piston rod when the spring strut is stored for later assembly.

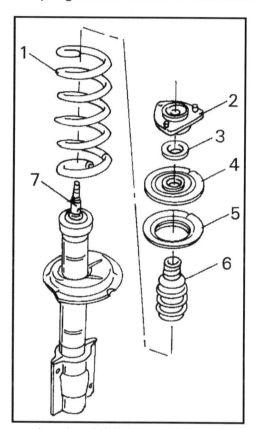

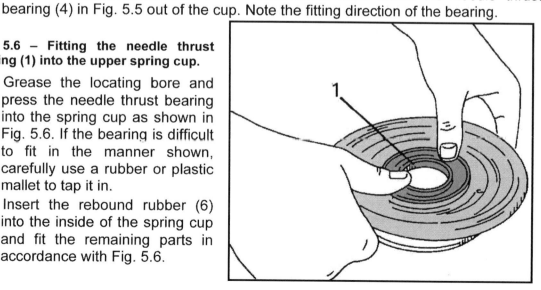

Fig. 5.5 – Dismantled spring strut.
1   Coil spring
2   Spring strut bearing
3   Thrust ring
4   Needle roller bearing
5   Upper spring seat
6   Rebound rubber
7   Spring strut

The shock absorber can be checked for correct operation by clamping the spring strut in upright position into a vice. Screw the back onto the piston rod and grip the nut with a pair of pliers. Move the piston rod up and down. The piston rod should move with even resistance. Any "dead play" indicates a faulty shock absorber.

5.2.2.   ASSEMBLY

Before assembly of the spring strut, prepare the upper spring strut bearing:

- Place the upper cap onto its edge (upright position) and, using a small chisel or a screwdriver then knock the needle thrust bearing (4) in Fig. 5.5 out of the cup. Note the fitting direction of the bearing.

Fig. 5.6 – Fitting the needle thrust bearing (1) into the upper spring cup.

- Grease the locating bore and press the needle thrust bearing into the spring cup as shown in Fig. 5.6. If the bearing is difficult to fit in the manner shown, carefully use a rubber or plastic mallet to tap it in.

- Insert the rebound rubber (6) into the inside of the spring cup and fit the remaining parts in accordance with Fig. 5.6.

- Clamp the spring strut in upright position into a vice and pull the piston rod out of the spring strut as far as it will go. Fit the compressed spring over the spring strut, engaging the lower coil with its stop. Place the upper spring seat over the spring.
- Fit the assembled spring strut bearing over the piston rod, followed by the spacer washer.
- Fit a new self-locking nut to the end of the piston rod and tighten the nut to 7.0 kgm (50.5 ft.lb.). The piston rod must be held against rotation until it is possible to apply a socket with torque wrench to the nut. The latter should be tight enough to keep the piston rod in position.
- Slowly release the spring compressor, at the same time checking that the spring coils enter the locations at top and bottom. The ends of the coils must be resting against the stop on the spring strut and a similar stop on the upper end.

5.2.3.   INSTALLATION

The installation of the spring strut is a reversal of the removal procedure. Note the following points:
- Insert the spring strut with the studs from below into the holes in the body panel and fit the three nuts without tightening them. Always use new self-locking nuts.
- Lift the complete front suspension unit with the jack and engage the spring strut. Fit the four bolts shown in Fig. 5.2. Tighten the bolts evenly across to 21.kgm (150 ft.lb.).
- Tighten the three nuts securing the upper spring strut bearing to 2.1 kgm (15 ft.lb.).
- Lower the vehicle to the ground and tighten the wheel bolts to the correct torque.

5.3.   Removal and Installation of a Front Suspension Unit on one Side

The following instructions must be followed when the complete steering knuckle together with the drive shaft is to be removed. It should be noted that the inner mounting of the suspension arm must be tightened when the weight of the vehicle is resting on the wheels. This will pre-load the rubber mountings to their correct operating position. Fig. 5.7 on the next page shows the front suspension on one side.

Attention: The hub grease cap is normally removed with a puller to be suitable for refitting. A damaged cap must be replaced.

- Slacken the wheel bolts and remove the hub grease cap with a strong screwdriver or a small chisel. It may be easier to remove the wheel as you will be able to insert the chisel straight into the gap. In this case slacken the drive shaft nut before the wheel is removed. *Never attempt to slacken the nut when the vehicle is on chassis stands*
- After slackening the drive shaft nut, place the front end of the vehicle on chassis stands and remove the wheel (as may be the case).
- Separate the connection between the brake hose and the metal pipe on the chassis. Plug the open ends of hoses/pipes in a suitable manner. Sticky tape is useful for this job.
- Disconnect the track rod ball joint from the steering lever and separate the connecting links for the stabiliser bar from the suspension strut.

Fig. 5.7 – View of the front suspension on one side.

- Slacken the bolts of the suspension arm mounting at the inside.
  In the engine compartment remove the three nuts securing the upper spring strut bearing, as described during the removal of the spring strut. Support the suspension assembly from below, as it will drop as soon as the last nut has been removed.

- Withdraw the steering knuckle towards the outside, guiding the drive shaft. If the drive shaft is to be removed, follow the instructions in Section 4 for the side in question. Otherwise withdraw the steering knuckle from the end of the drive shaft. Retain the drive shaft with a piece of wire as horizontally as possible.

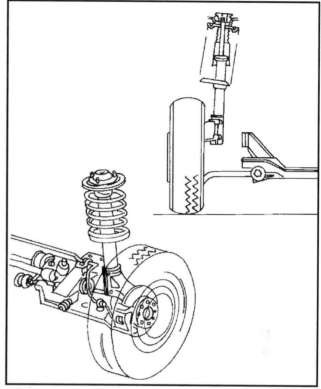

The installation is a reversal of the removal procedure. Observe the tightening torques at the end of this section or refer to the instructions already given for the installation of the spring strut. Bleed the brake system after re-connecting the brake hose to the pipe. Fit the drive shaft as described in Section 4.

5.4 Dismantling and Assembling a Front Axle Unit

After the front axle unit has been removed in the manner described above you will be able to dismantle it to replace individual parts. All tightening torques are given at the end of this chapter or have already been mentioned in earlier sections. Note the following:

Fig. 5.8 – Attachment of the suspension ball joint to the steering knuckle.

1 Bolts, joint to steering knuckle.

2 Nut, Joint to suspension arm (note the tightening torque).

- If the suspension arm is to be removed together with the suspension ball joint, remove the bolts from the bottom of the steering knuckle. Otherwise remove the ball joint nut from the bottom of the steering knuckle and separate the joint stud with a suitable puller. Fig. 5.8 shows the two possibilities.

- Remove the wheel bearings as described in the next section.

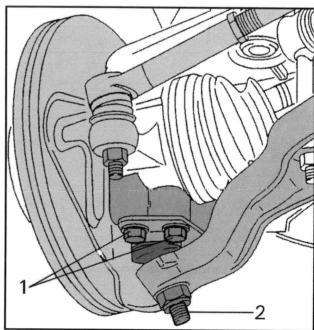

5.5   Steering Knuckle and Wheel Bearings

The replacement of the wheel bearings is not a straight-forward operation, as a dial gauge with a suitable holder is required to adjust the wheel bearing clearance. Required are also a puller and press mandrels, which can, however, be substituted by make-shift or conventional tools.

The steering knuckle must be removed, i.e. either the spring strut or the complete front axle unit must be removed as already described. A wheel bearing can then be removed as follows:

*   Remove the wheel hub from the steering knuckle. Alternative methods are available. Either you place the steering knuckle under a press and remove the hub from the rear, using a suitable press mandrel or you use a puller as shown in Fig. 5.9 and push out the wheel hub. The pressure of the centre spindle must be applied to the outer diameter of the hub, i.e. a suitable plate must be placed over the hub before the puller is applied. The spindle can then be tightened.

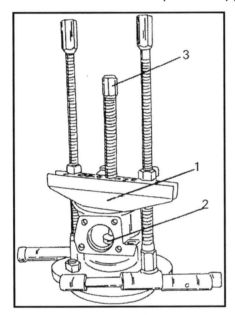

Fig. 5.9 – The wheel hub can be removed with a puller (1). Place thrust washer (2) over the wheel hub face. The spindle (3) is tightened to push out the hub.

*   The bearing race and the bearing adjustment spacer will remain on the wheel hub and must be withdrawn with a suitable puller. The claws of the puller must be engaged under the bearing race.
*   Place the steering knuckle over a vice and drive the two bearings out of the inside of the steering knuckle. The two grease seals will come away together with the bearing in question.
*   Remove the two outer bearing races from opposite sides of the steering knuckle. Collect the bearing spacer and the adjusting shims.

Thoroughly clean all parts and check them systematically for wear. Grease seals must always be replaced, once removed. Discoloured bearings are also due for replacement.

The wheel bearings are refitted in the following manner. The description is based on the use of the special tools, but suitable alternative tools can be used as applicable.

*   Make sure that the inside of the steering knuckle is clean and drive the outer bearing races from opposite sides into the steering knuckle, with the cone faces towards the outside. Take care not to damage the bearing running faces.

The bearing clearance (play) must now be adjusted. The work must be carried out with great care, as badly adjusted wheel bearings will soon lead to failure. The bearing clearance must be adjusted to 0.02 - 0.10 mm and must be measured with a dial gauge.

*   Clean the inside of the fitter outer bearing race, grease the bearing (6) in Fig. 5.10 and tap the bearing in position. The guide (2) and the assembly bolt are used for this purpose.
*   Insert the bearing spacer (7) into the outside of the steering knuckle and the inner wheel bearing (8) from the other side. Insert the two thrust pieces (3) and (4) into the opening. Fit the nut (5) to the assembly bolt (1) and tighten the nut to 1.0 kgm (7.2 ft.lb.). The bolt head must be held to prevent it from rotating.
*   Apply a ring spanner to the nut and rotate the wheel bearings a few times to settle them in position.

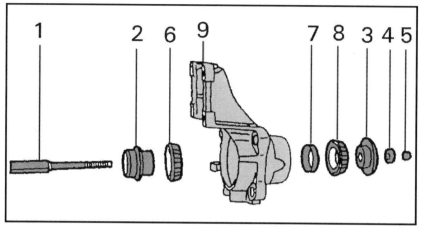

Fig. 5.10 – Fitting the wheel bearing to the steering knuckle, using the special tools.

1 Bolt
2 Thrust piece
3 Thrust piece
4 Washer
5 Nut

6 Inner wheel bearing
7 Bearing spacer
8 Outer wheel bearing
9 Steering knuckle

Assembly Note: If the special tools cannot be obtained (we would say in most cases), use a long bolt. Suitable sockets can be used in place of items (3) and (2). Large washers and a nut complete the make-shift arrangement.

The pre-load of the bearings must now be adjusted. Again the description is based on the special tools, but a suitable dial gauge, arranged as shown in Fig. 5.11, will do.

- Clamp the steering knuckle into a vice as shown in Fig. 5.11, attach the dial gauge holder and place the stylus onto the end of the bolt as shown in the illustration. Set the dial gauge to "Zero".

- Grip the end of the bolt (1) and move it to and fro (up and down), at the same time observing the dial gauge reading. The indication must be between 0.02 and 0.10 mm.

Fig. 5.11 – Checking the wheel bearing clearance. Place the stylus of the dial gauge (3) on the end of the bolt (1). Moving the bolt up and down will indicate the clearance of the wheel bearings. The dial gauge holder (2) is attached to the steering knuckle.

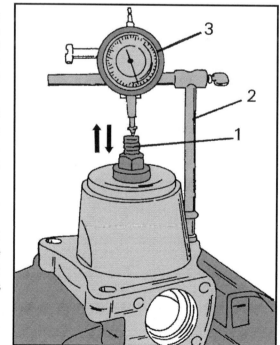

- If the clearance is not within the limits shown, increase or decrease the height of the bearing spacer (7) in Fig. 5.10. Bearing spacers are available in thicknesses from 21.29 to 21.97 mm, in increments of 0.04 mm between sizes.

- Remove the used tools and take out the wheel bearing cones, all of the bearing spacers must be replaced. In this case re-check the end float as described.

- Generously grease the bearing (6) in Fig. 5.10 and insert it into the steering knuckle. Fit the grease seal into the steering knuckle until the outside is flush.

Front Axle and Front Suspension

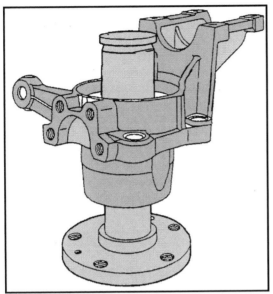

Fig. 5.12 – Fitting the wheel hub. Place the steering knuckle with the fitting bearing over the hub and press home

- Place the wheel hub with the flange onto the press table and drive the steering knuckle and the inserted bearing over the hub. A piece of tube of suitable diameter must be used. The tube must be placed against the inner bearing race. Drive the bearing fully over the hub. The hub and steering knuckle must be supported as shown in Fig. 5.12.
- Place the selected bearing spacer inside the steering knuckle.
- Fit the very well greased inner bearing race (6) in Fig. 5.10 into the steering knuckle (at least 50 g wheel bearing grease must be used). Drive the bearing in position with a piece of tube of suitable diameter. The wheel hub/steering knuckle remain in the position shown in Fig. 5.12. Grease a new oil seal and carefully fit it into the steering knuckle until the end is flush the knuckle face.

5.6. Suspension Arms - Removal and Installation

The following text describes the removal of the suspension arms. The remaining parts of the front suspension are not removed.

Before the front end of the vehicle is placed on a chassis stand, it will be necessary to remove the stabiliser bar from the bottom of the suspension arms, to release the tension from the arm. We would like to point out that the space is very confined to remove the mountings when the wheels are on the ground. The nuts (1) and (2) in Fig. 5.13 must be removed to release the outer ends of the stabiliser bar from the suspension. The bar can be left on the chassis. Removal takes place as follows:

Fig. 5.13 – The stabiliser bar connecting linkages are secured with nuts at the upper and lower ends. The nuts must always be replaced.

- Slacken the wheel bolts, place the front end of the vehicle on chassis stands and remove the wheel.
- Remove the protective shield underneath the vehicle.
- Refer to Fig. 5.8 and remove the ball joint nut (2). Separate the ball joint with a suitable puller from the suspension arm. *Note that the tightening torque for the nut is not the same on all models.*
- On the inside of the suspension arm remove the arm mounting bolts shown in Fig. 5.14. *The three bolts have a different tightening torque.*
- Remove the suspension arm.

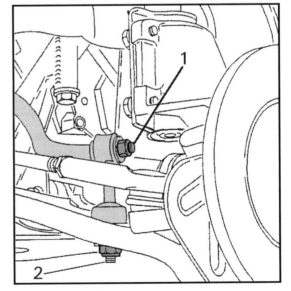

The installation is a reversal of the removal procedure, but the different tightening torques must be observed. The suspension arm mounting bolts must be tightened when the wheels are back on the ground. Note the following:

• Place the rear end of the suspension arm against the sub-frame. Use a jack to push the arm well against its mounting points.

• Fit the bolt (1) in Fig. 5.14, followed by the bolts (2) and (3). Tighten all bolts finger-tight. After the vehicle is on its wheels, tighten the bolt (1) with 25 kgm (180 ft.lb.), the bolt (2) with 20 kgm (144 ft.lb.) and the bolt (3) with 17 kgm (122.5 ft.lb.).

• Connect the lower ball joint to the steering knuckle and fit a new nut. The nut is tightened to 13 kgm (97.5 ft.lb.), with the exception of the "18Q" model. The nut on these vehicles is tightened to 23.5 kgm (170 ft.lb.). The nut can be tightened with the wheels off the ground.

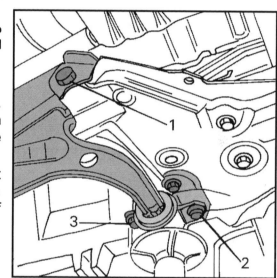

Fig. 5.14 – Attachment of a suspension arm to the sub-frame. The bolts (1) to (3) are tightened to the torque setting given in the text.

• Refit the stabiliser bar, referring to Fig. 5.13. Both nuts are tightened to 8.0 kgm (58 ft.lb.) when the vehicle is with the wheels on the ground.

• All other operations are now carried out in reverse order. Lower the vehicle on its wheels and tighten the elements of the front suspension as specified above.

5.7.   Suspension Ball Joint - Replacement

The replacement of the ball joint follows a similar pattern as described for the removal of the suspension arm. After the suspension arm has been separated from the ball joint (see Fig. 5.8), remove the two bolts (1). At the outside a protective panel is fitted, as can be seen in Fig. 5.15, which is removed after removal of the bolt. The ball joint can now be taken off.

The installation is a reversal of the removal procedure. Tighten the bolts (1) to 8.8 kgm (63.5 ft.lb.). Tighten the nut (2) as described during the installation of the suspension arm (Section 5.5).

5.8   Stabiliser Bar - Removal and Installation

As the track rod ball joint must be separated from the steering lever, a ball joint puller will be necessary.

• Slacken the wheel bolts, place the front of the vehicle on chassis stands and remove the wheel. Also remove the protective shield underneath the front end of the vehicle.

• Remove the track rod ball joint nut and separate the joint with a puller, as shown in Fig. 5.16 on the next page. Move the track rod upwards to have it out of the way.

• Refer to Fig. 5.17 (next page) and remove the nuts (2) and (3) securing the ends of the connecting links.

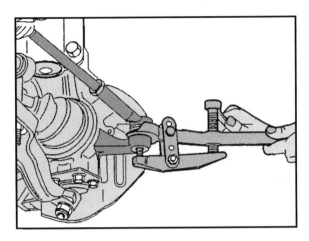

Fig. 5.16 – Separating a track rod ball joint.

- From below the vehicle remove the mounting clamp bolts on the L.H. and R.H. side at the locations shown in Fig. 5.18 and remove the stabiliser bar from the R.H. side of the vehicle. The bar must be lifted and rotated towards the bottom to release it from the suspension assembly.

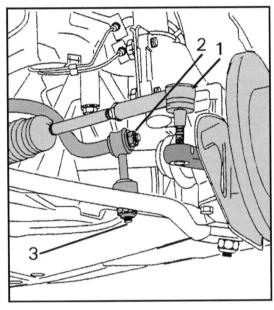

Fig. 5.17 – Stabiliser connecting linkage connected to the bar and the suspension arm. The track rod ball joint has already been separated.
1   Ball joint
2   Stabiliser end
3   Suspension arm end

The installation is a reversal of the removal procedure. The self-locking nuts must be replaced. Bolts and nuts are tightened with the wheels back on the ground. Bolts (1) in Fig. 5.18 are tightened to 20 kgm (145 ft.lb.), bolts (2) to 8.5 kgm (61 ft.lb.). Nuts (2) and (3) in Fig. 5.17 are tightened to 8.0 kgm (58 ft.lb.). Fig. 5.19 shows the attachment of the stabiliser bar together with other parts of the suspension.

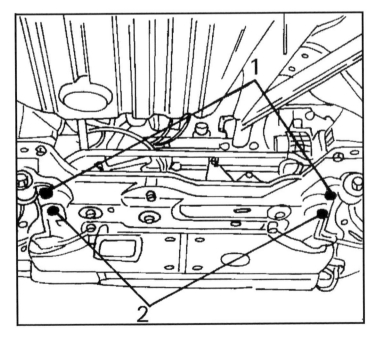

Fig. 5.18 – Bolts (1) and (2) secure the stabiliser bar mounting clamps to the bottom of the crossmember.

5.9 Vehicles with Four-Wheel Drive

The front suspension is in general of the same design and construction, but the following differences should be noted:

- The upper spring strut mounting has 30 mm thick inserts between spring strut and body panel.
- 10 mm thick inserts are fitted between the sub-frame and the body at the mounting points.

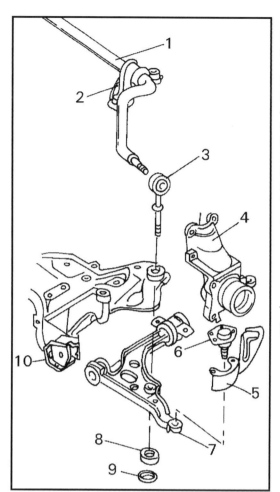

Fig. 5.19 — Stabiliser bar and lower suspension arm.

1   Stabiliser bar
2   Mounting clamp
3   Connecting rod
4   Steering knuckle
5   Protective cover
6   Suspension ball joint
7   Suspension arm
8   Rubber bush
9   Metal cup
10   Suspension crossmember

• The stabiliser bar, fitted as standard equipment, is pre-formed to avoid contact between the bar and the propeller shaft or the transfer box.

The repair operations described above are not influenced by the alterations specified above.

5.10   Tightening Torque Values

Ball joint to Suspension Arms:
- Models 10Q and 14Q   13.0 kgm (94 ft.lb.)
- Model 18Q   24.0 kgm (173 ft.lb.)

Ball joint plate to steering knuckle   8.8 kgm (63.5 ft.lb.)
Nuts, stabiliser connecting links   8.0 kgm (57.5 ft.lb.)

Stabiliser bar to crossmember (Fig. 5.18):
- Bolt 1   20.0 kgm (144 ft.lb.)
- Bolt 2   8.5 kgm (61.5 ft.lb.)

Suspension Arm to Chassis (Fig. 5.14):
- Bolt 1   25.0 kgm (180 ft.lb.)
- Bolt 2   20.0 kgm (144 ft.lb.)
- Bolt 3   17.0 kgm (122.5 ft.lb.)

Track rod ball joint nuts   7.0 kgm (50.5 ft.lb.)
Spring strut to steering knuckle   21.0 kgm (151.5 ft.lb.)
Spring strut to body   2.1 kgm (15 ft.lb.)

Drive Shaft Nuts:
- Models 10Q and 14Q   45.0 kgm (324 ft.lb.)
- Model 18Q   50.0 kgm (360 ft.lb.)

Brake caliper to spring strut   21.0 kgm (151.5 ft.lb.)
Brake caliper, guide bolts   2.7 kgm (19.5 ft.lb.)

Steering

Wheel Bolts:
- Models 10Q and 14Q   16.0 kgm (115 ft.lb.)
- Models 18Q   18.0 kgm (130 ft.lb.)

Brake disc to hub   1.0 kgm (7.2 ft.lb.)

ABS wheel speed sensor   1.0 kgm (7.2 ft.lb.)

---

6.   STEERING

6.0.   Technical Data

Type	Rack and pinion steering, without or with power assistance. Mainly power-assisted steering

Turning Circle between Kerb Stones/Walls:
- Short wheelbase (2.85 m)   11.00/11.50 m
- Medium wheelbase (3.20 m)   12.10/12.68 mm
- Long wheelbase (3.70 m)   13.70/14.14 m

Steering Pump:
- Drive   Belt drive
- Fluid pressure   100 bar (1420 psi.)

Steering Fluid:
- Filling capacity   1.3 litres
- Fluid type   ATF fluid, as in automatic transmissions
- Fluid level check   Every 6,000 miles

Front Wheel Alignment:
- Castor, not adjustable   1° +/- 30'
- Camber, not adjustable   0° +/- 30'
- Wheel to-in, adjustable   0° +/- 1 mm (0 +/- 0.04 in.)
- Checking conditions   Tyre pressures correct, vehicle empty

6.1.   Maintenance Operations - Steering

Checking Steering Rack Gaiters: The steering rack is closed of at both ends with black rubber gaiters. These should be checked periodically for cuts or other damage to prevent water, dust or other foreign matter from entering the steering. To check the gaiters, turn the steering wheel into full lock and check the stretched gaiter on one side for cuts. Replace if a cut is visible. Turn the steering to the opposite lock and check the other gaiter. Make sure that the gaiter securing clamps are properly tightened.

Checking rubber dust caps and ball joints: Check the rubber dust caps of each steering track rod ball joint for cuts. If cuts are detected, replace the joint as described later on.

The track rod ball joints can be checked for excessive wear. Jack up the front end of the vehicle and move the wheel to and fro, at the same time observing the track rod ball joint. Unusual movement of the joints can be seen. It is also possible to hold the ball joint where it enters the steering lever and ask a helper to turn the steering wheel to and fro (wheels on the ground). Movement in the joints requires the replacement of the joint(s).

Checking steering for play: Grip the steering wheel through the window and move the wheel to and fro, at the same time observing the front wheel. The road wheel must move immediately in response to the steering wheel movement. Otherwise: Excessive play in the steering rack, worn track rod ball joints, worn universal joint on the steering shaft.

Checking the fluid level: See description later on.

6.2 Steering unit
6.2.0. REMOVAL

Note: Before separating the steering shaft from the steering pinion, lock the steering wheel with the road wheels in the straight-ahead position. This will prevent damage to the cancelling switch underneath the steering wheel (use a piece of string in a suitable manner). **If an airbag is fitted, you will need some experience with that type of equipment. Otherwise have the steering changed by a workshop.**

- Disconnect the battery negative cable. If an airbag is fitted, wait at least 1 minute before carrying out any other operation.

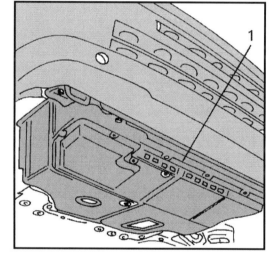

Fig. 6.1 – The protective shield (1) is fitted underneath the front end of the vehicle, can, however, have a different shape.

- Slacken the wheel bolts, place the front end of the vehicle on chassis stands and remove both wheels.

- Remove the protective shield underneath the front of the vehicle. Fig. 6.1 shows the shield in position, but different models have different arrangements. A second shield is fitted at the rear of the engine, which must also be removed.

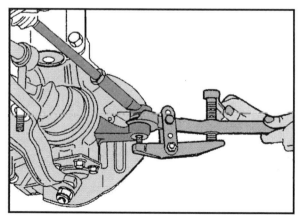

Fig. 6.2 – Separating a track rod ball joint.

- Turn the steering into full lock to one side and remove the nut securing the track rod ball joint to the steering lever. Use a suitable puller, as shown in Fig. 6.2 and separate the ball joint connection. Turn the steering wheel into the opposite lock and carry out the same operation on the other side.

- Slacken the stabiliser bar connecting rod nuts on both sides of the vehicle, i.e. slacken nuts (2) and (3) in Fig. 6.3.

Steering

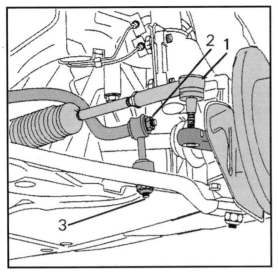

Fig. 6.3 – Details for the removal and installation of the steering.

1   Track rod

2   Nut, linkage to bar

3   Nut, linkage to suspension arm

- From the inside of the engine compartment remove the nut from the end of the clamp bolt. The bolt secures the upper part of the steering column universal joint. Mark the relationship between universal joint and steering shaft with paint.

- Disconnect the stabiliser bar connecting rods from the suspension arms (both sides).

- From the bottom of the suspension crossmember remove the four bolts (1) in Fig. 6.4.

Fig. 6.4 – The four bolts (1) secure the steering unit to the front crossmember.

- Using a tyre lever, push the stabiliser bar as far as possible towards the top and turn the steering until the steering universal joint can be disengaged from the steering pinion. Remove the steering sideways out of the vehicle (to the left or right). The removed steering is shown in Fig. 6.6.

If the track rod ball joints are to be replaced, clamp the track rod into a vice as shown in Fig. 6.5, slacken the locknuts and unscrew the track rod ends, counting the number of turns and if applicable half-turns necessary to fully unscrew a joint. Write the value down for each side for later

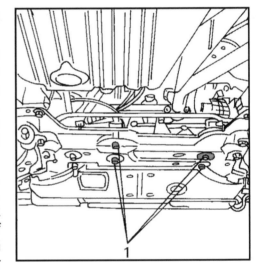

fitting of the track rod end. If the new joints are fitted in the same position, they will set the track rods to the correct length for the adjustment of the toe-in.

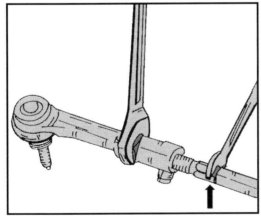

Fig. 6.5 – Removal of a track rod ball joint from the track rod. Apply an open-ended spanner at the position shown by the arrow.

6.1.1.   INSTALLATION

The installation is a reversal of the removal procedure, noting the following points:

- Check the condition of the steering rubber boots (gaiters) and make sure the boot clamps are tight.

- The securing bolts for the steering are tightened to 6.5 kgm (47 ft.lb.).

- If new track rod ball joints are to be fitted, screw them onto the end of the rod(s). Provisionally tighten the locknuts.

- Clean the ball joint studs of oil or grease and connect with the steering levers. Tighten the nuts to 8.8 kgm (63 ft.lb.).

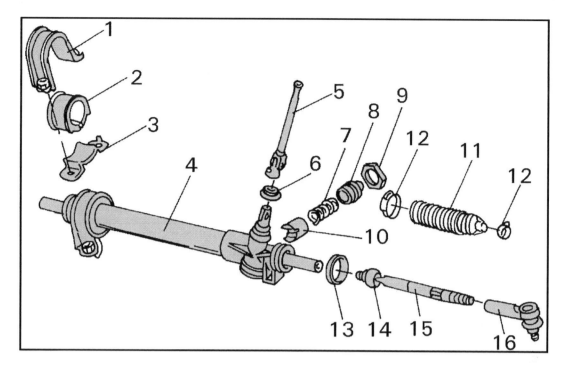

Fig. 6.5 – View of the removed and partially dismantled steering unit.

1 Mounting clamp	7 Spring	13 Sealing ring
2 Rubber bush	8 Threaded sleeve	14 Inner ball joint
3 Threaded holder	9 Locknut	15 Track rod
4 Rack housing	10 Plunger	16 Track rod ball joint
5 Steering shaft	11 Rubber gaiter	
6 Sealing grommet	12 Gaiter clamp	

- Set the steering to the central position and connect the steering universal joint to the steering column shaft. Make sure that the marks made before removal are in line, insert the bolt and tighten the nut to 4.5 kgm (32 ft.lb.).
- Check the toe-in setting of the front wheels as described in Section 6.5.

6.2.2.   STEERING REPAIRS

The steering should not be dismantled. In case of wear or damage fit a new steering or try to obtain an exchange steering. Steering with excessive play can, however, be adjusted. For safety reasons, however, we recommend to take the removed steering to a workshop where it can be checked and if necessary adjusted professionally.

The rubber gaiters can be replaced after disconnecting the track rods. You will have to assess how long the gaiter is damaged, as dirt may have entered the steering housing/rack. Before fitting a new gaiter, turn the steering wheel from lock to lock and clean off the old grease as good as possible. Then re-grease the steering rack and fit the gaiter.

The inner ball joints at the ends of the track rods can also be replaced. Proceed as follows:

- Remove the rubber gaiter from the track rod and the side of the rack housing. Cut the old clamp band. On the other side roll back the two rubber rings securing the gaiter to the track rod. Move the gaiter towards the outside of the track rod.
- Clamp the steering box into a vice (soft-metal jaws) and unscrew the ball joint housing from the steering rack. Workshops use a special wrench for this operation, you will have to use a pair of pliers or grips. The round-shaped ball joint housing is fairly sturdy as it is to be replaced, damage can be ignored. Unscrew the track rod as soon as the ball joint housing is free.

Steering

Fig. 6.7 – Locking a ball joint housing to the steering rack.

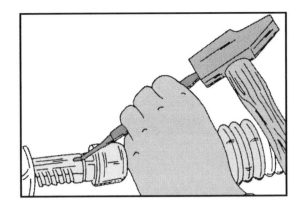

- Screw the new track rod with the new ball joint housing to the steering rack and tighten the housing with the grips as tight as possible.
- Secure the ball joint housing to the steering rack. The rack housing is clamped into a vice and the lug on the ball joint housing is peened into the groove of the rack, as shown in Fig. 6.7, without splitting the metal.
- Grease the steering rack and refit the rubber gaiter.
- Fit the track rod ball joint the same number of turns. Tighten the track rod locknut provisionally. The final tightening takes place after the toe-in has been checked and/or adjusted – **Do not forget to tighten the locknut after you have adjusted the toe-in.**

6.3 Steering Centre Position

The steering must be in the centre position during checks and adjustment of the toe-in or other operations, for example during the removal and installation of the steering gear. Proceed as follows:
- Turn the steering wheel fully into one lock and attach a piece of sticky tape at the top of the steering wheel rim. Mark a line with a pencil into the tape.
- Turn the steering wheel into the opposite lock, counting the exact number of rotations.
- Divide the counted turns by 2 and turn the steering wheel towards the centre. The steering wheel must be in the centre position. If this is not the case, adjust the track rod on the side in question to set the wheel to the centre position. Check the position of the steering wheel and re-set if necessary.

6.4. Front Wheel Geometry

The front wheel geometry must be checked when the vehicle has its kerb weight, i.e. unladen with coolant, fuel and oil.

6.4.0. CASTER ANGLE

The caster angle cannot be adjusted. The caster angle can be measured with conventional equipment, but an optical measurement by a specialist is preferred. If the obtained values are outside the limits, check the front suspension for distortion or better still, have it checked professionally. The same applies if the difference between the two sides exceeds 1°. Fig. 6.8 shows a diagram, showing the caster and camber settings. The caster diagram is demonstrated on the left.

6.4.1 CAMBER ANGLE

The camber angle should be checked optically, but cannot be adjusted. If a mechanical camber gauge is used, follow the instructions of the manufacturer. The difference between the two sides must not exceed 1°. Incorrect camber angles are mainly due to distortion in the front suspension. Have the suspension checked, as recommended above. Fig. 6.8 demonstrates the camber angle on the R.H. side.

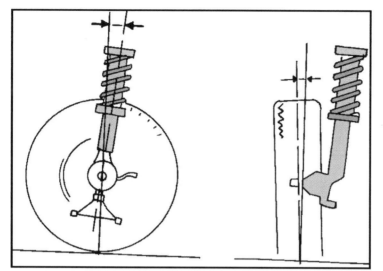

Fig. 6.8 – Diagram showing the caster angle (left) and the camber angle (right).

6.4.2 TOE-IN ADJUSTMENT

The front wheel toe-in can be measured with a mechanical tracking gauge. The front wheels are set to 0 mm, but with a tolerance of 1 mm towards toe-in or toe-out. Measure as follows:

- Check the tyre pressures and correct as necessary.
- Place the vehicle on level ground and turn the front wheels in the straight-ahead position.
- Place the tracking gauge with the pins against the wheel rims (level of wheel hubs) and set the gauge to "Zero". Mark the contact points with chalk or a spot of paint.
- Push the vehicle forward by half a turn of the wheels, i.e. the marked spot must now be at the rear, again level with the wheel hubs.
- Push the tracking gauge underneath the vehicle and place one pin against the marked spot. The pin on the other side will most probably not reach the rim. Unlock the moveable pin and pull it towards the outside until it can be placed against the rim. Lock the pin in position.
- Remove the tracking gauge and read off the measurement. The indication should be "0" (Zero) or within a tolerance of 1 mm more or less.
- If an adjustment is necessary, slacken the locknuts at the inside of the two track rod ball joints and turn the track rod by the same amount on both sides. Note that there must be a gap of at least 2.0 mm (0.08 in) between the track rod ball joint and the locknut face. Make sure that the rubber gaiters cannot twist when the rods are turned. Slacken, then re-tighten the gaiter clamp bands if necessary.
- Finally tighten the two locknuts to 6.0 kgm (43.5 ft.lb.). The track rods must be held against rotation.

6.5. Power-assisted Steering
6.5.0. REMOVAL AND INSTALLATION

Fig. 6.9 shows details of the steering. A ball joint puller must be available to remove the steering. It also advisable to have two clamps to pinch together the steering fluid hoses to prevent the draining of the complete system.

The removal and installation is carried out in a similar manner as described for the mechanical steering, with the difference that the pipes and hoses must be disconnected from the steering housing.

Fill the steering system after installation as follows:

- Fill the fluid reservoir to the "Max" mark with the recommended steering fluid (Dexron II, ATF fluid). 1.3 litres will be necessary if the system has been completely drained.
- Move the steering wheel a few times from one lock to the other (vehicle on chassis stands), with the engine switched off. Correct the fluid level if necessary.

Steering

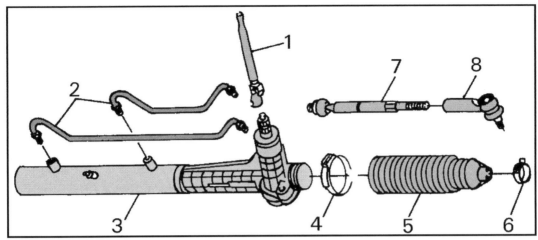

Fig. 6.9 – Component parts of the power-assisted steering.

1 Lower steering shaft	5 Steering gaiter
2 Fluid pipes	6 Outer gaiter clamps
3 Rack housing	7 Track rod
4 Inner gaiter clamp	8 Track rod ball joint

- Lower the vehicle to the ground, start the engine and again turn the steering wheel a few times from one lock to the other, until the fluid level in the reservoir remains steady. Refit the reservoir cap.

- After installation of the steering check the toe-in setting or have it checked professionally.

6.5.1.   STEERING FLUID LEVEL

The steering fluid reservoir has a "Max" and a "Min" mark. Every 6,000 miles the fluid level should be checked as part of a regular maintenance. Unscrew the cap to check the level. Never overfill the system. Make sure the correct fluid is used to top up the system.

If the fluid level has dropped below the minimum mark, bleed the system as described under "Removal and Installation of the power-assisted Steering" in Section 6.5.1.

To replace the fluid, disconnect the hose from the reservoir and let the fluid drain into a suitable container. Move the steering wheel to and fro to eject the fluid. Fill the system with 1.3 litres DEXRON II ATF fluid as described in Section 1.6.0.

6.6.   Tightening Torque Values

Steering securing bolts	6.5 kgm (47 ft.lb.)
Track rod ball joints locknuts	6.0 kgm (43.5 ft.lb.)
Track ball joints to steering levers	7.0 kgm (50.5 ft.lb.)
Locknuts at inside of track rods	12.0 kgm (86.5 ft.lb.)
Wheel bolts:	
- Models 10Q and 18Q	16.0 kgm (115 ft.lb.)
- Model 18Q	18.0 kgm (130 ft.lb.)
Steering universal joint clamp bolts/nut	4.5 kgm (32.5 ft.lb.)
Nuts for stabiliser bar connecting linkages	8.0 kgm (58.0 ft.lb.)
Hydraulic pipe connections	3.0 kgm (22 ft.lb.)
Fluid pipe clamp	0.9 kgm (6.5 ft.lb.)
Steering wheel nut	5.0 kgm (36.0 ft.lb.)

7. REAR AXLE AND REAR SUSPENSION

The rear suspension consists of two leaf springs, fitted in longitudinal direction to the chassis side members. Each spring consists of a single spring leaf. It is obvious that due to the different load capacities of the various makes and models there are differences in the carrying capacity of the springs. Whenever a spring is replaced, quote the model and the chassis number, i.e. 10Q, 14Q or 18Q. The springs are marked at the shackle mountings, at the rear ends of the springs.

The springs are secured at the centre by two "U" bolts to the rear axle tube. A spring pin with a detachable bracket secures each spring at the front. A spring shackle arrangement with welded-in bolts and detachable shackles is used to attach the springs at the rear. Spring pins and spring shackle pins are rubber-mounted.

Two-way acting telescopic shock absorbers complete the rear suspension. The lower mounting points are located below the spring. Springs and shock absorbers are generally the same for vehicles with two-wheel and four-wheel drive. Figs. 7.1 and 7.2 show views of the rear suspension from different angles.

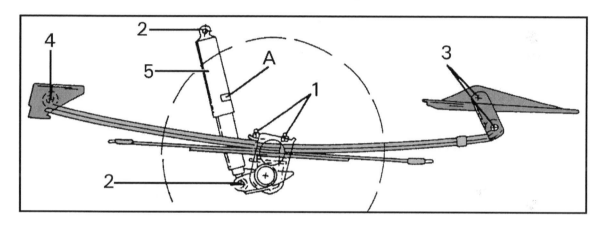

Fig. 7.1 – View of the rear suspension from one side.

1 Spring "U" bolt Nut	4 Spring pin nut
2 Shock absorber bolts, 18 kgm	5 Shock absorber
3 Spring shackle nut	A Shock absorber marking

7.0 Technical Data

Type	Leaf spring, one or two leaves and two-way acting telescopic shock absorbers.
Spring identification	Colour-marking, depending on load capacity. Only fit springs with the same colour-marking if a spring is replaced.
Rear wheel hubs/bearings	Two taper roller bearings
Bearing end float	0.025 - 0.10 mm
Shock Absorbers:	
- Type	Different depending on Model
- Colour code	10Q/14Q black, 18Q blue

Rear Axle and Rear Suspension

Tracking of rear wheels

0 +/- 1 mm (0 +/- 0.04 in.), not adjustable

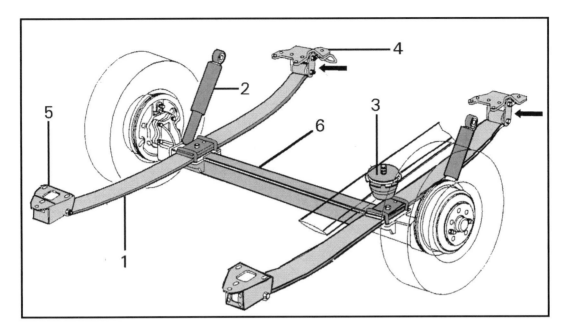

Fig. 7.2 – View of the assembled rear suspension together with the rear springs. The arrows show where the colour code can be found. Models with 4 x 4 drive have a packing underneath the rebound rubber.

1	Rear spring	4	Spring shackle mounting bracket
2	Shock absorber	5	Spring eye mounting bracket
3	Rebound rubber	6	Rear axle

7.1.   Removal and Installation of a Rear Spring

It should be noted that rear springs must be set to a certain height after installation. The necessary operations must therefore be followed.

- Remove the spare wheel to improve the access.
- Slacken the wheel bolts and jack up the rear end of the vehicle. Place chassis stands underneath the sides of the body.
- On the side where the spring is to be removed, place the jack underneath the axle tube and lift the axle until just under tension.
- Remove the nuts shown in Fig. 7.3 from the spring "U" bolts and carefully drive out the bolts towards the top. Take care not to damage the threads. To prevent thread damage, tap each side of the bolts alternatively until the "U" bolt is free. Remove the second "U" bolt in the same manner.
- At the rear of the spring unscrew the two nuts securing the spring shackle, at the front of the spring remove the nut at the inside of the spring pin. Do not remove the bolts at this stage.
- Remove the lower shock absorber mounting below the rear axle.
- Lower the rear axle a few inches on the jack and drive out the spring pin at the front.   Take care that no part of the rear axle is under tension during this operation (for example break the brake hose).
- At the rear of the spring take off the spring shackle plate and drive out the two mounting bolts. The spring can drop during the operation and care must be taken to keep it "balanced". The spring can now be removed.

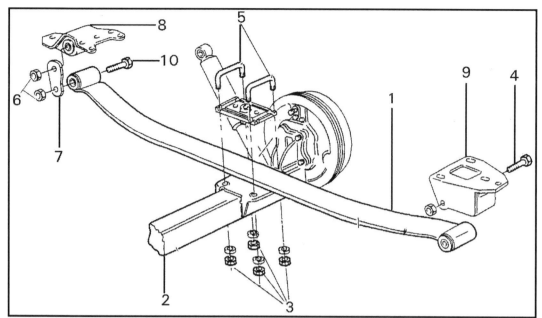

Fig. 7.3 – Details for the removal and installation of the rear springs (except 4 x 4).

1 Leaf spring	4 Spring pin	7 Spring shackle mounting bracket
2 "Rear axle tube	5 "U" Bolts	8 Spring shackle bolt
3 "U" bolt nuts	6 Nuts	9 Mounting bracket
		10 Rear spring bolt

The installation of the rear spring is carried out in reverse order. The self-locking nuts must be replaced. The spring must be set to a specific height. The mountings of the spring at the front and the rear and the shock absorber bolt must be tightened when the correct installation height has been obtained.

- Lift the spring into the correct position and fit the spring pin at the front of the spring and the bolt into the spring shackle at the rear end. Fit the nuts, but do not tighten them (only hand-tight).

- Lift the axle on the jack until it rests against the spring. The centre bolt in the spring must engage into the hole in the axle pad.

Drive the "U" bolts from the top into the axle. If they cannot be inserted with a slight tap, check them for distortion. Distorted bolts can be straightened in a vice. Place a piece of tube over the legs of the bolt and bend them inwards or outwards as applicable. Screw on the nuts and tighten them evenly to 13 kgm (94 ft.lb.).

- Connect the shock absorber at the bottom of the axle.

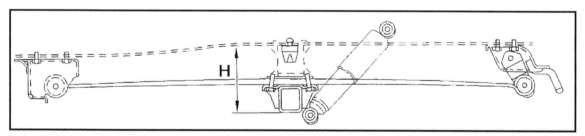

Fig. 7.4. – Measure the height "H" before tightening the rear spring and shock absorber bolts are tightened. Either lift the axle or place weights in the cargo room, depending which operations are being carried out.

The axle must now be lifted to bring it to the correct position in relation to the spring. To do this, lift the axle until dimension "H" in Fig. 7.4 is 192 mm in the case of models 10Q and 14Q or 297 mm in the case of model 18Q. A metric ruler should be used for the check.

Rear Axle and Rear Suspension

- Leave the axle and spring in this position and tighten the bolts (1) and (3) in Fig. 7.3 with 15.5 kgm (112 ft.lb.). Tighten the shock absorber bolt to 16 kgm (115 ft.lb.).
- Refit the wheel, lower the vehicle to the ground and tighten the wheel bolts to the specified torque.

7.2. Removal and Installation of the Rear Axle

- Slacken the wheel bolts, jack up the rear of the vehicle and place chassis stands underneath the sides of the body. The axle is removed without rear wheels.
- Follow the routing of the brake pipes and separate the connections between the brake pipe and the brake hose on the frame. First unscrew the union nut and pull out the pipe end. Immediately protect the open end in a suitable manner (sticky tape). Knock out the spring plate and remove the hose fitting out of the metal bracket. Again protect the open hose end by closing it off. Fig. 7.5 shows the brake hose/pipe connection.

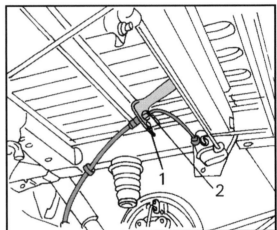

Fig. 7.5 – Separate the brake hose/brake pipe connections at (2) and drive out the spring plate (1).

- If ABS is fitted, separate the hydraulic pipe connections, drive out the clips securing the brake hose, disconnect the plugs for the wheel speed sensors on the cable harness and free the cable harness from its attachment on the body. Plug open connections to prevent the entry of dirt.
- Remove the nut from the end of the handbrake cable on the brake compensation lever and disengage the cable end. The outer sleeves of the handbrake cables must be detached from the bracket on the frame and pulled out.
- Remove the spring clip from the brake pressure regulator linkage and disengage the linkage. Push the linkage to one side where it cannot be in the way.
- Place a jack underneath the centre of the rear axle and lift the axle until the shock absorbers are compressed. Remove the upper and lower shock absorber mountings and lift out the two units. Another possibility is to remove the shockers from their upper mountings and leave them attached at the bottom.
- Check that the axle is securely supported on the jack and remove the bolts securing the spring pin bracket at the front of the spring and the bolts securing the spring shackle to the chassis frame at the rear. 12 bolts must be removed in total. There is no need to remove the nuts securing the spring pins and the spring shackle plates. The spring eyebolts at the front can, however, are slackened if it is intended to remove them later on.
- Undo the exhaust system mounting to make sure it cannot be in the way during the removal of the axle.
- Lower the rear axle on the jack until it can be removed towards the rear. A helper should steady the axle on the jack. Make sure that none of the removed items can get caught in the axle.

The installation of the rear axle is made easier when the spring pin and the shackle plate nuts are slackened before the axle is lifted in position.

- Roll the axle underneath the vehicle and lift it in position until the rear mounting bracket is snug against the mounting face on the chassis. Fit the mounting bolts without tightening them fully.
- The mounting bracket must now be centred. The workshop used special centering pins, which are inserted, into one of the mounting holes. As these will not be available, insert a drift of suitable diameter. Fit the bracket securing bolts and tighten them to 14 kgm (101 ft.lb.).
- Lift the axle further, as required, until the front spring mounting bracket is against the chassis. Fit the bolts without tightening them fully. Check that all bolts are situated in the centre of the elongated holes and then tighten them to 14 kgm (101 ft.lb.).
- Re-connect the shock absorbers without tightening the bolts and nuts.
- Insert the brake hose through the hole in the bracket and secure it with the spring plate. Re-connect the brake pipe to the brake hose and tighten the union nut. Take care not to twist the hose. Also connect the linkage for the brake pressure regulator and the handbrake cable.
- The rear suspension must now be loaded down as specified during the installation of the rear springs in Section 7.1. Important is dimension "H" in Fig. 7.4.
- Tighten the spring shackle and the spring eye pin to 15.5 kgm (112 ft.lb.) and the shock absorber mounting nuts to 16 kgm (115 ft.lb.).
- Finally adjust the handbrake and bleed the brake system as described in section "Brakes".

Fig. 7.6 – The shock absorber mounting at the lower end.

7.3   Dampers – Removal and Installation

- Place the rear of the vehicle on chassis stands and place the jack underneath the centre of the rear axle. Lift the axle until the shock absorbers are compressed, i.e. they are no longer under tension from the springs.

Remove the shock absorber mountings at the top and at the bottom and remove the shock absorber. Figs. 7.6 and 7.7 show the attachment of a shock absorber.

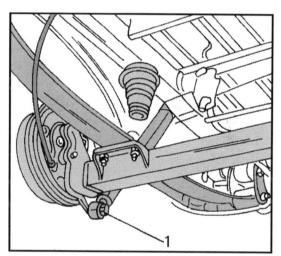

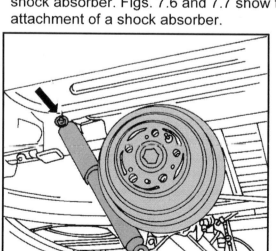

Fig. 7.7 -   The shock absorber mounting at the upper end.

A shock absorber can be tested as follows:

- Clamp the unit in upright position into a vice and slowly pump it up and down. The resistance must be even through the travel. "Dead" play indicates a faulty shock absorber, which must be replaced.
- Make sure that the shock absorber is the correct one for the vehicle in question, i.e. model year, carrying capacity, etc.

Rear Axle and Rear Suspension

The installation is a reversal of the removal procedure, but the vehicle must be weighted down as described during the replacement of the rear springs, i.e. the dimension "H" in Fig. 7.4 must be set to the specific value. In this case this can be obtained by placing weights in the cargo room of the vehicle, when the vehicle is resting on its wheels. Tighten both mountings to 16 kgm (115 ft.lb.).

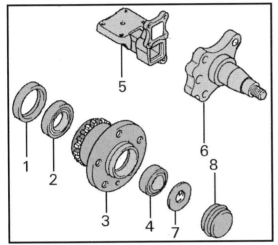

Fig. 7.8 – Rear wheel hub and wheel bearing.

1	Oil seal
2	Inner wheel bearing
3	Wheel hub and toothed rotor (ABS)
4	Outer wheel bearing
5	Rear axle housing
6	Axle stump
7	Thrust washer
8	Grease cap

7.4. Rear Hubs and Wheel Bearings

The rear wheel bearings must be adjusted after the brake drums have been fitted. After the adjustment the nut is peened in position, preventing it from coming loose. Fig. 7.8 shows the component parts of a wheel hub/wheel bearing assembly. The wheel hub shown is for a vehicle with ABS (toothed rotor fitted to the wheel hub).

A wheel hub is removed as follows:

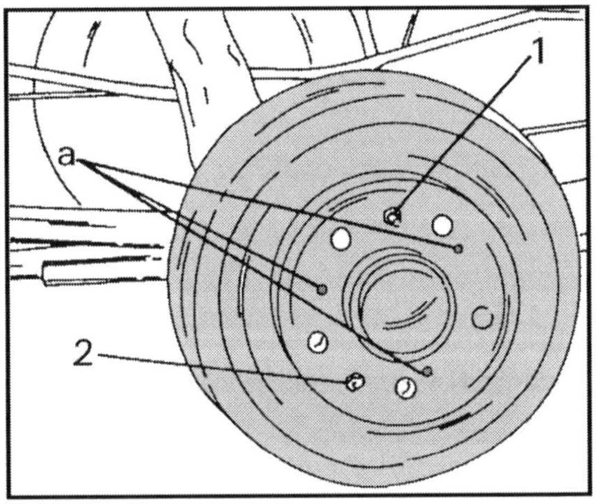

Fig. 7.9 – When removing a brake drum, unscrew the guide pin (1) and the screw (2). Screw three screws into the threaded holes "a" to remove a tight drum.

- Slacken the wheel bolts, place the rear end of the vehicle on chassis stands and unscrew the wheel or wheels.
- Unscrew the guide pin for the wheel (1) and the screw (2) in Fig. 7.9 and remove the brake drum. The brake drum will be very tight and you will need three M20 x 1.25 bolts to withdraw it. Screw the bolts into the threaded bores "a" and tighten them alternatively until the drum can be taken off.
- Remove the hub grease cap with a small chisel. We must warn you that the cap may be damaged.
- Find the peening of the wheel bearing nut (2 places) and knock it back. The wheel bearing nut must now be slackened and removed. Remove the thrust washer underneath the nut. 7.10 shows the operation at this stage.
- If the axle stump must be removed, remove the bolts (2) in Fig. 7.11. The axle stump (1) can now be removed.
- From the inside of the wheel hub remove the wheel bearing. The outer bearing race is driven out of the wheel hub, if the bearing is to be replaced.
- Thoroughly clean all bearing parts. If the bearing requires replacement, dismantle the wheel hub as described above.

Assemble and refit a wheel hub as follows:
- Fill the inside of the wheel hub with heat-resisting grease (wheel bearing grease).

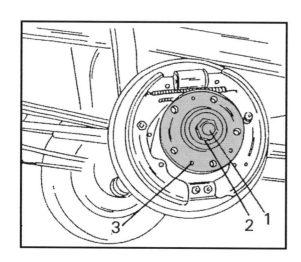

Fig. 7.10 – View of the fitted wheel hub.
1   Wheel bearing nut
2   Thrust washer
3   Wheel hub

- Drive the two outer wheel bearing races from opposite sides into the wheel hub. Use a good drift to avoid damage.

- Insert the inner wheel bearing cage and fit a new oil seal.

- If the axle stump has been removed, refit it with new bolts. The bolts are tightened to 15 kgm (108 ft.lb.).

Fig. 7.11 – View of the rear axle without brake drum. The axle stump (1) is secured with bolts (2).

- Slide the wheel hub over the axle stump and drive it in position, using a soft-metal hammer or plastic mallet. Grease the outer bearing cage, insert it into the wheel hub and place the washer in position. Fit a new wheel bearing nut and tighten it finger-tight.

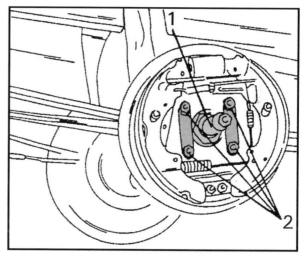

The wheel bearing must now be adjusted. Important is the bearing clearance of 0.025 – 0.10 mm. Proceed as follows:

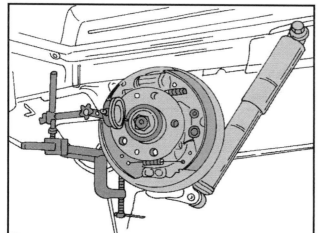

Fig. 7.12 – Checking the bearing clearance.

- Tighten the wheel bearing nut to 2.0 kgm (14.5 ft.lb.). Rotate the brake drum during the tightening process to settle the wheel bearings in their races.

- Completely slacken the nut and then re-tighten it again to 2.0 kgm.

- Fit a dial gauge as shown in Fig. 7.12, with the stylus resting on the outside of the wheel hub flange. Push the wheel hub fully in and set the dial gauge to "Zero". Pull the hub outwards and read off the indication on the gauge. The result is the end float of the wheel hub.

- If the clearance is not within the values given above, slacken or tighten the nut.

- In the final position peen the wheel bearing nut into the axle stump to secure it. Do not split the metal of the nut collar.

- Remove the dial gauge.

- Fit the brake drum and tighten it in position by means of the guide pin and the two securing screws (see Fig. 7.9).

Rear Axle and Rear Suspension

• Fit the hub grease cap and the wheel and lower the vehicle to the ground. Tighten the wheel bolts.

7.5. Rear Drive Shafts (4WD)

The rear drive shafts have a tri-axe joint on the axle side and a constant velocity joint on the wheel side. Both shafts are of the same length. The arrangement of the tow shafts is the same as described for the front wheel drive shafts.

7.6. Rear Axle (with 4WD)

The rear axle of a vehicle with four-wheel drive is secured by means of two rubber-metal bearings to a bracket on the body and two rubber-metal bearings to the sub/frame. The front end of the axle drive is connected to the propeller shaft. Fig. 7.13 shows a sectional view of the axle together with the location of the mountings.

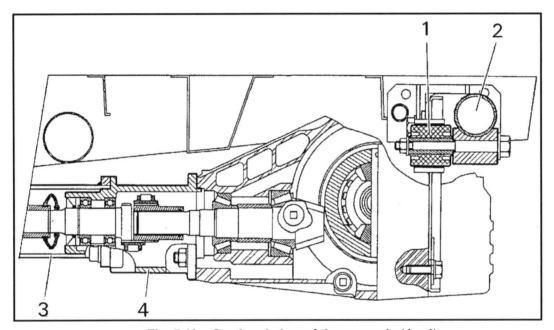

Fig. 7.13 – Sectional view of the rear axle (4 x 4).
1 Rubber/metal bearing on sub/frame
2 Sub/frame
3 Propeller shaft tube
4 Selector housing for 4 x 4

The oil level in the rear axle case should be checked every 6,000 miles. Change the oil every 20,000 miles. The axle oil capacity is 2.3 litres (approx. 4 pints). An oil filler/level plug is inserted into the rear of the rear axle housing. A drain plug is fitted to the bottom of the housing. Warm oil will speed up the draining operation.

Make sure that the sealing washers of the plugs are in good condition before they are fitted.

Further information is given in Chapter 3 in conjunction with the transmission.

7.7. Propeller Shaft (4WD)

The propeller shaft consists of two parts. The front part is fitted with a universal joint and a sliding joint which is inserted into the rear of the transmission to compensate for to and fro movements of the power unit. The rear propeller shaft consists of a shaft which rotates inside a tube.

Depending on the version, one or two intermediate bearings are fitted (vehicles with short or long wheelbase). The drive is transmitted to the propeller shaft when the four-wheel drive is engaged.

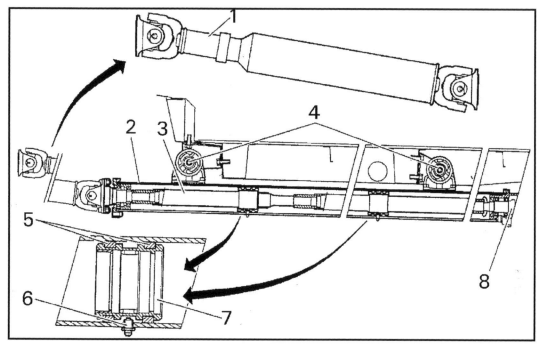

Fig. 7.14 – Arrangement of the propeller shaft (4 x 4). The arrows show the location of the grease nipple.

1	Propeller shaft
2	Propeller shaft tube
3	Propeller shaft with 3 intermediate bearings (long wheelbase)
4	Intermediate bearing (long wheelbase)
5	Rubber bearing mounting
6	Grease nipple
7	Mounting bearing
8	Splined end

Fig. 7.14 shows details of the propeller shaft mounting. Removal and installation can be carried out by referring to the illustration. It will be noted that the universal joints of the shaft and the sliding joint have grease nipples (depending on the length of the shaft one or two nipples in the joints). The nipples should be filled every 6,000 miles with a suitable grease (grease gun).

7.8.   Rear Axle – Tightening Torques

Shock absorber mountings..16.0 kgm (115 ft.lb.)
Rear spring mounting, front and rear..15.5 kgm (112 ft.lb.)
Spring "U" bolt nuts...13.0 kgm (94 ft.lb.)
Spring hanger brackets to chassis...14.0 kgm (101 ft.lb.)
Spring shackle mounting to spring and chassis..............................15.5 kgm (112 ft. lb.)
Rear axle shaft stump to axle...15.0 kgm (108 ft.lb.)
Rear hub nut..2.0 kgm, then adjust and lock
Wheel Bolts:
- Models 10Q and 14Q...16.0 kgm (115 ft.lb.)
- Model 18Q..18.0 kgm (120 ft.lb.)

8. BRAKE SYSTEM

8.0. Technical Data

Type fitted	Dual-circuit system. System without ABS diagonally split, system with ABS split front/rear circuit. With load-sensitive brake pressure regulator, brake servo unit. Handbrake acting on rear wheels. ABS fitted as optional extra.

Front Brakes

Type	Lucas (Girling) sliding-type brake callipers with two pistons of different diameters. Calipers different for models 10Q/14Q and 18Q.

Brake discs:
- Models 10Q and 14Q   Solid discs
- Model 18Q   Ventilated discs

Brake Cylinder Diameter:
- Models 10Q and 14Q   40 and 48 mm (1.59 and 1.9 in.)
- Model 18Q   45 and 48 mm (1.79 and 1.9 in.)

Brake Disc Diameter:
- Models 10Q and 14Q   280.0 mm (11.12 in.)
- Model 18Q   300.0 mm (11.92 in.)

Brake Disc Thickness:
- Models 10Q and 14Q   18.0 mm (0.72 in.)
- Model 18Q   24.0 mm (0.95 in.)

Min. permissible Thickness:
- Models 10Q and 14Q   15.9 mm (0.63 in.)
- Model 18Q   21.9 mm (0.87 in.)

Brake pad thickness (all models)	18.2 mm (0.72 in.)
Min. brake pad thickness (without metal plate)	1.0 mm (0.04 in.)
Brake disc run-out	0.15 mm (0.006 in.), measured 2 mm (0.08 in) from the outer edge.

Rear Drum Brakes

Type	With leading and trailing brake shoes, automatic adjustment

Wheel Brake Cylinder Diameter:
- Models 10Q and 14Q, without turbo   25.0 mm (0.99 in.)
- Models 10Q and 14Q, with turbo   27.0 mm (1.07 in.)
- Model 18Q   28.6 mm (1.14 in.)

Brake drum diameter, all models	254.0 mm (10.09 in.)
Max. brake drum diameter, all models	255.6 mm (10.15 in.)
Min. Thickness of brake linings	1.0 mm (0.04 in.)

Master Brake Cylinder:
- Piston diameter – Models 10Q and 14Q   22.2 mm (0.88 in.)

- Piston diameter – Model 18Q   25.4 mm (1.0 in.)
- from chassis number 15 091 011   23.81 mm (0.95 in.) – only 10Q/14Q

Brake Fluid:
- Type   SAE J1703 Dot 4
- Regular replacement   Every 25,000 miles or 2 years

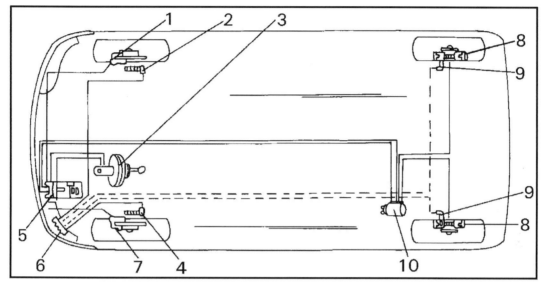

Fig. 8.1 – Layout of the brake system component parts with ABS.

1 R.H. front brake caliper   6 Electronic ABS control unit
2 R.H. front wheel speed sensor   7 L.H. front brake caliper
3 Master brake cylinder with brake servo   8 Brake drums
4 L.H. front wheel speed sensor   9 Rear wheel speed sensor
5 ABS hydraulic control unit   10 Brake pressure regulator

8.1.   Short Description

All models covered in this manual have disc brakes at the front. The brakes are made by Girling. Each front disc brake assembly has two pistons of different diameter, supplied independently by separate circuits. Sliding callipers are employed, i.e. the pressure is applied to the pistons on one side and the complete brake calliper is moved sideways on slide bolts to press the brake pad on the opposite side against the brake disc. Different calipers are fitted to models 10Q/14Q and 18Q. The smaller of the two pistons has a larger diameter on the 18Q model. Also note the different disc diameters and disc thicknesses.

The tandem master cylinder works on the dual-line principle, but there are differences. On models without ABS the system is diagonally split. The rear circuit of the cylinder supplies the upper piston of each front caliper and the rear brakes. The front circuit of the cylinder supplies the lower pistons of each calliper. The front and rear circuit are split if ABS is fitted, i.e. one circuit supplies the front brakes and the other one the rear brakes. Fig. 8.1 shows the layout of a circuit with ABS. The circuit without ABS looks similar, with the difference that the parts belonging to the ABS system are not shown.

Not all models have the same master cylinder, differing in the diameter. If a cylinder must be changed, make sure the correct part is fitted.

A brake servo unit is fitted, the vacuum being supplied by a separate vacuum pump, driven by the engine camshaft. A brake pressure regulator regulates the brake pressure to the rear wheels.

The handbrake operates the rear wheels. The rear wheels should be locked when the handbrake lever is pulled 4 to 5 notches.

8.2.   Front Disc Brakes

8.2.0.   REPLACING THE BRAKE PADS

To check the remaining thickness of the brake pad material, remove the front wheels and check the two brake pads through the inspection 'window'. Always check on both sides, as uneven wear is possible. If this is the case, check the brake caliper on the side with the increased wear thoroughly, as the calliper could be sticking. If the thickness is less than 4 mm, replace the brake pads.

If the brake pads are removed for other reasons than replacement, mark each pad as you take it out, i.e. L.H. and R.H. side and inner and outer pad. Incorrect fitting could lead to brake pull to one side.

Replace the brake pads as follows:

*   Slacken the wheel bolts on both sides, jack up the front end of the vehicle and place chassis stands underneath the sides of the body. The suspension must be allowed to hang down under its own weight.

*   Disconnect the cables from the pad wear indicator on the side of the spring strut/brake calliper.

    Grip the brake caliper and with a sharp pull move it towards the outside. This will force the piston back into their bores. Care must be taken when the fluid reservoir is fairly full, as it can overflow. Check and if necessary draw off some fluid.

Fig. 8.2 – Removal of a brake caliper. When removing the slide bolts (1), counterhold the hexagon at the inside (2) with an open-ended spanner. It may be possible to ground down the spanner to insert it as shown.

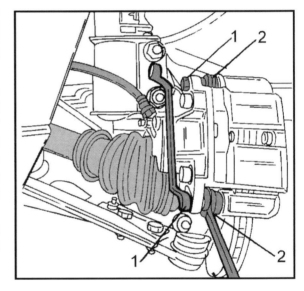

*   Using a ring spanner and an open-ended spanner as shown in Fig. 8.2 then unscrew the slide bolts. The lower bolt is removed, the upper bolt is slackened. The two bolts are self-locking and must be replaced. In emergency it is, however, possible to use "Loctite" during installation.

*   Swing the calliper towards the top, as shown in Fig. 8.3 and remove the inner and outer brake pads.

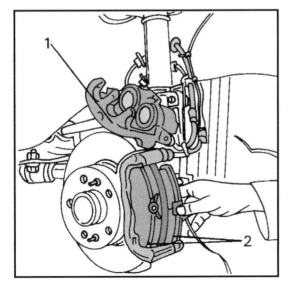

Fig. 8.3 - Removal of a brake caliper. The caliper (1) is moved upwards and tied up. The brake pads (2) can be removed from both sides of the brake disc.

Fig. 8.4 shows a detailed view of the removed brake calliper together with the brake pads.

Important: The brake pedal must not be depressed after the brake pads have been removed.

Clean the inside of the brake calliper opening with a stiff brush to remove brake dust. The pistons must now be pressed into their bores, if they appear to be protruding above the calliper bore. Use a hammer handle, but have a helper observing the fluid level in the reservoir, as the fluid will rise, as the pistons are pushed in. If necessary, remove some fluid out of the reservoir or open the bleed screw whilst the first piston is pushed in. Careful handling will not allow air into the system – otherwise the brake system must be bled of air.

If the sealing rubbers for the slide bolts are in bad condition, unscrew the guide bolt. Clean the bolt and refit it with the new rubber part. The guide bolt is fitted with rubber grease.

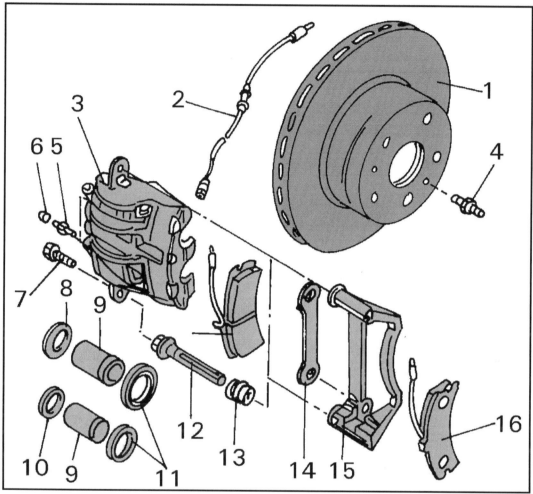

Fig. 8.4 – Exploded view of a brake caliper with two pistons (without ABS).

1 Ventilated disc
2 Brake pad wear indicator cable
3 Brake caliper cylinder
4 Brake disc screw
5 Bleed screw
6 Rubber dust cap
7 Guide bolt, 2.7 kgm
8 Cylinder seal, upper piston
9 Brake cylinder piston
10 Cylinder seal, lower piston
11 Rubber dust seal
12 Slide bolt
13 Rubber grommet
14 Plate
15 Caliper mounting bracket
16 Brake pad set

The installation of the brake pads follows the description below:

• Insert the inner brake pad (with the cable for the pad wear indicator), making sure that the cable is properly routed. Now fit the outer brake pad.

• Check once more that the brake pads are fitted correctly and swing the caliper over the brake pads. Fit the new bolt at the bottom of the caliper. New bolts are normally included in the brake pad repair kit. *If none is supplied, coat the threads with "Loctite".*

Brake System

Remove the upper slide bolt, coat the threads with "Loctite" and refit it into the caliper.

- Now tighten both bolts to 2.7 kgm (20 ft.lb.). First tighten the lower bolt. Again hold the hexagon at the inside with an open-ended spanner, as shown in Fig. 8.2. Now tighten the upper bolt in the same manner.
- Re-connect the cable for the brake pad wear indicator. Check that the cables cannot touch other parts of the front suspension, when the wheels are turned from lock to lock.
- Operate the foot brake a few times to set the new pads against the brake discs. You will also find out, if the brake system requires bleeding. Pump the pedal with quick strokes. A rising pedal normally indicates air in the system.
- Refit the wheels and lower the vehicle to the ground. Tighten the wheel bolts with the specified torque (depending on the vehicle models).
- Check and if necessary correct the fluid level in the reservoir.

Remember that new brake pads need a while to "bed" in, before the brakes obtain the full performance. Treat the brakes with care when you first drive off.

8.2.1.   BRAKE CALIPER – REMOVAL AND INSTALLATION

The removal and installation of a brake caliper follows in general the description above. The brake caliper cylinder can then be unscrewed from the suspension steering knuckle (the two outer bolts in Fig. 8.5) or is free after both slide bolts are removed. The parts shown in Fig. 8.4 will now be free.

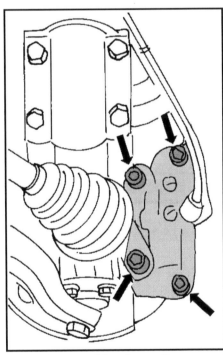

Fig. 8.5 – Attachment of a brake caliper on the steering knuckle. The bolts on the right show the location of the slide bolts, the bolts on the left are the bolts for the mounting bracket.

As two brake hoses are fitted, separate the connection between the hoses and the pipes, i.e. it is not possible to remove the brake caliper and then the brake hose. Brake pipes/brake hoses are connected with union nuts and spring plates. Close the ends of the brake pipes in suitable manner to prevent entry of dirt.

If the brake caliper mounting bracket is to be removed, unscrew the two inner bolts in Fig. 8.5. Below the mounting frame is a washer, which must not be omitted during installation.

Note the following during installation, also assuming that the mounting bracket has been removed:

- Fit the brake hoses to the caliper body and tighten them to 1.3 kgm (11 ft.lb.).
- Thoroughly clean the mounting face of the caliper and steering knuckle, coat the caliper bolts with "Loctite", fit the mounting bracket in position and fit the bolts. Tighten the bolts in several stages to a torque of 21 kgm (151 ft.lb.).
- Fit the brake pads as already described.
- Insert the brake hoses into the bracket and secure with the spring plates. Fit the brake pipes and tighten the union nuts. Move the wheels from one lock to the other and check that the brake hoses cannot rub against other parts of the front suspension. If necessary, slacken the union nuts and rotate the hose(s) accordingly.

- Finally bleed the brake system as described later on. Operate the foot brake a few times before driving off.

8.2.2. BRAKE CALIPER OVERHAUL

Note the following general rules when overhauling brake calipers or for that matter any other hydraulic part:

- The work must be carried out on a clean workbench.
- All rubber cups and seals must be replaced if the part has been dismantled, even if rubber parts still look useable, replace them. Before dismantling a caliper, make sure that repair kits are available.
- Never refit a piston or caliper if corrosion or other blemishes can be found. Always replace the part in question. Only use alcohol, white spirit or brake fluid to clean parts. Even a small amount of petrol can damage the rubber parts sooner or later. Any marks left by the use of white spirits can be cleaned-off with a lint-free cloth.

Fig. 8.6 - Removal of a piston. A wooden block is placed underneath the piston.

A caliper can be dismantled as follows:

- Unscrew the two brake hoses from the caliper and remove the two bleeder screws.
- Remove the dust seal(s) from the piston bores.
- The pistons are blown out. Place a piece of hardwood into the caliper opening to allow the piston to "hit" the wood and not the metal (see Fig. 8.6). Remember that you have two pistons, i.e. it may be necessary to deal with one piston at the time. Keep the fingers away from the area of the

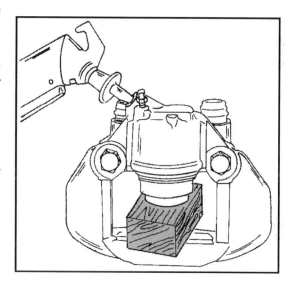

piston opening when the piston is ejected. You may be able to carry out the operation at a petrol station.

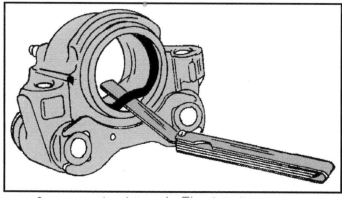

Fig. 8.7 – Removal of a cylinder sealing ring.

- From the inside of the cylinder bore remove the cylinder sealing ring(s) with a blunt, pointed instruments, as for example shown in Fig. 8.7. Do not damage the bore(s).
- Clean all parts in clean brake fluid or alcohol. All parts in the repair kit must be used, i.e. do not use any of the old parts.
- Coat the cylinder seal(s) with clean brake fluid and insert them into the grooves(s), using the fingers only.
- Fit the dust seals to the pistons and slowly insert the piston into the caliper bore. Insert the seal lip into the cylinder grove and push the piston fully in. Check that the dust seals are correctly fitted.

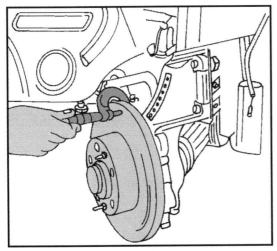

Fig. 8.8 – Measuring the thickness of a brake disc with a micrometer.

8.2.3. BRAKE DISCS

Brake discs must be replaced, if the friction faces show grooves or other damage. Grooves can develop if the brake pads have been allowed to wear down to the metal plates. Measure the thickness of the brake discs with a micrometer, as shown in Fig. 8.8 and compare the results with the dimensions given in Section 1.8.0. If in doubt, you may be able to get information for your particular vehicle from your dealer.

If the discs show slight wear, you may have them re-ground.

Remove brake discs as follows:

• Slacken the wheel bolts, place the front end of the vehicle on chassis stands and remove the wheel.

• Remove the brake pads as described and remove the brake caliper completely. Also remove the caliper mounting bracket. Tie the complete assembly with a piece of wire to the front suspension.

Fig. 8.9 – Brake discs are secured with guide studs at the positions shown. Rear brake drums are secured in a similar manner.

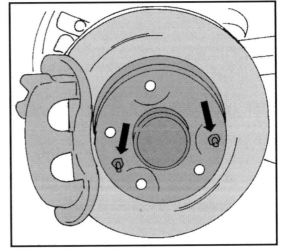

• Remove the two guide bolts from the outside of the wheel hub, shown in Fig. 8.9. The brake disc has a tight fit on the hub. M10 x 1.25 bolts can be screwed into the threaded bores and used as extractor bolts to pull off the disc. Sometimes it is enough to knock off the disc with a rubber mallet.

• During installation fit the disc over the hub and tap it in position with a rubber or plastic mallet. Fit the guide bolts and tighten them alternatively to 1.0 kgm (7.2 ft.lb.).

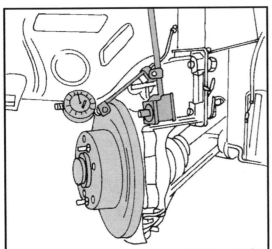

Fig. 8.10 – Checking a disc brake for run-out.

• Arrange a dial gauge with a suitable holder as shown in Fig. 8.10 and apply the stylus approx. 2mm from the outer edge of the disc. Slowly rotate the wheel hub/disc and observe the dial gauge reading. The highest run-out 0.15 mm (0.006 in.). Higher readings can be due to dirt between disc and hub. In this case remove the disc once more and check the surfaces.

• Refit the brake calliper assembly, noting the tightening torque for the mounting bracket and the caliper slide bolts. Fit the wheel, lower the vehicle to the ground and tighten the wheel bolts.

8.3. Rear Brakes

8.3.0. BRAKE DRUMS – REMOVAL AND INSTALLATION

Normally the brake drums can be removed after removal of two guide bolts, similar as shown in Fig. 8.9 on the example of the brake discs. Sometimes it is, however, necessary to pull off the drums. To do this, screw three M10 x 1.25 bolts into the holes shown in Fig. 8.11. By tightening the three bolts alternatively, the drum will slowly come off. If a sticking drum is experienced, release the handbrake and insert a screwdriver into the hole "a" in Fig. 8.11. The screwdriver will push against the adjuster lever of the automatic shoe adjustment, and disengages a pin from the brake shoe. The brake drum will now come off as described.

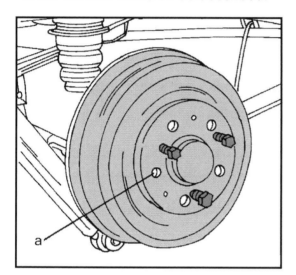

Fig. 8.11 – Three bolts can be used to withdraw the brake drum as described. Insert a screwdriver into the bore "a" to release the automatic adjustment lever.

8.3.1. REPLACING THE BRAKE SHOES

All models have the same rear brakes. After removal of the brake drum, make a sketch of the fitted shoe return springs to facilitate the installation. Specially note which way the spring hooks are inserted.

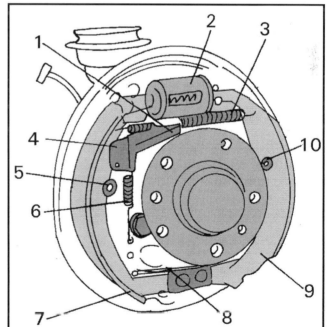

Fig. 8.12 – View of a rear brake assembly.
1   Adjuster strut
2   Wheel brake cylinder
3   Upper return spring
4   Adjuster lever
5   Brake shoe hold-down pin
6   Lever return spring
7   Brake shoe
8   Lower return spring
9   Brake shoe
10 Brake shoe hold-down pin

Brake shoes must only be replaced in sets. Never fit brake shoes of different manufacturers or with different lining materials. When we are talking brakes, we are talking original spare parts from the manufacturer. Fig. 8.12 shows a view of a brake assembly after the drum has been removed. Fig. 8.13 shows an exploded view of the brake assembly which will help during removal and installation of the brake shoes.

• Disengage the return spring (6) with a pair of pliers and remove the adjuster mechanism (4).

• The upper return spring (3) and the lower return spring (8) must be removed with a pair of pliers or use a screwdriver and carefully lift the spring hooks out of their anchorage. The thrust piece, i.e. the strut for the self-adjusting mechanism of the brake shoes, in the centre can be released and can be taken out.

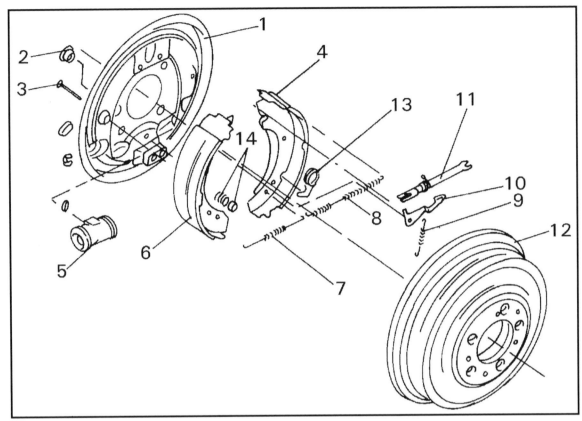

Fig. 8.13 – Exploded view of a rear brake assembly.

1 Brake back plate	8 Upper shoe return spring
2 Closing plug	9 Adjusting lever return spring
3 Brake shoe hold-down pin	10 Adjusting lever
4 Brake shoe	11 Adjuster strut with wheel
5 Wheel brake cylinder	12 Brake drum
6 Brake shoe	13 Adjuster pawl
7 Lower shoe return spring	14 Spring and spring seat

- Remove the brake shoe hold-down pins. Normally a special tool is now required, but a pair of pliers is suitable. Push with a finger from the rear of the brake back plate against the hold-down pin (10) and rotate the spring seat on the outside with a pair of pliers (1/4 of a turn) until the end of the pin can be guided through the slot in the spring seat. Remove the spring seat and the spring and withdraw the pin from the rear. Carry out the same operations on the other side of the vehicle.

- Lift the bottom end of the two brake shoes (7) and (9) off the brake back plate. Remove the return spring if still engaged in one of the shoes.

- Pull the two brake shoes at the upper ends apart and carefully disengage them from the wheel cylinder pistons. Place an elastic band around the wheel cylinder to keep the pistons in place. Otherwise the wheel cylinder can be removed.

- Lift off the brake shoes and disengage the handbrake cable. To do this, compress the spring and disconnect the cable end as soon it is possible.

Thoroughly clean all parts, including the back plate. If petrol is used, make sure it cannot come near the wheel brake cylinder (if still fitted). The brake shoe linings can have a minimum thickness of 1.0 mm above the rivet heads, but if the thickness has worn down to 2.0 mm, we recommend to have the brake shoes replaced, to avoid the same work within a short time. Leaking wheel brake cylinders should be replaced.

8.3.2. INSTALLATION OF BRAKE SHOES

Place the brake shoes and other parts onto a bench as shown in Fig. 8.14 before commencing the installation.

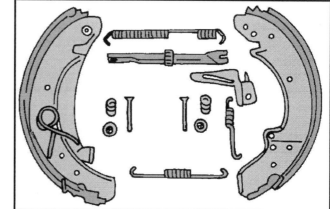

Fig. 8.14 – Arrange the rear brake parts on a bench as shown before installation.

- Refit the wheel brake cylinder to the brake back plate and connect the brake pipe at the rear (if removed).

- Fit the brake shoes to the brake back plate, engaging the handbrake cable with the rear shoe.

- Remove the elastic band from the wheel cylinder (if still fitted) and insert the upper shoe ends into the wheel cylinder pistons, without damaging the rubber caps. Place the lower ends against the abutment at the bottom of the brake back plate.

- Insert the brake shoe hold-down springs from the rear and place the spring and the spring seat over the pin from the front. Apply pressure to the pin from the rear, grip the spring seat with a pair of pliers and push it over the pin. As soon as the pinhead appears above the spring seat, turn the spring seat to lock the pin in position. Attach both brake shoes in the same manner.

- Insert the strut between the two brake shoes, but note that the strut with the R.H. thread is fitted to the L.H. brake assembly.

- Fit the upper and lower brake shoe springs between the brake shoes. First engage the spring hook on one side and then stretch the spring with a pair of pliers, until the other end of the spring can be engaged. Make sure the spring hooks are engaged as before dismantling.

- The next operation is carried out by referring to Fig. 8.15. Engage the spring (3) with the brake shoe and the other end with the adjuster lever (1).

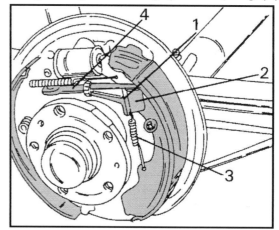

Fig. 8.15 – Details for the installation of the brake shoes.
1   Adjuster lever anchorage
2   Adjuster lever
3   Return spring
4   Adjuster strut with wheel

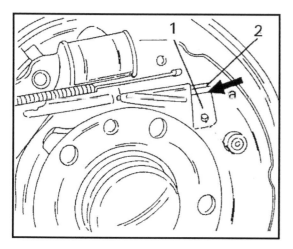

Fig. 8.16 – When fitting the adjuster lever (1) insert it at "a" underneath the strut (2).

- Fit the adjuster lever (1). Fig. 8.16 shows more details of the installation. The end "a" of the lever must be placed under the link (2) and above the pin (3).

- Centre the brake shoes on the brake back plate. Have a last look at the fitted brake shoes by comparing the assembly with Fig. 8.17, to make sure that all parts have been fitted correctly.
- Fit the brake drum and fit the two guide bolts (1.0 kgm/7.2 ft.lb.).
- Operate the hand brake and the foot brake a few times to set the self-adjusting mechanism into operation. This will also centre the brake shoes inside the drums.

Fig. 8.17 – Before fitting the brake drums compare the fitted brake shoes with the illustration.

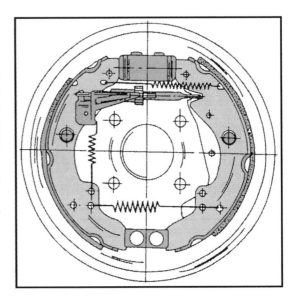

- If the wheel cylinder has been removed, i.e. the brake pipe disconnected, bleed the brake system as described later on. Remember that each front caliper has two bleed screws (except models with ABS).
- Refit the wheels and lower the vehicle to the ground. Tighten the wheel bolts. Treat the brakes with the necessary care for the first few miles.

8.3.3.   WHEEL BRAKE CYLINDERS

Wheel cylinders should not be overhauled. In case of failure, fit a new cylinder. (**Attention:** Different diameters). To remove a cylinder, remove the brake shoes as described above, disconnect the brake pipe at the rear of the back plate (union nut) and unscrew the cylinder securing bolts. A cylinder can also be removed with the brake shoes in position after unhooking the upper return spring(s) and pushing the brake shoes apart. In this case you will have to be careful when the new cylinder is fitted, to avoid damage to the rubber caps.

Installation is a reversal of the removal procedure. Tighten the cylinder bolts to 2.0 kgm (14.5 ft.lb.) and the pipe union nut to 1.7 kgm (12 ft.lb.).

8.4.   Brake Master Cylinder

Master cylinders of different diameters are used within the model range covered. Always make sure that the correct cylinder for the vehicle in question is fitted.

8.4.0.   REMOVAL AND INSTALLATION

Note: The operation of the brake fluid level warning light can be checked by depressing the fluid reservoir cap. With the ignition switched on, the warning light in the dashboard must be illuminated.

The removal and installation of the cylinder is a fairly easy operation. The cylinder is bolted to the front of the brake servo unit.

- Disconnect the battery earth cable.

Fig. 8.18 – Master brake cylinder and brake servo unit.

1   Clip for reservoir
2   Securing nut for cylinder
3   Master brake cylinder
4   Reservoir
5   Brake servo
6   Vacuum hose

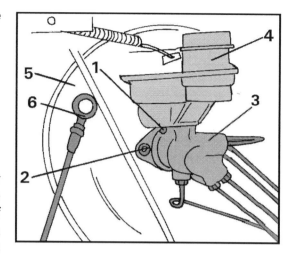

- Remove the connector plug from the brake fluid level warning switch.

- Clean the area around the reservoir cap and the brake fluid pipes. Remove the reservoir cap and remove some of the brake fluid in the reservoir. A syringe can be used. Fig. 8.18 shows the fitted cylinder.

- Remove the securing clip at the bottom of the fluid reservoir and rock the reservoir to and fro until it is free of the rubber grommets in the cylinder. The reservoir is now taken out.

- Remove the brake pipe union nuts, withdraw the pipes and carefully bend the pipes to one side. Note where each pipe is connected and also take care not to spill brake fluid over the painted parts in the engine compartment.

- Remove the two nuts securing the cylinder to the front face of the brake servo unit and carefully lift out the cylinder. Take care not to drip brake fluid on painted surfaces. Hold a rag underneath the cylinder when lifting it out. Fig. 8.19 shows details of the corresponding parts.

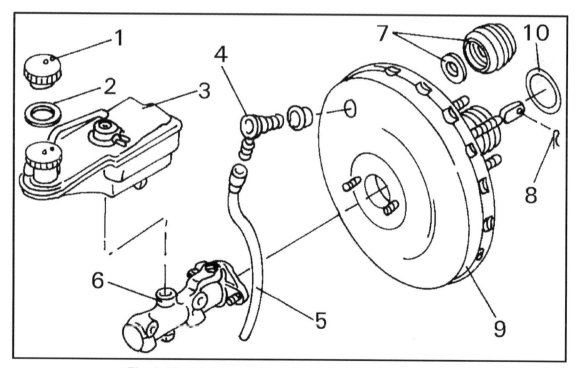

Fig. 8.19 – Master brake cylinder and brake servo unit.

1 Reservoir cap	6 Master brake cylinder
2 Sealing ring	7 Rubber seal with filter
3 Fluid reservoir	8 Clevis pin (clip)
4 Non-return valve	9 Brake servo unit
5 Vacuum hose (to pump)	10 Sealing ring

Brake System

The installation of the cylinder is a reversal of the removal procedure.

The nuts are tightened to 2.0 kgm (14.5 ft.lb.). After installation of the cylinder, push the reservoir with the two connections into the rubber grommets of the cylinder body and secure it in position with the securing clip at the bottom. Make sure the clip is entered properly into its location.

Fill the fluid reservoir with clean brake fluid and bleed the brake system as described later on, noting the differences between vehicles with and without ABS. There are two bleed screws on the hydraulic ABS control unit.

8.4.1.   CYLINDER REPAIRS

Master cylinders can be overhauled, but we recommend to fit a new cylinder, if the original one has developed a fault. Make sure a cylinder with the correct diameter is fitted.

8.5.   Brake Servo Unit

Repair of the brake servo unit should not be attempted. Loss of the brake servo assistance will not influence the operation of the brake system, but you will find that the pedal pressure necessary to brake the vehicle will be substantially higher. Never allow the vehicle to free-wheel downhill with the engine switched off, as the vacuum for the brake servo unit will be used up very soon, leaving you without servo assistance.

Before the brake servo unit is removed, check its operation as follows:

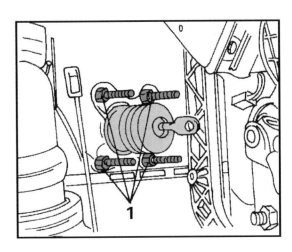

Fig. 8.20 – The nuts (1) secure the brake servo unit to the brake pedal bracket.

Switch off the engine and operate the brake pedal a few times until the vacuum is used up.

* Depress the brake pedal to the floor and start the engine. The pedal

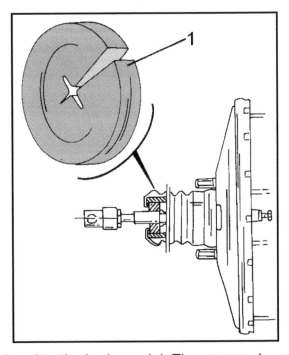

Fig. 8.21 – The filter (1) is located around the push rod in the end of the brake servo unit. Cut the filter as shown to fit a new one.

must "sink" under pressure. If this is not the case, there is a fault in the brake servo system. As a further check make sure that the vacuum hose is connected between the unit and the vacuum pump.

The master cylinder must be removed to gain access to the servo unit. It is also necessary to remove the pedal bracket inside the vehicle. The latter is secured with the four nuts shown in Fig. 8.20.

A clevis pin is used to connect the push rod to the brake pedal. The vacuum hose must be disconnected.

Repairs are restricted to replacing the servo unit filter at the push rod end. To do this, push back the rubber boot, remove the retainer and remove the old filter with a pointed tool. The new filter must be cut with a pair of scissors from the outside towards the inside and then pushed over the push rod. Fig. 8.21 demonstrated the operation.

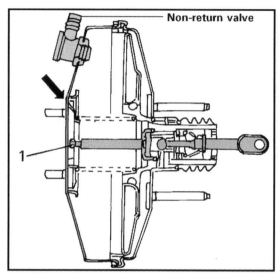

Fig. 8.22 – Adjusting the brake servo unit push rod. Measure from the end face (arrow) to the tip of the push rod (1).

The check valve, i.e. non-return valve can also be replaced. The location of the valve can be seen in Fig. 8.22. The valve is pushed into the servo unit and can be pulled out after disconnecting the vacuum hose. Check the condition of the rubber grommet, before the new valve is fitted.

If a new brake servo unit is fitted, adjust the length of the push rod. The end of the push rod must be below the end face of the servo unit. The end of the push rod tip must be 0.1 to 0.3 mm below the end face, a very small clearance, but important for the correct operation of brake servo unit and master brake cylinder. Check by placing a steel ruler over the end face and measuring the clearance between end face and push rod tip. To adjust, slacken the locknut, rotate the push rod and re-tighten the locknut.

The securing nuts in Fig. 8.20 are tightened to 2.0 kgm (14.5 ft.lb.).

8.6. Bleeding the Brake System

Bleeding of the brake system is required, when the circuit has been opened or air has entered into the system, for example, if the fluid level in the reservoir has dropped too far. Before bleeding the system, clean the area around the reservoir filler cap and around the bleeding screws.

If only one wheel brake cylinder or one brake calliper has been disconnected, it may be sufficient to bleed just the circuit connected to this brake unit, i.e. rear right and front left or rear left and front right, or the front axle and the rear axle, depending on the design of the brake circuit. Start the bleeding operation at the rear brakes and then the front brakes, if no ABS is fitted. The upper bleed screw of the front brakes is bled first. If ABS is fitted, proceed in the order rear right, front left, rear left and front right. You will need a helper, as the fluid level in the reservoir must be continuously observed, as it must not drop below the minimum level and of course, to operate the brake pedal.

Important Note: Vehicles with ABS have two bleeding screws in the hydraulic control unit. These must be bled first. We must stress that you will need some experience with the bleeding of brake system to undertake the operations on such a vehicle.

Two bleed screws are fitted to the front brake calipers on vehicles without ABS. Vehicles with ABS only have one bleed screw.

Proceed as follows:

• Remove the rubber dust cap from the bleed screw and push a transparent bleeder hose over the bleed screw. Bleeder hoses are available from accessory shops. Hold the other end of the hose into a glass jar, filled with some brake fluid. Make sure that the bleeder hose remains at all times below the level of the brake fluid.

- Ask the helper to operate the brake pedal with slow strokes and to signal you, when the pedal is contacting the floor. Open the bleeder screw by half a turn. Fluid will run through the hose and into the jar. Close the bleed screw.
- Repeat the "pumping" operation and opening and closing of the bleed screw until brake fluid, free of air bubbles, is emerging into the glass jar. Remember to replenish the fluid reservoir in between.
- Repeat the bleeding operation in the given order on the other brake units. Finally top-up the fluid reservoir to the required level. *Brake fluid drained out of the system into the glass jar must, however, not be used to fill the system.*

Final Note: The brake fluid should be changed every two years. Experience has shown that this necessity is normally overlooked. For your own safety, we strongly recommend it. Brake fluid is subject to heat and will deteriorate in service.

8.7.　　　Adjusting the Handbrake

The rear wheels must be locked when the handbrake lever has been pulled by 1 to 5 notches. Place the rear of the vehicle on chassis stands. First rotate the rear wheels to check whether the wheels can rotate freely. The handbrake requires only adjustment when the brake shoes or the handbrake cables have been replaced. If an adjustment is necessary, proceed as follows:

- Pull the handbrake to the third notch and jack up the rear end of the vehicle.
- Tighten the nut in the centre of the handbrake equaliser lever until the rear wheels can just be rotated under a fair effort. Re-tighten the locknut.
- Release the handbrake lever and then pull it once more to the third or fourth notch. Check that the rear wheels can no longer be rotated.
- Fully release the handbrake lever and check that both rear wheels can be rotated freely.
- Lower the vehicle to the ground.

8.8.　　　Brake Pressure Regulator

The brake pressure regulator can only be adjusted with the help of two pressure gauges. Practically every model in the covered range has a different pressure setting, depending on the fitted engine, the wheelbase, the carrying capacity and the type of body. Only your workshop will be able to check and/or adjust the regulator. The brake pressure regulator cannot be repaired and must be replaced if a fault has developed. The adjustment of the regulator takes place on the linkage, by shortening or lengthening it.

As the brake regulator must be adjusted, if it has been replaced, we recommend to entrust the operation to a workshop.

8.9.　　　Vacuum Pump

Details of the vacuum pump have already been given in conjunction with the engine.

8.10.　　　Tightening Torque Values – Brakes

Bleeder screws	0.8 kgm (6 ft.lb.)
Brake pipe union nuts	1.4 kgm (10 ft.lb.)
Front brake disc securing screws	1.0 kgm (7.2 ft.lb.)
Caliper mounting bracket bolts	21 kgm (151 ft.lb.)
Caliper slide (guide) bolts	2.7 kgm (19 ft.lb.)

Rear wheel hub nuts	2.0 kgm (14.5 ft.lb.), adjust and then lock by peening
Front Drive Shaft Nuts:	
- Models 10Q and 14Q	45. 0 kgm (324 ft.lb.)
- Model 18Q	50.0 kgm (360 ft.lb.)
Wheel Bolts:	
- Models 10Q and 14Q	16.0 kgm (115 ft.lb.)
- Model 18Q	18.0 kgm (130 ft.lb.)
Brake pipes, rear wheel cylinder	2.0 kgm (14.5 ft.lb.)
Brake pipes, master brake cylinder	1.5 kgm (10 ft.lb.)
Master cylinder securing nuts	2.0 kgm (14.5 ft.lb.)
Brake servo securing nuts	2.0 kgm (14.5 ft.lb.)

9. ELECTRICAL SYSTEM

9.0. Battery

Voltage ....12 Volts
Polarity: ....Negative earth (ground)
Capacity: ....450 amps
Location .... Engine compartment
State of Charge:
   Fully discharged: .... 1.120, specific gravity
   Fully charged:.. 1.280, specific gravity

9.0.0. BATTERY CARE

The 12 volts battery consists of six cells, made up of positive and negative plates. Surrounded by a sulphuric acid solution. The battery provides the current to start the engine, for the glow plug system, the lighting of the vehicle and other current consumers.

The following maintenance operations should be carried out at regular intervals to extend the life of the battery and to always keep it at its peak performance.

- Check the battery level once a week. If the battery is translucent, the level can be seen through the case. Otherwise the filler plugs will have to be removed for inspection. If the electrolyte is below the separator plates, add distilled water (available from every petrol station). Do not over-fill the battery and wipe away any spilled water before replacing the filler plugs. Tap water must not be used to top-up the battery.

- Some batteries incorporate a battery checker, which enables an easy check of the battery condition. If a green spot can be seen, there is no need for further attention, i.e. the battery is sufficiently charged. If the battery checker turns dark, the battery must be re-charged. If the checker turns a light colour, electrolyte is missing in the battery.

If frequent topping-up is necessary, it may be that the battery is over-charged by the alternator and the latter should be checked accordingly. A cracked battery case can also be the cause.

Electrical System

Fig. 9.1 – A hydrometer will show the spec. gravity of the electrolyte by the position of the float inside the glass tube.

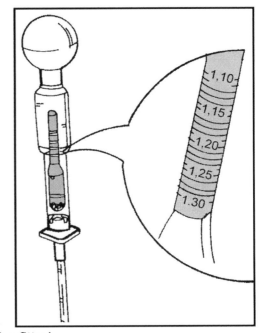

- The battery cables should always be firmly clamped and the battery terminals must be free of corrosion to ensure good electrical conduct. Corroded areas can be cleaned with a soda solution and a wire brush. A thin coating of petroleum jelly should be smeared on battery posts before the cables are re-connected.

- Check the gravity of the electrolyte in each cell, using a hydrometer, as one is shown in Fig. 9.1. This is an indication of the charge condition of the battery. All cells should give the same reading. If there is a great variation in one cell, then either the electrolyte in the cell is weak due to being topped-up with distilled water or that cell is defective. In this case, a new battery must be fitted.

- The battery can be charged with a home-charger, but follow the instructions of the manufacturer to avoid damage to the battery.

- Note that the radio security code must be known and **handy** after the battery is re-connected. All pre-programmed radio stations will also have been lost, after the battery has been re-connected.

9.1.   Alternator

9.1.0.   ROUTINE PRECAUTIONS

The vehicles covered in this manual employ an alternator with an output of either 80 or 120 amps (also 95 amps), depending on the equipment. The alternator can be made by Bosch, Valeo or Mitsubishi. The alternator fitted to the 1.9 litre engine is driven by a belt from the crankshaft pulley, driving at the same time the compressor of an air conditioning system, if one is fitted. The alternator of a 2.5 litre engine is driven together with the steering pump. This equipment contains polarity sensitive components and the precautions below must be observed to avoid damage.

- Check the battery polarity before connecting the terminals. Immediate damage will result to the silicon diodes from a wrong connection - even if only momentarily.

- Never disconnect the battery or alternator terminals **whilst the engine is** running.

- Never allow the alternator to be rotated by the engine unless **ALL** connections are made.

- Disconnect the alternator multi-pin connector **before** using electric welding equipment anywhere on the vehicle.

- Disconnect the battery leads if a rapid battery charger is to **be** used.

- If an auxiliary battery **is** used to start the engine, take care that the polarity is correct. **Do not** disconnect the cables from the vehicle battery.

- When a new alternator is required, fit one as originally found in the vehicle.

9.1.1.   SERVICING

Overhaul and checking of the alternator is best entrusted to a specialist or dealer who will have available the special equipment necessary. It is recommended that the owner should not use test instruments on the unit, unless he or she is familiar with the procedures and precautions necessary. Incorrect applications of meters and test equipment can quite easily cause damage to the diodes.

The alternator bearings are pre-lubricated and require no routine maintenance. The brushes can be inspected after a high mileage has been covered and can be replaced if necessary. It should be noted, however, that the brush life can be expected to be quite long under normal conditions. Again, this is a job for a specialist shop.

9.1.3.   ALTERNATOR MAINTENANCE

Periodically wipe away any dirt or grease which has accumulated on the outside of the alternator. If a water hose is used to clean the outside of the engine, cover the alternator to prevent water from entering. Check the security of the electrical cable connections on the alternator. The tension of the alternator drive belt should be checked at regulator intervals. Refer to Section. 9.1.5.

Take extreme care when connecting the battery leads to the battery – positive to positive and negative to negative.

9.1.4.   REMOVAL AND INSTALLATION

Before removal of the alternator, we must point out that the tension of the drive belt is adjusted by means of a checking instrument for the tension. We recommend that you read Section 9.1.5 before you attempt to remove the alternator.

- Disconnect the battery negative cable, followed by the positive cable.
- Note the location of the battery supply wires and disconnect them from the rear cover.
- Remove the drive belt, following the instructions in Section 9.1.5 and remove the alternator securing bolts. Lift the alternator carefully from the vehicle.

The installation is a reversal of the removal procedure. Fit the drive belt as described in the next section.

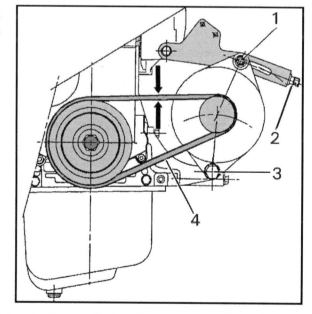

Fig. 9.2 – Alternator drive belt fitted to a 1.9 litre engine. The deflection is measured between the arrows.
1   Adjuster locknut
2   Adjusting bolt
3   Lower alternator bolt
4   Drive belt

9.1.5.   DRIVE BELT

With 1.9 litre engine

Fig. 9.2 shows the routing of the belt, together with the arrangement for the adjustment of the tension. As already mentioned, a checking instrument is required to adjust the tension professionally. The following instructions are given therefore for reference only. Experienced D.I.Y. mechanics will obviously know how tight a belt should be. Remove a belt as follows, noting the differences when an A/C system is fitted.

- Disconnect the battery negative cable.

Electrical System

- Place the front end of the vehicle on chassis stands and remove the protective shield below the engine compartment. If an air conditioning system is fitted, remove the R.H. front wheel.

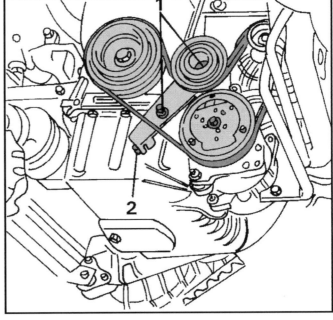

Fig. 9.3 – Details for the removal and installation of the drive belt in the case of a 2.5 litre engine.
1   Belt tensioner bolts
2   Adjusting bolt

- On vehicles **without A/C system** slacken the bolt (3) at the bottom of the alternator and the nut (1) at the top, until the belt is slack and can be lifted off.

- **If an A/C system is fitted**, refer to Fig. 9.3. In this case, slacken the two bolts (1) securing the belt tensioner and the belt tensioner bolt, until the belt is slack and can be lifted off.

- Place the new belt over the belt pulleys, making sure it is engaged properly in the grooves. Turn the tension adjusting bolt, as applicable, until the belt is tensioned. In our description the belt should deflect approx. 5 mm between the arrows in Fig.9.2. Tighten the nut (1) in Fig. 9.2 to 2.2 kgm (21 ft.lb.) and the bolt (3) to 4.0 kgm (30 ft.lb.). Tighten the two bolts (1) of the belt tensioner (Fig.9.3), if an A/C system is fitted.

Fig. 9.4 – Place the tension tester (2) over the drive belt as shown and read the indication on the instrument (1).

To complete the description, we will include the instructions on the use of the tension measuring instrument. The tester is placed against the belt as shown in Fig. 9.4. The indication of the tension is expressed in so-called "Seem" units.

- Place the tester over the tight drive belt and rotate the adjuster bolt until an indication of 120 Seems is obtained (plus or minus 19 Seems).

- Remove the tester and rotate the crankshaft three full turns in the direction of rotation. Place the tester in position once more, as shown and tighten the adjusting bolt until the reading is 140 Seem, with the tolerance given above. Remove the tester and tighten the bolt and nut as given above.

- Re-connect the battery and start the engine. After approx. 10 minutes switch off the engine and check the tension as described above. The tension must not be less than 100 Seems. Otherwise re-tension the belt.

- In all cases carry out the remaining operations in reverse order.

Note: If the belt has been adjusted without using the tension checker, have the tension checked in a workshop, if you are not absolutely satisfied with your adjustment. The above description will take you to the next dealer.

2.5 Litre Engine

Carry out the preliminary operations described for the 1.9 litre engine, but in this case remove the R.H. front wheel.

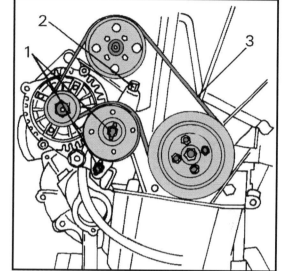

Fig. 9.5 – Details for the adjustment of the drive belt – 2.5 litre engine.
1   Lock bolts
2   Adjusting bolt with locknut
3   Drive belt

* Slacken the bolts (1) in Fig. 9.6 and slacken the locknut of bolt (2) at the bottom. *Re-tighten* the bolt (2). This will slacken the belt, which can now be removed.

* Fit the new belt and tighten the bolts (1) to 1.0 kgm (7.2 ft.lb.). The belt tension is now adjusted by means of bolt (2), i.e. the bolt is *tightened against the normal tightening direction*, until the tension has been obtained. Again you will have to judge the correct tension (see description below, if a tension checker is used). Measure the tension between the arrows in Fig. 9.6.

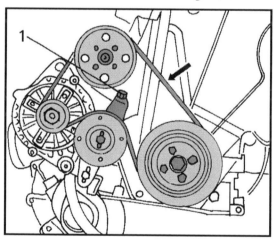

Fig. 9.6 – The tension of the belt is checked at the position shown by the arrow. The adjusting bolt (1) is rotated to adjust the tension.

* Turn the crankshaft three turns in the direction of rotation and re-check the tension. If satisfied, tighten the bolts (1) to 2.0 kgm (14.5 ft.lb.) and tighten the locknut. All other operations are carried out in reverse order.

If a tension checker is used, follow the description given above, but the indication should be around 65 Seem. There is no need to run the engine to re-check the tension.

9.2.   Starter Motor

9.2.0.   TECHNICAL DATA

Make:..Bosch (1.7 or 2.1 kW), Valeo (1.7 kW)
.... or Mitsubishi
Min. brush length:..3.0 mm (0.52 in.)

9.2.1.   REMOVAL AND INSTALLATION

The starter motor can be removed from the clutch housing after the battery and the cables at the solenoid switch have been disconnected.   The front of the vehicle should

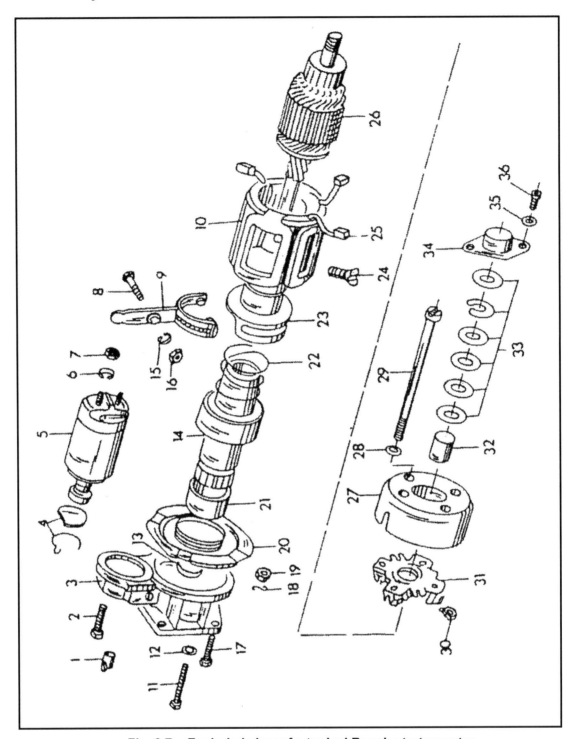

Fig. 9.7 – Exploded view of a typical Bosch starter motor.

1	Starter motor bush	13	Stop ring	25	Carbon brush
2	Starter motor bolt	14	Starter motor drive	26	Armature
3	Drive end bracket	15	Spring washer	27	Commutator end
4	Sundry parts	16	Spring washer	28	Plain washer
5	Solenoid switch	17	Bolt, M8	29	Through bolt
6	Spring washer	18	Spring washer	30	Brush spring
7	Nut, M8	19	Nut, M8	31	Brush holder
8	Bolt, engagement lever	20	Intermediate bracket	32	Commutator end bush
9	Engagement lever	21	Engagement bush	33	Sundry parts, com. end
10	Field coils	22	Engagement spring	34	Cover
11	Bolt, M10	23	Engagement bush	35	Spring washer
12	Plain washer	24	Pole piece screw	36	Screw, M4

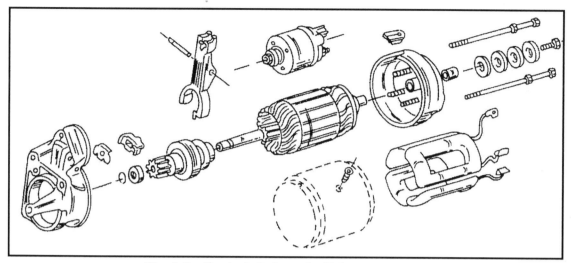

Fig. 9.8 – Exploded view of a Valeo starter motor.

be placed on chassis stands to facilitate the access to the starter motor. The installation is a reversal of the removal procedure.

9.2.1.   SERVICING

Starter motors are manufactured by Valeo, Bosch and also by Mitsubishi. We recommend to fit an exchange starter motor, if the original unit is no longer functioning. Various specialised companies are around and always have a starter motor for your specific model. There are, however, two exploded views of the starter motors used (Fig. 9.7 and 9.8).

9.3.   Fuses

Different models use different fuses. Your Owner's Manual will give you the protected circuits for a particular model.

Before replacing a fuse, is it necessary to trace the cause of the fuse failure and to rectify it. To check whether a fuse is burnt out, inspect the metal strip across the top of the fuse. There should be no breaks in the centre. If the metal strip is interrupted, fit a fuse of the same value. Never fit a fuse with a smaller value to a position where a fuse with a higher value should be situated, or visa versa. Fuses are colour-coded, but again there are no particular guide lines. If a fuse is required, take the old fuse to the parts department of your dealer. This way you will be assured to obtain the correct fuse for the circuit in question. Never repair a fuse with a make-shift piece of metal across the fuse terminals.

9.4.   Headlamps

As headlamps must be adjusted after one of them has been removed and the alignment must be checked optically, we refrain from giving any information on the removal and installation of the headlamps. We would like to, however, point out, that driving with misaligned headlamp beams is against the law.

9.5   Bulb Table

Headlamp main beams   H4, 55/60 watts
Fog lamps   H1
Brake/tail lamps   21/5 watts
Rear fog lamp   21 watts

Reversing light	21 watts
Indicator lights	5 watts
Number plate lights	5 watts
Front parking lights	5 watts

FAULT FINDING SECTION

The following section lists some of the more common faults that can develop in a motor car, both for petrol and diesel engines. For the purpose of this manual, references to diesel engines are of course, first and foremost. The section is divided into various categories and it should be possible to locate faults or damage by referring to the assembly group of the vehicle in question.

The faults are listed in no particular order and their causes are given a number. By referring to this number it is possible to read off the possible cause and to carry out the necessary remedies, if this is within the scope of your facilities.

ENGINE FAULTS

Engine will not crank:	1, 2, 3, 4
Engine cranks, but will not start:	5, 6, 7, 8
Engine cranks very slowly:	1, 2, 3
Engine starts, but cuts out:	5, 6, 9, 10
Engine misfires in the lower speed ranges:	5, 6, 9, 11
Engine misfires in the higher speed ranges:	5, 6, 11, 12
Continuous misfiring:	5, 6, 7, 10 to 15, 21, 22
Max. revs not obtained:	5, 6, 12, 22
Faulty idling:	5, 6, 8 to 11, 13, 15, 16, 21 and 22
Lack of power:	3, 5 to 11, 13 to 15, 22
Lack of acceleration:	5 to 8, 12, 14 to 16
Lack of max. speed:	5 to 8, 10, 12, 13 to 15, 22
Excessive fuel consumption:	3, 5, 6, 15, 16
Excessive oil consumption:	16 to 19
Low compression:	7, 11 to 13, 16, 20 to 22

CAUSES AND REMEDIES

1. Fault in the starter motor or its connection. Refer to "Electrical Faults".
2. Engine oil too thick. This can be caused by using the wrong oil, low temperatures or using oil not suitable for the prevailing climates. Depress the clutch whilst starting (models with manual transmission).

Otherwise refill the engine with the correct oil grade, suitable for diesel engines (for example TOTAL DIESEL).

3. Moveable parts of the engine not run-in. This fault may be noticed when the engine has been overhauled. It may be possible to free the engine by adding oil to the fuel for a while.

4. Mechanical fault. This may be due to seizure of the piston(s), broken crankshaft, connecting rods, clutch or other moveable parts of the engine. The engine must be stripped for inspection.

5. Faults in the glow plug system. Refer to "Glow Plug Faults".

6. Faults in the fuel system. Refer to "Fuel Faults".

7. Incorrect valve timing. This will only be noticed after the engine has been reassembled after overhaul and the timing belt has been replaced incorrectly. Re-dismantle the engine and check the timing marks on the timing gear wheels.

8. Compression leak due to faulty closing of valves. See also under (7) or leakage past worn piston rings or pistons cylinder head gasket blown.

9. Entry of air at inlet manifold, due to split manifold or damaged gasket.

10. Restriction in exhaust system, due to damaged exhaust pipes, dirt in end of exhaust pipe(s), kinked pipe(s), or collapsed silencer. Repair as necessary.

11. Worn valves or valve seats, no longer closing the valves properly. Top overhaul of engine is asked for.

12. Sticking valves due to excessive carbon deposits or weak valve springs. Top overhaul is asked for.

13. Cylinder head gasket blown. Replace gasket and check block and head surfaces for distortion.

14. Camshaft worn, not opening or closing one of the valves properly, preventing proper combustion. Check and if necessary fit new camshaft.

15. Incorrect valve (tappet) clearance. There could be a fault in the hydraulic tappets (2.5 litre) or have clearances adjusted (1.9 litre).

16. Cylinder bores, pistons or piston rings worn. Overhaul is the only cure. Fault may be corrected for a while by adding "Piston Seal Liquid" into the cylinders, but will re-develop.

17. Worn valve guides and/or valve stems. Top overhaul is asked for.

18. Damaged valve stem seals. Top overhaul is asked for.

19. Leaking crankshaft oil seal, worn piston rings or pistons, worn cylinders. Correct as necessary.

20. Loose glow plugs, gas escaping past thread or plug sealing washer damaged. Correct.

21. Cracked cylinder or cylinder block. Dismantle, investigate and replace block, if necessary.

22. Broken, weak or collapsed valve spring(s). Top overhaul is asked for.

GLOW PLUG FAULTS

Check a suspect glow plug as follows (except DJ5 TED engine):

- Remove the glow plug lead from the rear glow plug and from the remaining plugs the bus bars.
- Connect a 12 volts test lamp to the plus terminal of the battery and with the other lead of the lamp touch in turn the connecting threads of each glow plug. The faulty plug is detected when the test lamp does not light up.

LUBRICATION SYSTEM FAULTS

The only problem the lubrication system should give is excessive oil consumption or low oil pressure, or the oil warning light not going off.

Excessive oil consumption can be caused by worn cylinder bores, pistons and/or piston rings, worn valve guides, worn valves stem seals or a damaged crankshaft oil seal or leaking gasket on any of the engine parts. In most cases the engine must be dismantled to locate the fault.

Low oil pressure can be caused by a faulty oil pressure gauge, sender unit or wiring, a defective relief valve, low oil level, blocked oil pick-up pipe for the oil pump, worn oil pump or damaged main or big end bearings. In most cases it is logical to check the oil level first. All other causes require the dismantling and repair of the engine. If the oil warning light stays on, switch off the engine IMMEDIATELY, as delay could cause complete seizure within minutes.

COOLING SYSTEM FAULTS

Common faults are: Overheating, loss of coolant and slow warming-up of the engine:

Overheating:

1. Lack of coolant: Open the expansion tank cap with care to avoid injuries. Never pour cold water in to an overheated engine. Wait until engine cools down and pour in coolant whilst engine is running.

2. Radiator core obstructed by leaves, insects, etc.: Blow with air line from the back of the radiator or with a water hose to clean.

3. Cooling fan not operating: Check fan for proper cut-in and cut-out temperature. If necessary change the temperature switch or see your Citroen / Peugeot / Fiat dealer.

4. Thermostat sticking: If sticking in the closed position, coolant can only circulate within the cylinder head or block. Remove thermostat and check as described in section "Cooling".

5. Water hose split: Identified by rising steam from the engine compartment or the front of the vehicle. Slight splits can be repaired with insulation tape. Drive without expansion tank cap to keep the pressure in the system down, to the nearest service station.

6. Water pump belt torn: Replace and tension belt (if possible).
7. Water pump inoperative: Replace water pump.
8. Cylinder head gasket blown: Replace the cylinder head gasket.

Loss of Coolant:
1. Radiator leaks: Slight leaks may be stopped by using radiator sealing compound (follow the instructions of the manufacturer). In emergency a egg can be cracked open and poured into the radiator filler neck.
2. Hose leaks: See under 5, "Overheating".
3. Water pump leaks: Check the gasket for proper sealing or replace the pump.

Long Warming-up periods:
1. Thermostat sticking in the open position: Remove thermostat, check and if necessary replace.

DIESEL FUEL SYSTEM FAULTS

Engine is difficult to start or does not start	1 to 13
Engine starts, but stops soon afterwards:	14 to 20
Engine misfires continuously:	1 to 13
Bad idling:	14 to 20
Black, white or blue exhaust smoke:	21 to 29
Lack of power:	30 to 39
Excessive fuel consumption:	40 to 47

CAUSES AND REMEDIES

1. Fuel tank empty. Refuel.
2. Pre-glowing time too short. Operate until warning light goes "off".
3. Cold starting device not operated. Pull cable and push in after approx. 1 minute.
4. Glow plug system inoperative. Refer to "Glow Plug Faults".
5. Electro-magnetic cut-off device, loose or no current. Check cable to cut-off at top of injection pump. Ask a second person to operate ignition key and check if a "click" is heard. Either interrupted current supply or defective cut-off device.
6. Air in fuel system. Operate starter motor until fuel is delivered.
7. Fuel supply faulty. Slacken the injection pipes at injectors, and check if fuel is running out. Other faults: kinked, blocked or leaking injection pipes, blocked fuel filter, tank breathing system blocked. Wrong fuel for cold temperatures.
8   Injection pipes refitted in wrong order. Alter repair.
9. Injection timing of pump out of phase: Have the adjustment checked

and corrected.

10. One or more injectors faulty, dirty or incorrect injection pressure. Have injectors repaired or replace them.

11. Injection pump not operating properly. Fit an exchange pump or have it repaired.

12. Valves not opening properly.

13. Compression pressures too low. See item "8" under "Engine Faults".

14. Idle speed not properly adjusted. Adjust.

15. Throttle cable not properly adjusted or sticking. Re-adjust or free-off.

16. Fuel hose between filter and pump not tightened properly. Tighten connections.

17. Rear mounting of injection pump loose or cracked. Tighten or replace.

18. See items 6, 7, 9, 11, 12 and 13.

19. Engine mounting not tightened properly or worn. Tighten or replace.

20. Sticking accelerator pedal. Free-off pedal.

21. Engine not at operating temperature. Check exhaust smoke colour again when engine is warm.

22. Too much acceleration at low revs. Use individual gears in accordance with acceleration.

23. Air cleaner contaminated. Clean or replace.

24. Fuel filter contaminated. Replace.

25. Max. speed adjustment incorrect. Re-adjust.

26. Injectors are dripping. Have them checked or replace faulty ones.

27. Injector nozzles sticking or broken. Replace injector.

28. Injection pressure too low. Have injectors checked and adjusted.

29. See items 9, 11, 12 and 13.

30. Throttle cable travel restricted. Re-adjust. Check that floor mats cannot obstruct pedal movement.

31. Throttle cable not correctly adjusted. Re-adjust.

32. Operating lever loose on pump. Re-tighten.

33. Max. speed not obtained. Re-adjust max. speed or have it adjusted.

34. Injector pipes restricted in diameter (near connections). Disconnect pipes and check that diameter is at least 2.0 mm (0.08 in.).

35. Heat protection sealing gaskets under injectors not sealing or damaged. Remove injectors and check. Replace if necessary. Fit the washers correctly.

36. Injection pressure of injectors wrong. Have them re-adjusted.

37. See items 6, 7, 9, 11 and 13.

38. See item 20.

39. See items 23, 24, 26 and 27.

40. Road wheels dragging. Brakes seized or wheel bearings not running freely.

41. Engine not running "free". Refers to new or overhauled engine.

42. Fuel system leaking. Check hoses, pipes, filter, injection pump, etc. for

leaks.

43. Fuel return line blocked. Clean with compressed air if possible.
44. Idle speed too high. Re-adjust.
45. Max. speed too high. Re-adjust.
46. See items 10, 11, 12 and 13.
47. See items 24, 26, 27 and 28.

CLUTCH FAULTS

Clutch slipping:	1, 2, 3, 4, 5
Clutch will not disengage fully:	4, 6 to 12, 14
Whining from clutch when pedal is depressed:	13
Clutch judder:	1, 2, 7, 10 to 13
Clutch noise when idling:	2, 3
Clutch noise during engagement:	2

CAUSES AND REMEDIES

1. Insufficient clutch free play at pedal. Adjust in accordance with instructions in section "Clutch" (if applicable).
2. Clutch disc linings worn, hardened, oiled-up, loose or broken. Disc distorted or hub loose. Clutch disc must be replaced.
3. Pressure plate faulty. Replace clutch.
4. Air in hydraulic system (only applicable to models with hydraulic clutch control). Low fluid level in clutch cylinder reservoir.
5. Insufficient play at clutch pedal and clutch release linkage (the latter in the case of mechanical operation). Adjust as described.
6. Excessive free play in release linkage (only for cable operated clutch). Adjust or replace worn parts.
7. Misalignment of clutch housing. Very rare fault, but possible on transmissions with separate clutch housings. Re-align to correct.
8. Clutch disc hub binding on splines of main drive shaft (clutch shaft) due to dirt or burrs on splines. Remove clutch and clean and check splines.
9. Clutch disc linings loose or broken. Replace disc.
10. Pressure plate distorted. Replace clutch.
11. Clutch cover distorted. Replace clutch.
12. Fault in transmission or loose engine mountings.
13. Release bearing defective. Remove clutch and replace bearing.
14. A bent clutch release lever. Check lever and replace or straighten, if possible.

• The above faults and remedies are for hydraulic and mechanical clutch operation and should be read as applicable to the model in question, as the clutch fault finding section is written for all types of clutch operation.

STEERING FAULTS

Steering very heavy:	1 to 6
Steering very loose:	5, 7 to 9, 11 to 13
Steering wheel wobbles:	4, 5, 7 to 9, 11 to 16
Vehicle pulls to one side:	1, 4, 8, 10, 14 to 18
Steering wheel does not return to centre position:	1 to 6, 18
Abnormal tyre wear:	1, 4, 7 to 9, 14 to 19
Knocking noise in column:	6, 7, 11, 12

CAUSES AND REMEDIES

1. Tyre pressures not correct or uneven. Correct.
2. Lack of lubricant in rack and pinion steering.
3. Stiff steering linkage ball joints. Replace ball joints in question.
4. Incorrect steering wheel alignment. Correct as necessary.
5. Steering needs adjustment. See your dealer for advice.
6. Steering column bearings too tight or seized or steering column bent. Correct as necessary.
7. Steering linkage joints loose or worn. Check and replace joints as necessary.
8. Front wheel bearings worn, damaged or loose. Replace bearing.
9. Front suspension parts loose. Check and correct.
10. Wheel nuts loose. Re-tighten.
11. Steering wheel loose. Re-tighten nut.
12. Steering gear mounting loose. Check and tighten.
13. Steering gear worn. Replace the steering gear.
14. Steering track rods defective or loose.
15. Wheels not properly balanced or tyre pressures uneven. Correct pressures or balance wheels.
16. Suspension torsion bars (front) or springs (rear) weak or broken. Replace bar or spring in question or both.
17. Brakes are pulling to one side. See under "Brake Faults".
18. Suspension out of alignment. Have the complete suspension checked by a dealer.
19. Improper driving. We don't intend to tell you how to drive and are quite sure that this is not the cause of the fault.

BRAKE FAULTS

Brake Failure: Brake shoe linings or pads excessively worn, incorrect brake fluid (after overhaul), insufficient brake fluid, fluid leak, master cylinder defective, wheel cylinder or caliper failure. Remedies are obvious in each instance.

Brakes Ineffective: Shoe linings or pads worn, incorrect lining material or brake fluid, linings contaminated, fluid level low, air in brake system (bleed brakes), leak in pipes or cylinders, master cylinder defective. Remedies are obvious in each instance.

Brakes pull to one side: Shoes or linings worn, incorrect linings or pads, contaminated linings, drums or discs scored, fluid pipe blocked, unequal tyre pressures, brake back plate or caliper mounting loose, wheel bearings not properly adjusted, wheel cylinder seized. Rectify as necessary.

Brake pedal spongy: Air in hydraulic system. System must be bled of air.

Pedal travel too far: Linings or pads worn, drums or discs scored, master cylinder or wheel cylinders defective, system needs bleeding. Rectify as necessary.

Loss of brake pressure: Fluid leak, air in system, leak in master or wheel cylinders, brake servo not operating (vacuum hose disconnected or exhauster pump not operating). Place vehicle on dry ground and depress brake pedal. Check where fluid runs out and rectify as necessary.

Brakes binding: Incorrect brake fluid (boiling), weak shoe return springs, basic brake adjustment incorrect (after fitting new rear shoes), piston in caliper of wheel cylinder seized, push rod play on master cylinder insufficient (compensation port obstructed), handbrake adjusted too tightly. Rectify as necessary. Swelling of cylinder cups through use of incorrect brake fluid could be another reason.

Handbrake ineffective: Brake shoe linings worn, linings contaminated, operating lever on brake shoe seized, brake shoes or handbrake need adjustment. Rectify as necessary.

Excessive pedal pressure required: Brake shoe linings or pads worn, linings or pads contaminated, brake servo vacuum hose (for brake servo) disconnected or wheel cylinders seized. Exhauster pump not operating (diesel engines). Rectify as necessary.

Brakes squealing: Brake shoe linings or pads worn so far that metal is grinding against drum or disc. Inside of drum is full of lining dust. Remove and replace, or clean out the drum(s). Do not inhale brake dust.

Note: Any operation on the steering and brake systems must be carried out with the necessary care and attention. Always think of your safety and the safety of other road users. Make sure to use the correct fluid for the power-assisted steering and the correct brake fluid.

Faults in an ABS system should be investigated by a dealer.
Change the brake fluid in regular Intervals (approx. every 2 years).

ELECTRICAL FAULTS

Starter motor failure:	2 to 5, 8, 9
No starter motor drive:	1 to 3, 5 to 7
Slow cranking speed:	1 to 3
Charge warning light remains on:	3, 10, 12

Fault Finding Section

Charge warning light does not come on:	2, 3, 9, 11, 13
Headlamp failure:	2, 3, 11, 13, 14
Battery needs frequent topping-up:	11
Direction indicators not working properly:	2, 3, 9, 13, 14
Battery frequently discharged:	3, 10, 11, 12

CAUSES AND REMEDIES

1. Tight engine. Check and rectify.
2. Battery discharged or defective. Re-charge battery or replace if older than approx. 2 years.
3. Interrupted connection in circuit. Trace and rectify.
4. Starter motor pinion jammed in flywheel. Release.
5. Also 6, 7 and 8. Starter motor defective, no engagement in flywheel, pinion or flywheel worn or solenoid switch defective. Correct as necessary.
9. Ignition/starter switch inoperative. Replace.
10. Drive belt loose or broken. Adjust or replace.
11. Regulator defective. Adjust or replace.
12. Generator inoperative. Overhaul or replace.
13. Bulb burnt out. Replace bulb.
14. Flasher unit defective. Replace unit.

WIRING DIAGRAM LEGEND
Not all current consumers are fitted to all models

BB00	Battery	1041	Emergency stop	2325	Front R.H. flasher
BB10	Supply box		switch	2340	L.H. side flasher
BF00	Fuse box	1042	General relay	2345	R.H. side flasher
BMF1	Max. fuse box	1043	Re-arming push button	2520	Horn
BMF2	Max. fuse box	1044	Diode unit	2600	Lamp rotator
CA00	Ignition switch	1104	Electro valve, advance	2605	Dipped beam relay
C1300	Engine test connector	1150	Pre-heating control unit	2606	Main beam relay
C4640	Tachograph fuse	1156	Post-heating relay	2610	L.H. headlamp
	connector	1157	Post-heating thermal	2615	R.H. headlamp
C7000	ABS diagnostic	1160	Glow plugs	2630	Rear L.H. lamps
	connector	1203	Inertia switch		on body shell
MF175	Fuse, 175 A	1204	Impact safety relay	2633	R.H. number plate
PS00	Connector board,	1208	Diesel injection pump		light
	4 x 4 system	1211	Fuel gauge	2634	Rear R.H. lamps
V1000	Charge warning light	1220	Coolant temperature		on body shell
V1150	Pre-heating warning		sensor	2635	L.H. number plate
	lamp	1252	Advance corrector relay	3000	Front L.H. door
V1300	Engine diagnostic	1254	Load lever switch		aperture switch
	warning lamp	1255	Fuel cut-out valve	3001	Front R.H. door
V2000	Rear fog lamp	1316	Engine speed sensor	3010	Front interior lamp
V2300	warning light,	1331	Injector, No. 1	3019	Interior lamp
V3310	Flasher warning light	1332	Injector, No. 2	3020	Rear interior lamp
V2600	Side light warning	1333	Injector, No. 3	3029	Central interior lamp
	lamps	1334	Injector, No. 4	3030	Central interior lamp
V2620	Main beam warning	1400	TDC sensor	3086	Blue interior lamp
	lamp	1500	Cooling fan relay		switch
V2660	Warning light, front	1505	Cooling fan thermal	3087	Parking lamp switch
	fog lamps		switch	3088	Parking lamps relay
V4010	Warning light,	1506	Cooling fan resistor	4025	Engine coolant thermal
	coolant level	1510	Cooling fan		switch and temperature
V4020	Warning light,	1526	Coolant fan resistor		sensor
	coolant, temperature	1620	Vehicle speed sensor	4026	Engine coolant tem-
V4050	Warning light, water	2000	Rear fog lamp switch		temperature switch
	in fuel	2001	Light/wiper switch	4050	Water in fuel sensor
V4110	Oil pressure	2100	Stop lamp switch	4110	Engine oil pressure
	warning lamp	2200	Reversing lamp switch		switch
V5300	Warning lamp, low	2300	Hazard warning	4310	Fuel gauge
	fuel	2305	Flasher unit	4311	Fuel gauge stabiliser
V4420	Warning light, hand-	2320	Front, L.H. flasher	4315	Fuel gauge rheostat
	brake and brake fluid,			4400	Handbrake switch
	also brake pad wear			4410	Brake fluid level switch
V6235	Warning light,			4430	L.H. brake pad wear
	anti-theft device				indicator contact
V7000	Warning light, ABS			4431	R.H. brake pad wear
V8110	Heated rear screen				indicator contact
	warning light			4640	Tachograph
0004	Instrument cluster			5015	Wiper motor
1005	Starter inhibitor switch			5100	Pump, screen washer
1010	Starter motor			5405	Pump, headlamp
1020	Alternator				washer
1021	General support relay				

Wiring Diagrams

5410	L.H. headlamp washer motor		7020	ABS control unit
5415	R.H. headlamp washer motor		7025	Brake pressure unit
6004	Window switch, driver side		7029	ABS pump fuse
6005	Window switch, passenger side		7030	Electric pump unit
6021	Window relay		7020	Clock
6040	Window motor, driver side		8000	A/C switch
6235	Door locking control unit		8005	Slow-speed air blower relay
6240	L.H. door locking motor		8006	Evaporator thermal sensor
6245	R.H. door locking motor		8007	Pressostat
6255	R.H. side door locking motor		8020	A/C compressor
6260	Rear door locking motor		8040	Air blower speed control
6406	Rear view mirror switch		8041	Additional heating switch
6410	Drivers door mirror		6046	Air blower speed resistor
6415	Passenger door mirror		8048	Additional heating relay
6540	Seat belt unit		8049	Air blower motor
6700	Control switch, differential lock		8060	Additional air blower motor
6701	Electro valve, differential lock		8061	A/C unit relay
6702	4 x 4 selector valve		8100	Front cigar lighter
6703	4 x 4 selector valve 4 x 4 selector relay		8110	Heated rear window switch
			8115	Heated rear window relay
6706	4 x 4 selector switch		8120	Heated rear window
6712	Differential unlocking switch		8121	Control module transponder
6740	Differential locking relay		8122	Digital electro-valve
7000	Front L.H. ABS sensor		8310	Heated rear seat
7005	Front R.H. ABS sensor		8410	Radio
7010	Rear L.H. ABS sensor		8420	L.H. loudspeaker
7015	Rear R.H. ABS sensor		8425	R.H. loudspeaker

Wiring Looms - Abbreviations

AVID	Wiring loom, front right		AVIG	Wiring loom, front left
FIAF	Wiring loom, front panel		GMV	Wiring loom, cooling fan
ES/P	Wiring loom, headlamp washer		MOT	Wiring loom, engine
ABR	Wiring loom, ABS		ABR/AV	Wiring loom, ABS, front
ABR/PB	Wiring loom, ABS, dashboard		S/CH	Wiring loom, seat heater
CSL	Wiring loom, 4 x 4 operation		PLAF/C	Wiring loom, interior lamp
P/B/C	Wiring loom, add. dashboard		P/B	Wiring loom, dashboard
PLAF	Wiring loom, interior lights		PLAF/AR	Wiring loom, rear interior lamp
CLM	Wiring loom, A/C system		CL/AD	Wiring loom, add. Heater
PR AV/G	Wiring loom, L.H. front door		PR AR/G	Wiring loom, L.H. rear door
PR AR	Wiring loom, rear door		PR AV/I/D	Wiring loom, 2nd front door
PR AV/D	Wiring loom, R.H. front door		PR AR/D	Wiring loom, R.H. rear door
LI PR	Wiring loom, door connection harness		AR/G	Wiring loom, L.H. rear
AR/D	Wiring loom, R.H. rear		AR/SP	Wiring loom, rear under floor
INT/F/AV G	Front L.H. door switch		INT/F/AF D	Front R.H. door switch
CHR/MOT	Wiring loom, tachograph		CHR/PB	Wiring loom, dashboard, tachograph

Cable Colour Code

BA	=	white		MV	=	Mauve		VE	=	green
BE	=	blue		NR	=	black		VI	=	violet
BG	=	beige		OR	=	orange		AY	=	light blue
GR	=	grey		RG	=	red				
JN	=	yellow		RS	=	pink				
MR	=	brown								

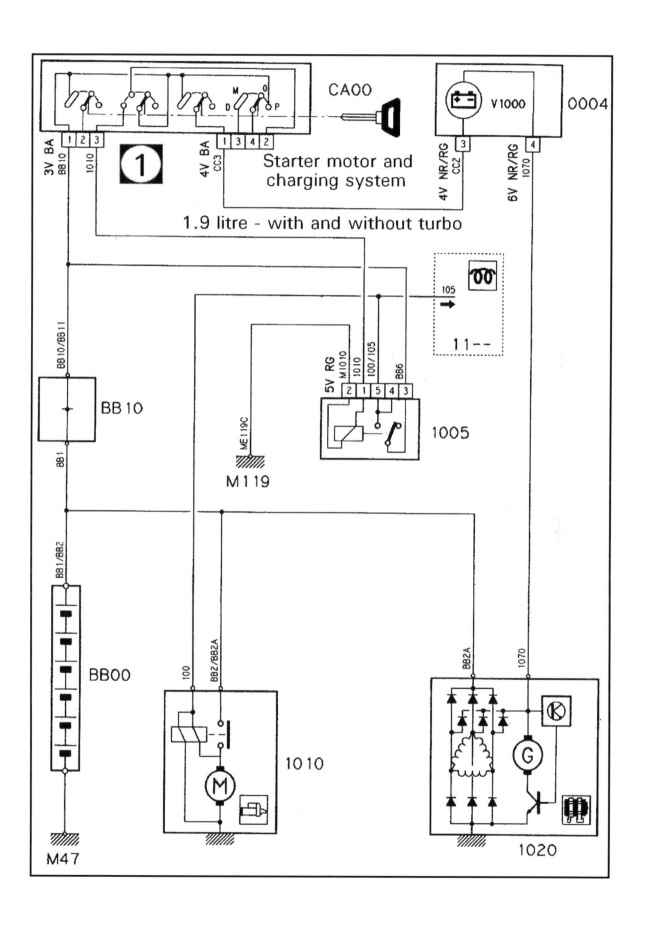

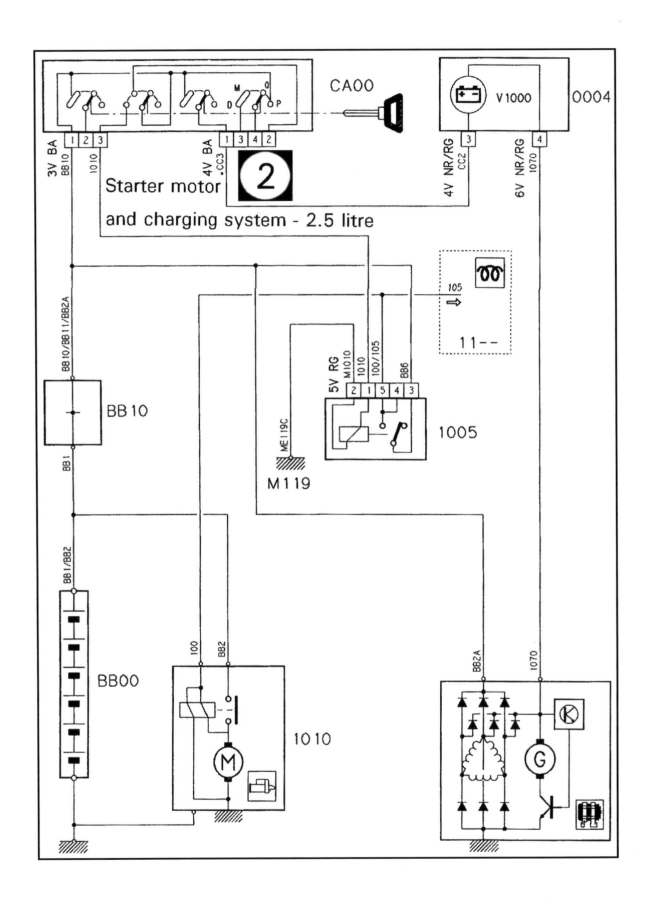

CA00

V 1000   0004

Starter motor

and charging system - 2.5 litre

BB 10

M 119

1005

BB00

1010

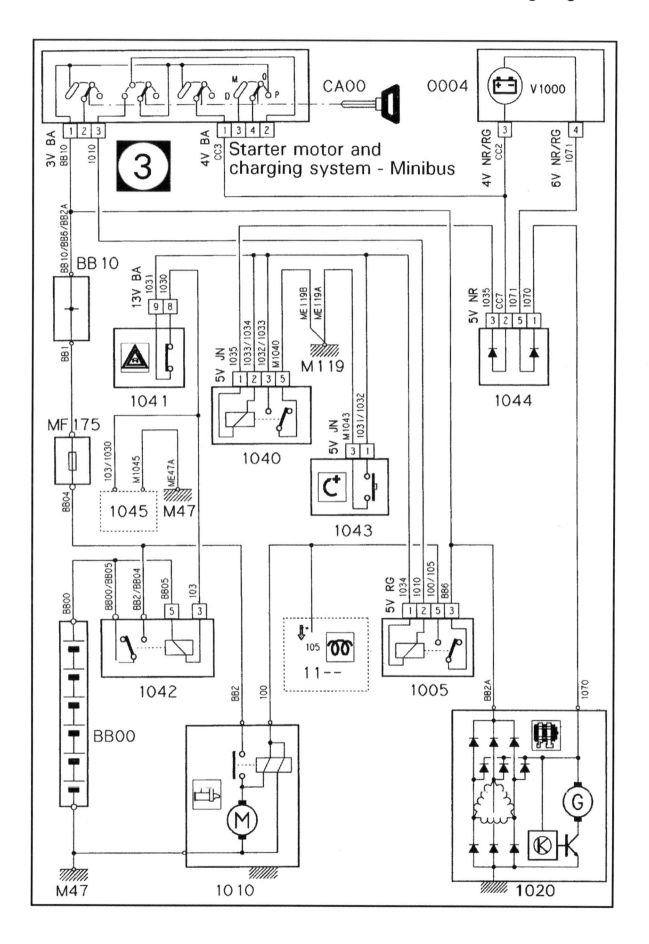

CA00   0004   V1000

③ Starter motor and charging system - Minibus

BB 10

13V BA

M 119

1041

5V JN

1040

5V JN

1043

5V NR

1044

MF 175

1045   M47

BB00

1042

11 --

1005

M47   1010   1020

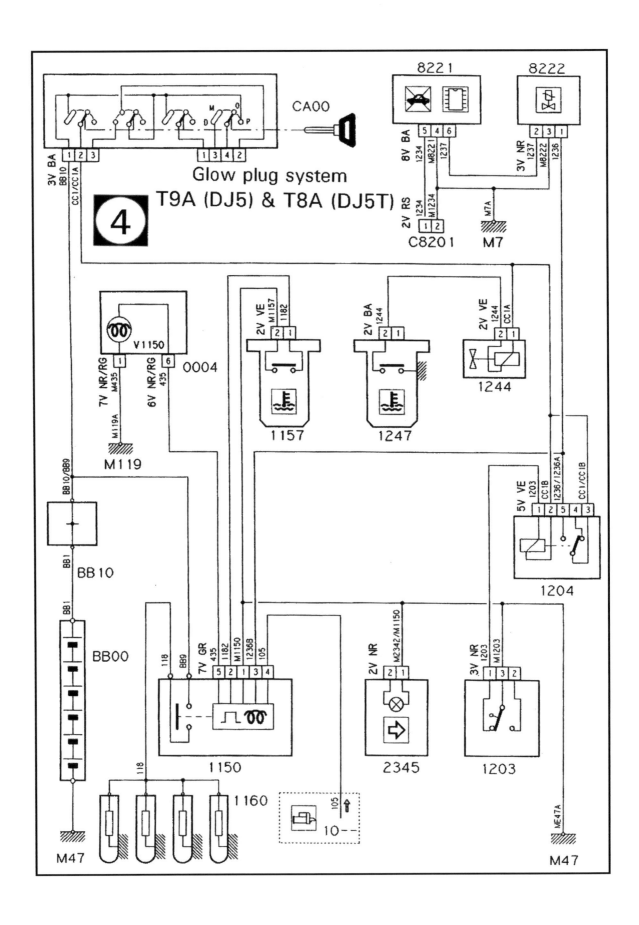

Glow plug system
T9A (DJ5) & T8A (DJ5T)

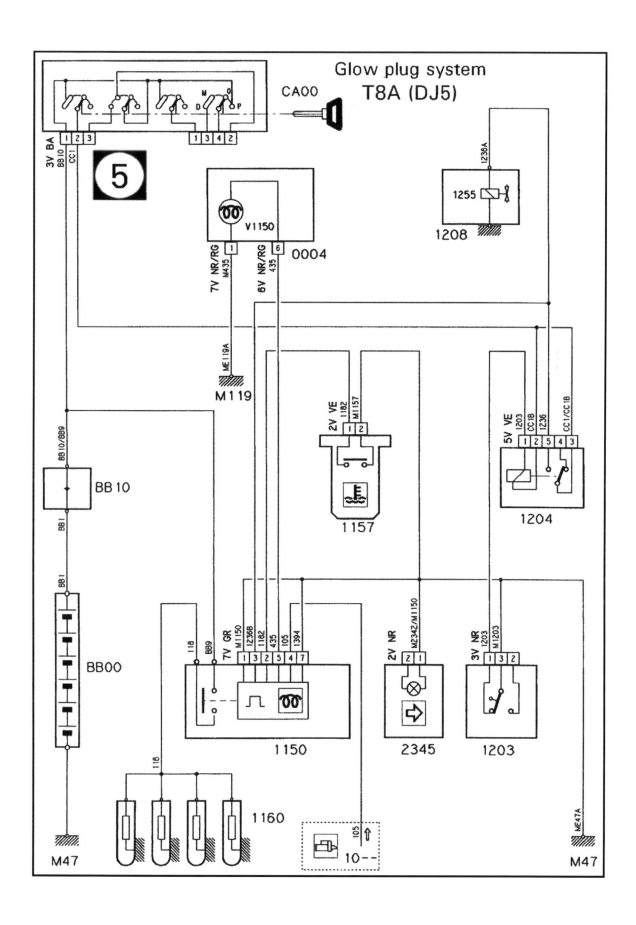

Glow plug system
T8A (DJ5)

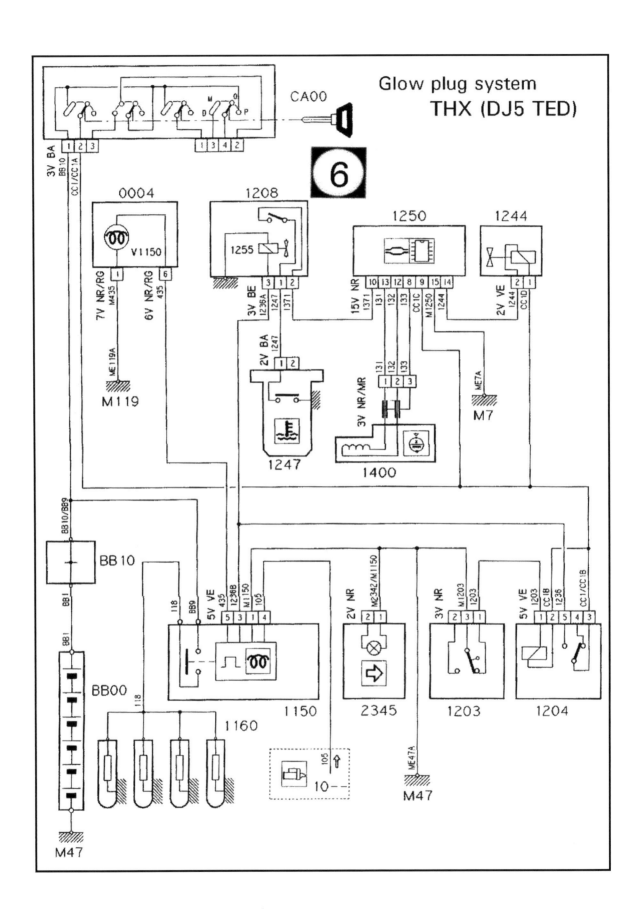

Glow plug system
THX (DJ5 TED)

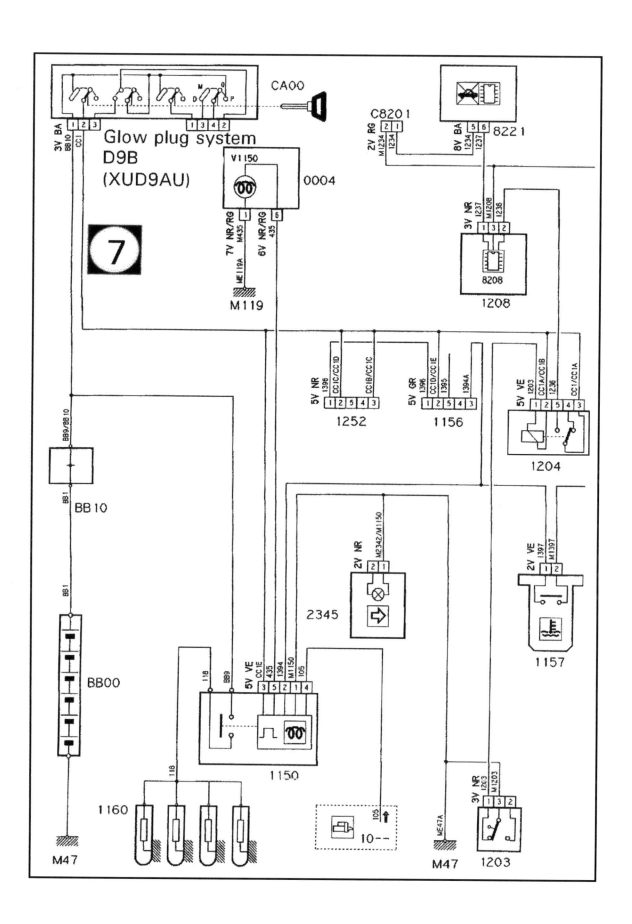

Glow plug system
D9B
(XUD9AU)

CA00

⑦

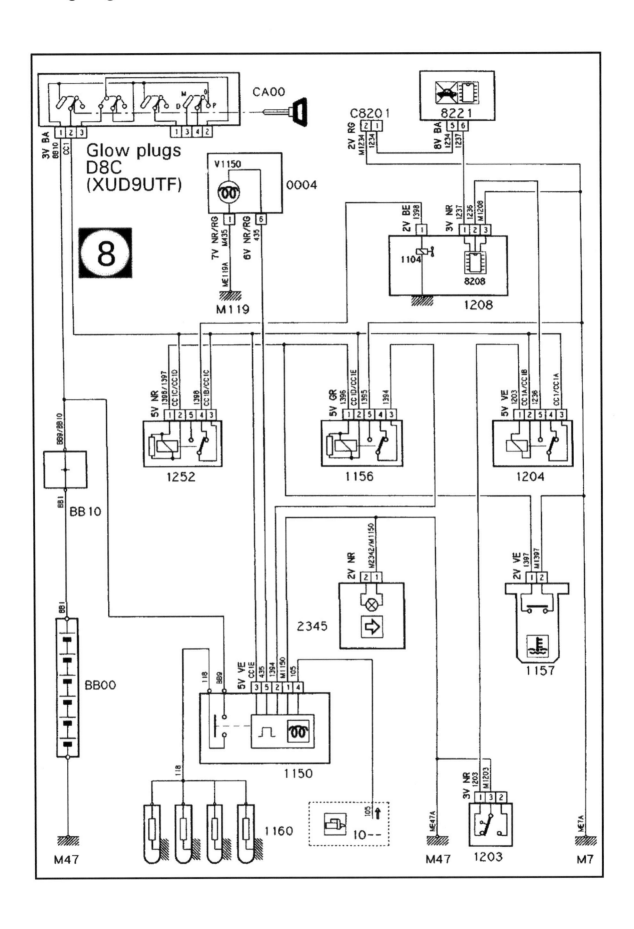

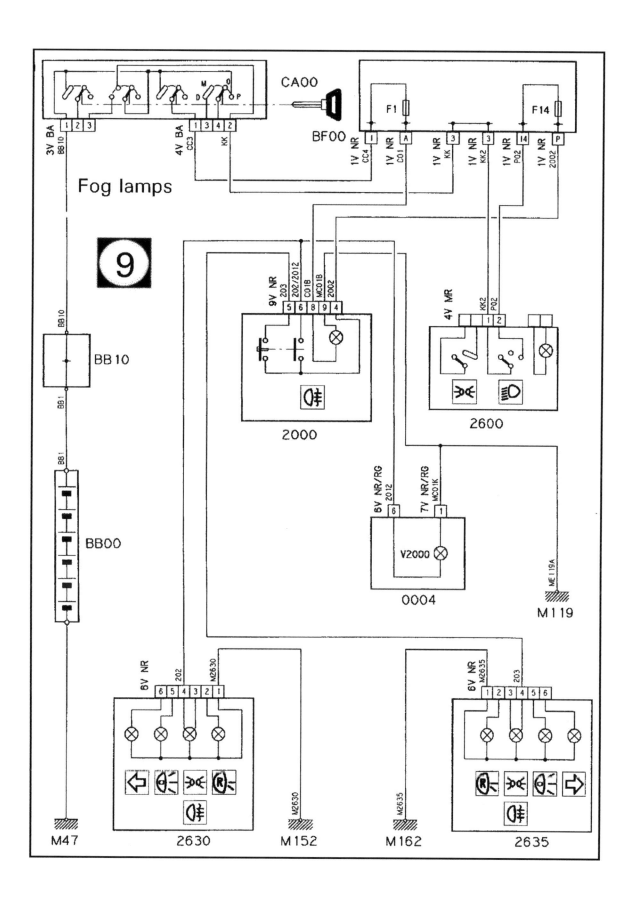

Fog lamps

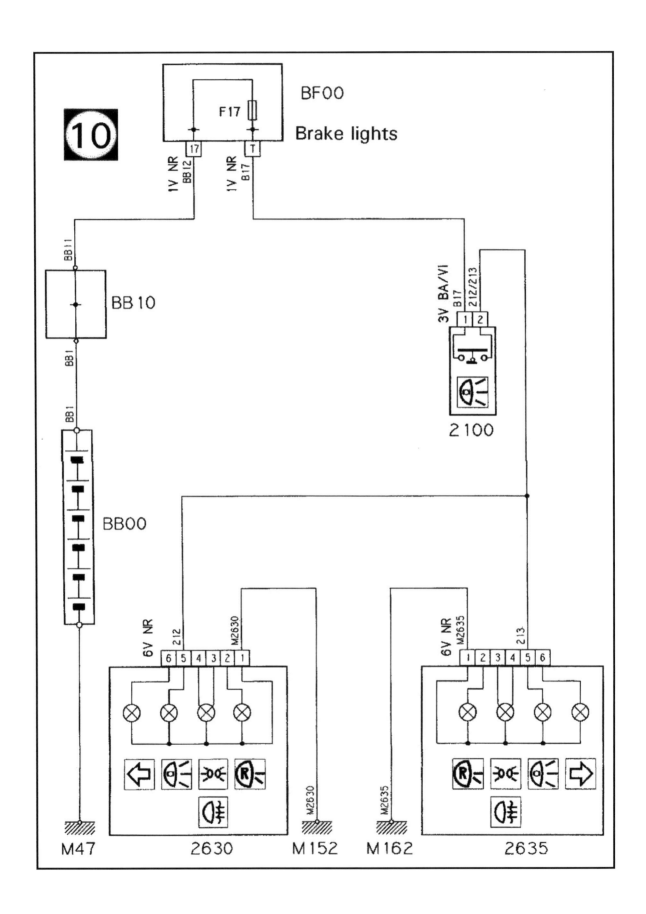

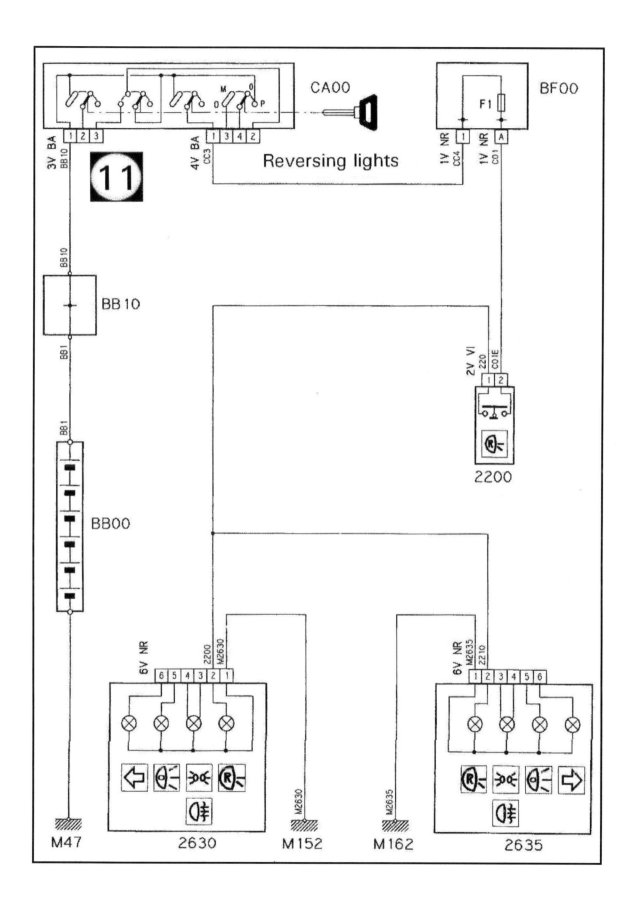

Wiring Diagrams

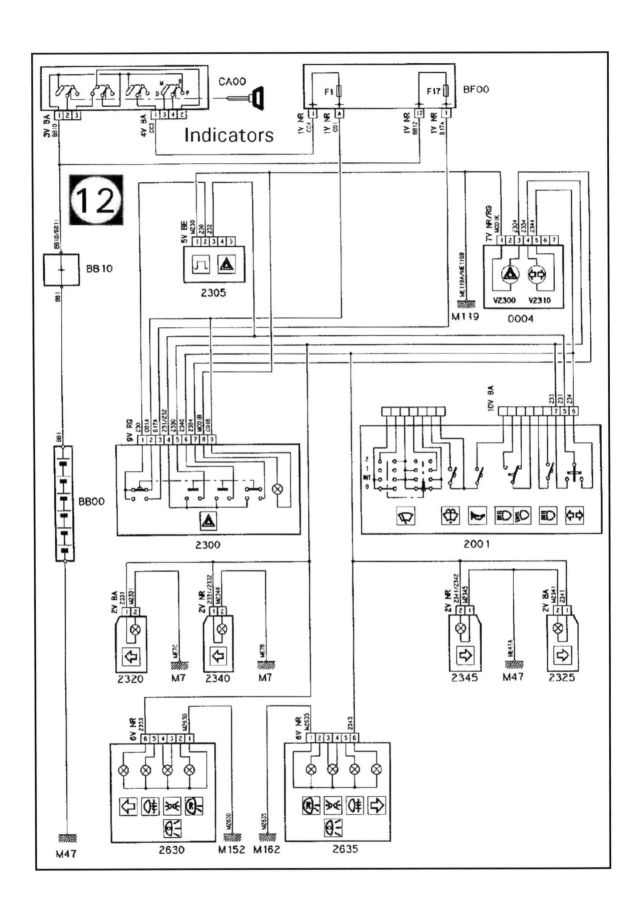

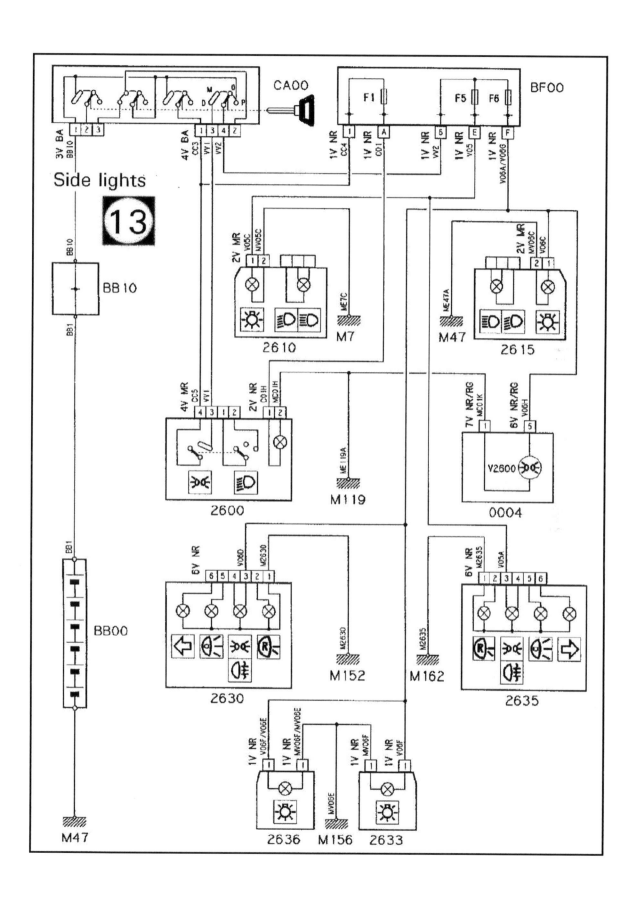

Side lights

13

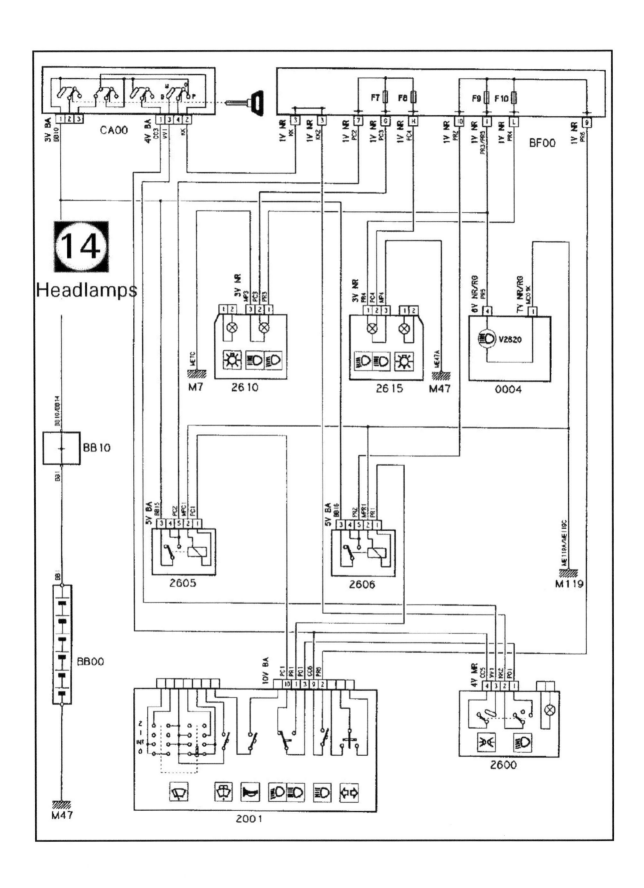

14

Headlamps

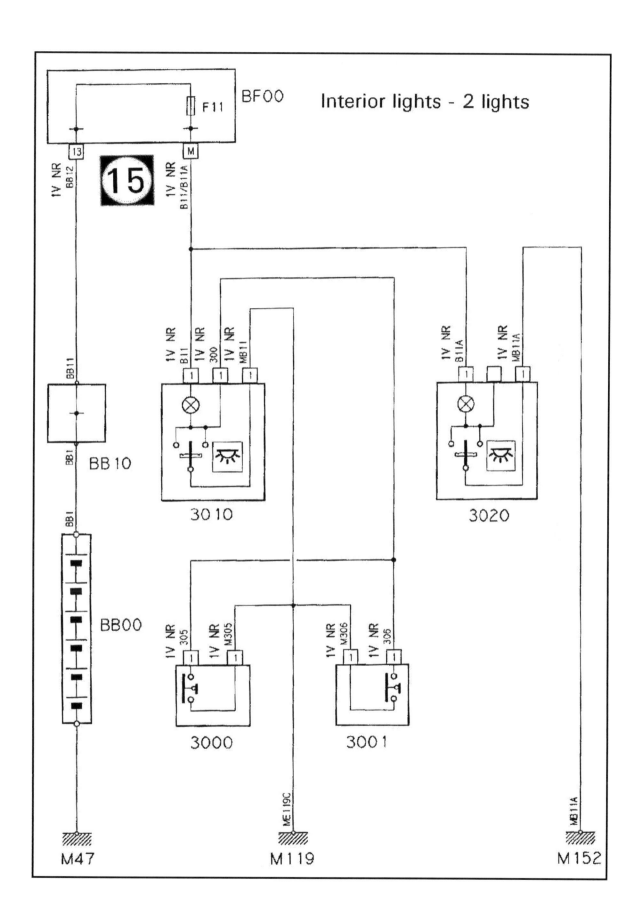

Interior lights - 2 lights

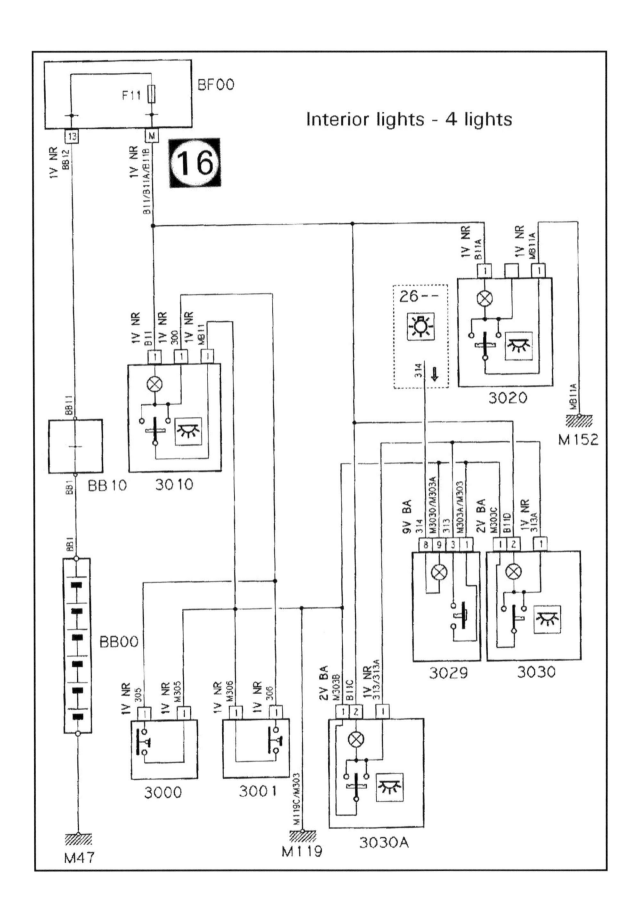

Interior lights - 4 lights

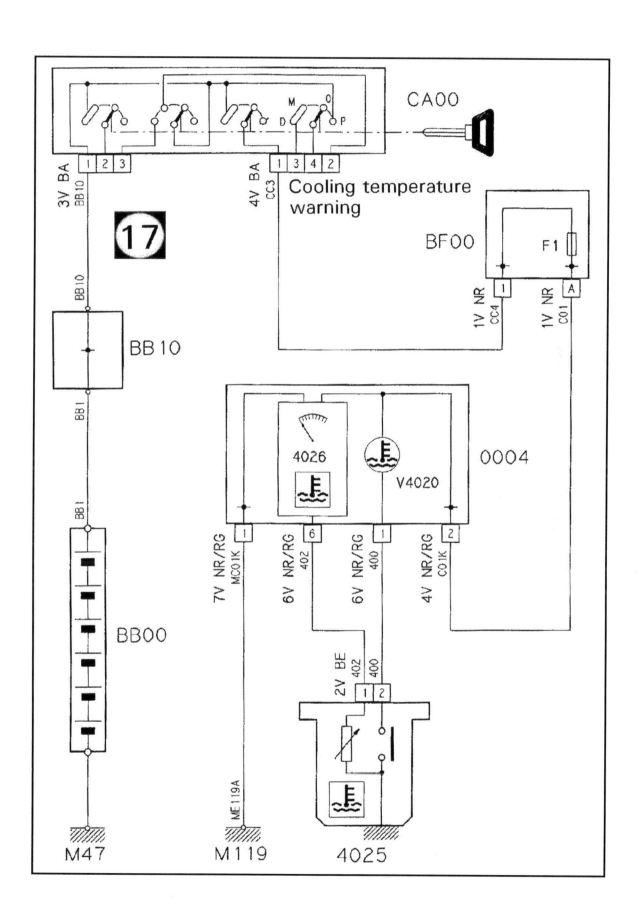

Cooling temperature warning

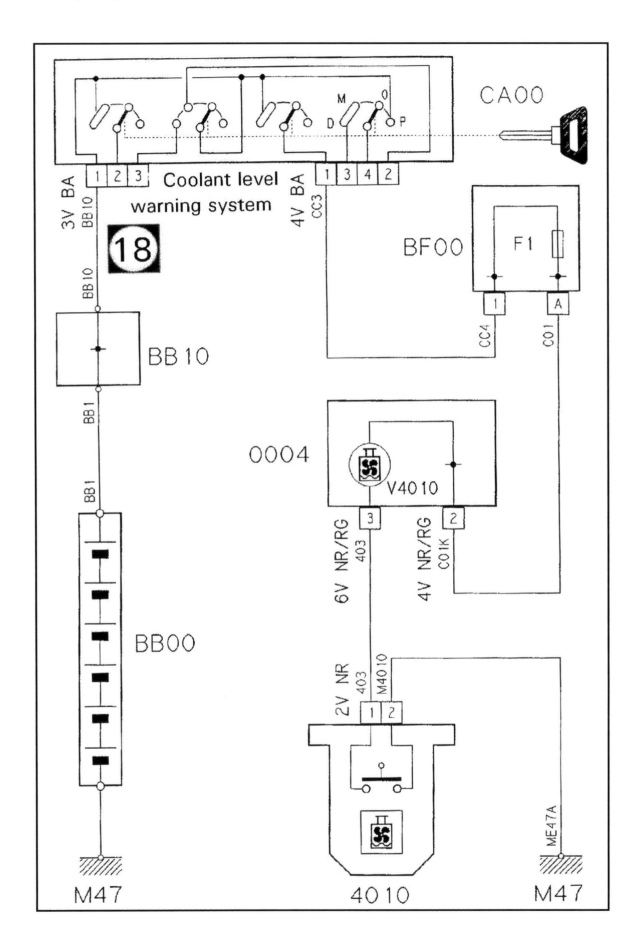

Coolant level warning system

CA00

3V BA

4V BA

BB10

CC3

18

BF00   F1

BB10

BB10

BB 10

BB1

CC4   C01

0004

V4010

BB1

BB00

6V NR/RG   4V NR/RG

403   C01K

2V NR

403   M4010

M47   4010   M47

ME47A

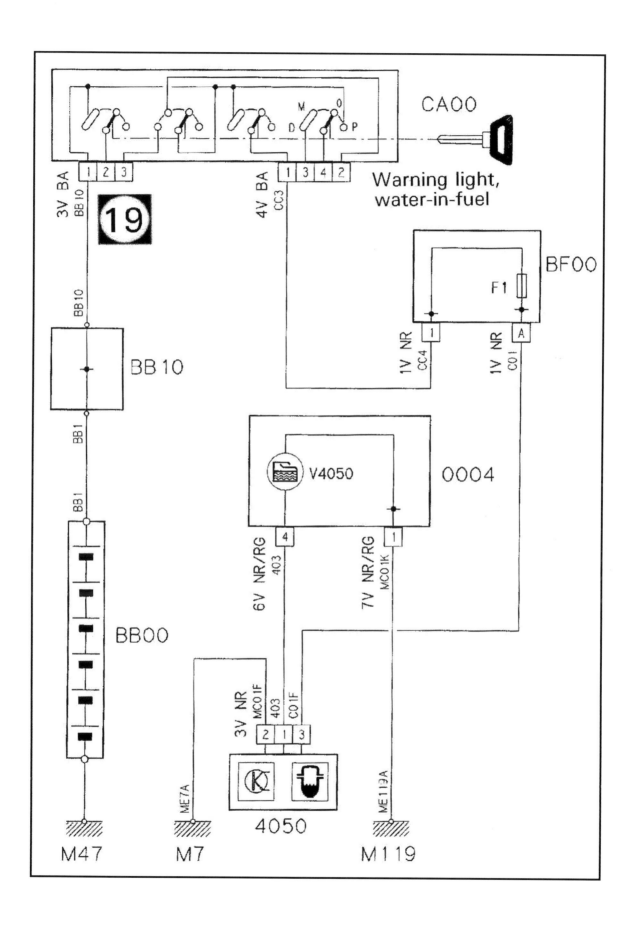

CA00

Warning light,
water-in-fuel

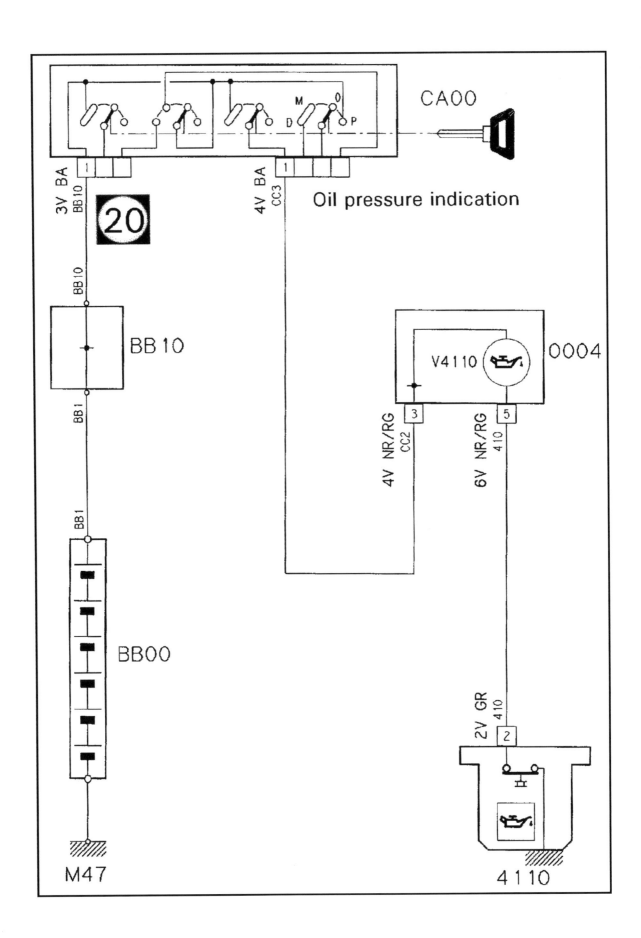

CA00

Oil pressure indication

3V BA
BB10

20

BB10

BB10

BB1

BB1

BB00

M47

V4110

0004

4V NR/RG
CC2

6V NR/RG
410

2V GR
410

4110

4V BA
CC3

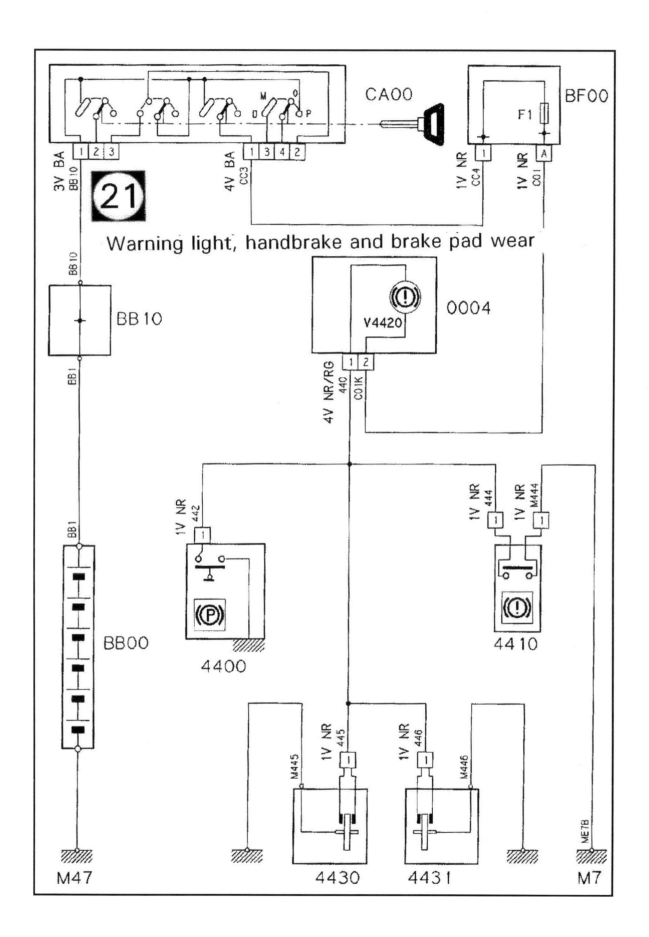

Warning light, handbrake and brake pad wear

CA00

BF00

3V BA
BB10

4V BA
CC3

1V NR
CC4

1V NR
C01

BB10

BB10

BB10

BB1

BB00

BB1

BB1

V4420

0004

4V NR/RG
440   C01K

1V NR
442

4400

1V NR
444

1V NR
M444

4410

M445

1V NR
445

1V NR
446

M446

ME7B

M47

4430

4431

M7

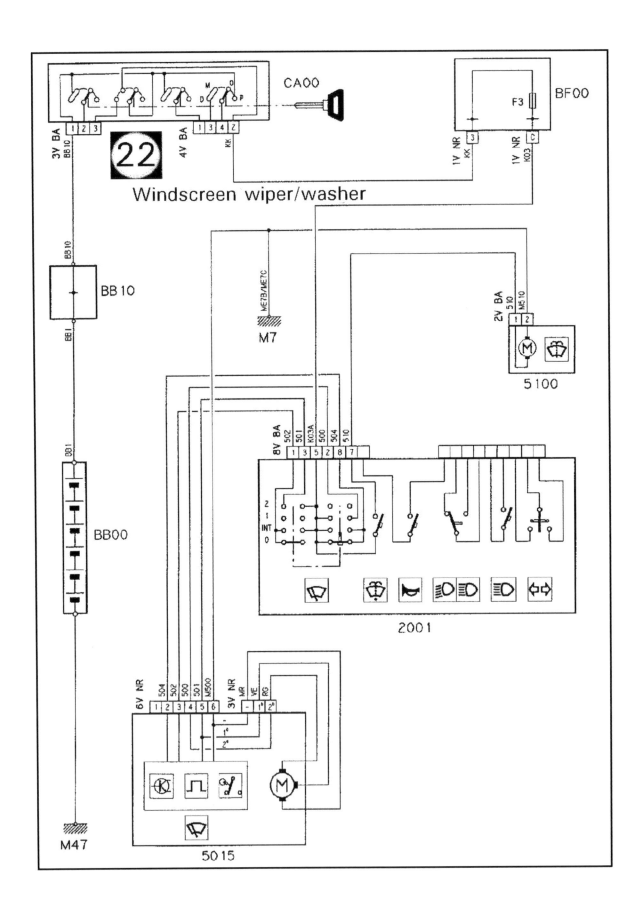

Windscreen wiper/washer

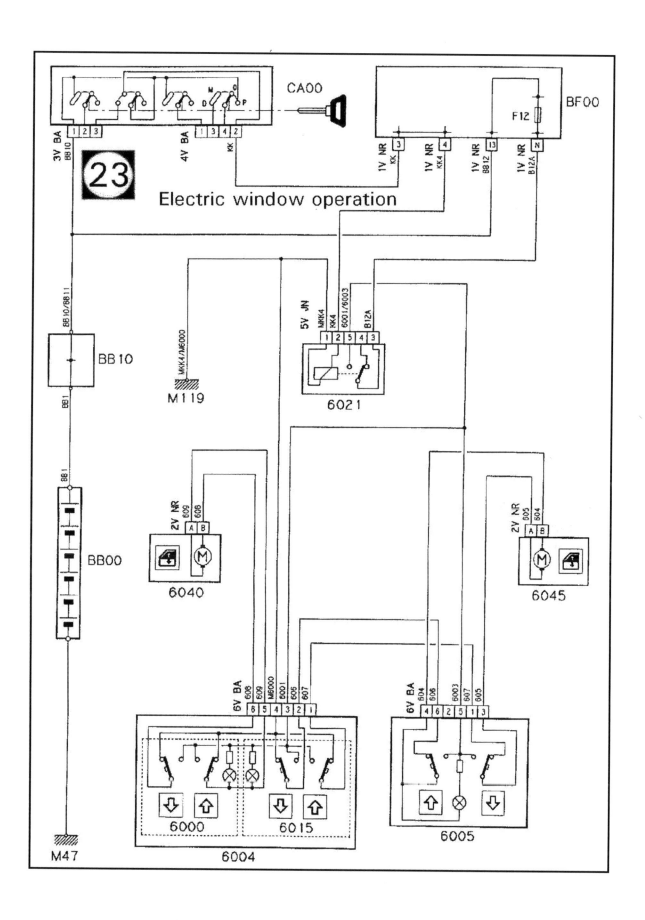

Electric window operation

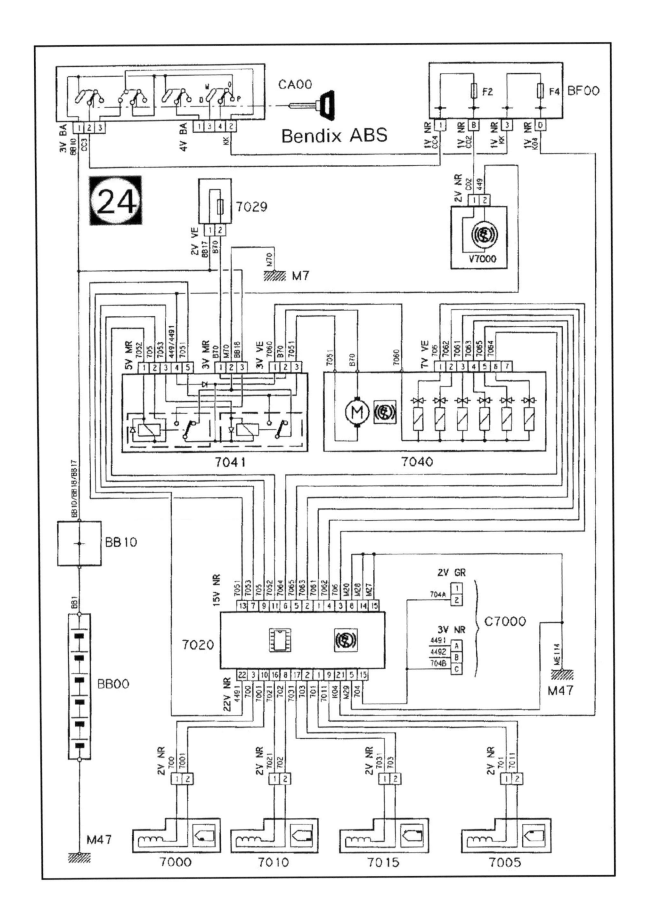

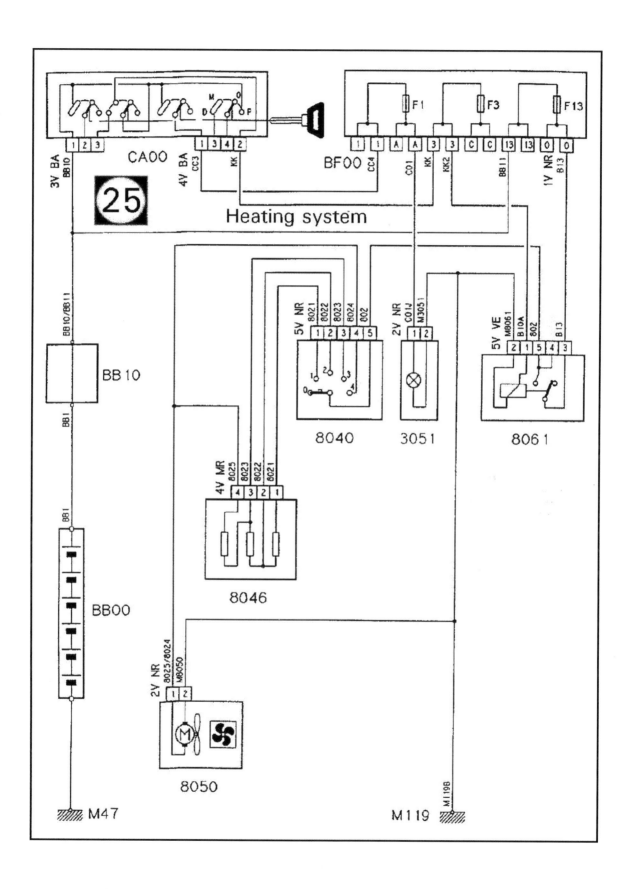

Heating system

8040

3051

8061

8046

BB10

BB00

8050

M47

M119

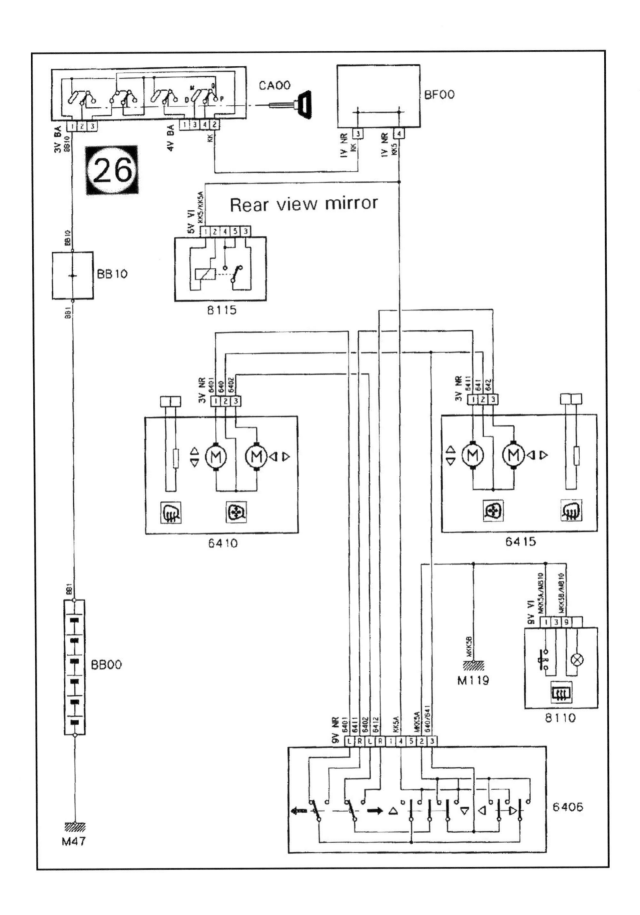

Rear view mirror

Printed in Great Britain
by Amazon

45169511R00113